Instructor's Resource Manual to Accompany

BIOLOGY

third edition

BY ARMS & CAMP

FLORENCE C. RICCIUTI, Ph.D.

Albertus Magnus College

 SAUNDERS COLLEGE PUBLISHING

Philadelphia Fort Worth Chicago
San Francisco Montreal Toronto
London Sydney Tokyo

Instructor's Resource Manual to accompany BIOLOGY, 3/e

ISBN # 0-03-003647-X

Printed in the United States of America.

9 018 9876543

Saunders College Publishing
Holt, Rinehart and Winston
The Dryden Press

TABLE OF CONTENTS

Preface

Teaching introductory biology has been made easier because of the availability and amount of supplementary material. The ancillary package for Biology (3/E) includes:

(1) A SET OF OVERHEAD TRANSPARENCIES of figures from text;

(2) A SET OF OVERHEAD TRANSPARENCIES OF ELECTRON MICROGRAPHS of cells and subcellular organelles;

(3) A STUDENT STUDY GUIDE;

(4) A TEST BANK containing over 1000 multiple choice questions organized as two sets of 10 questions per chapter and unit examinations;

(5) A LABORATORY MANUAL with its own INSTRUCTOR'S MANUAL:

and

(6) this INSTRUCTOR'S RESOURCE MANUAL.

This instructor's resource manual is intended to assist the professor in several ways. First, the manual provides a comparison of contents of the second and third editions. Secondly, the manual provides alternate chapter sequences for a one term course or a course with a particular focus. Thirdly, it provides a partial listing of distributors for audiovisual materials, and for computer software, and a listing of magazines and journals that contain articles suitable for this type of course.

Lastly, each chapter in this manual coordinates the various ancillary materials for each chapter in the textbook and includes the following items (with few exceptions):

I. Chapter Outline

II. Chapter Summary

III. Chapter Learning Objectives

IV. What's new or expanded in the third edition

V. Suggestions for Lecture Preparation and Enrichment

    a. CUSTOMIZED ANCILLARY PACKAGE

        1. overhead transparencies of text figures customized to this text.

        2. correlative laboratory exercises

    b. Supplemental Readings

    c. Films

    d. Student Activities

    e. Ideas for Demonstrations

    f. Topics for Discussion and Library Research

VI. Essay Questions

The chapter summary and learning objectives are reprinted for the instructor's convenience. The outline highlights the main topics in the chapter.

In the lecture preparation/enrichment section overhead transparencies of text figures are listed. Suggestions are made concerning the use of the overhead transparencies while lecturing and the nature of questions to be asked of students.

Correlative laboratory exercises from Carolyn Eberhard's Biology Laboratory 3/E. (1986), Saunders College Publishing) are listed and described briefly as to the types of activities that students will be doing.

Major changes between the second and third editions are described in the section on what's new or expanded. New figures are pointed out, and new topics and reorganization of old topics are also indicated.

Articles from many of the journals and magazines listed in the front of this manual are listed according to chapters. Some of the articles are annotated. These could also be assigned as supplemental readings for class discussions or used as references or starting points for term papers. The articles are varied in type. Some are more "scientific" and provide experimental details while others are written more for the nonscience person and focus on the societal aspects of biological research and technology.

Many films are available for an introductory biology course. Only a few are listed. It is suggested that the instructor look through catalogs from distributors to see what films are available.

It is believed that students who are more actively involved in their educational experience will learn more than those who are not. The activities described in this manual provide students with a "hands on" experience or exercise that emphasizes a biological concept. Some can be done in class while others can be assigned as homework. Also provided are suggestions for classroom demonstrations.

Subjects that could be the focus of small/large group discussions and term papers are listed. In many cases these subjects are accompanied by references to articles in magazines and journals.

Several essay questions are provided for each chapter. These could be used in conjunction with the unit examinations in the test bank or they could be assigned as homework. Some are appropriate as a problem solving exercise to be given at the beginning of a class.

It is hoped that this instructor's resource manual will be a useful aid for the professor. Any criticisms and suggestions for improvement are most welcome.

<u>A Comparison of the Contents of the</u>

<u>Second and Third Editions</u>

    This table is designed to help instructors switch from the second edition (2/E) of Arms and Camp to the third edition (3/E). In the center column the headings for sections are listed according to chapters in the second edition. In the left column is the section letter and page number ir parentheses. In the right column is the section letter and the chapter in the third edition plus the page number in parentheses. New sections or topics are indicated by "new" in the left column. Sections in the second edition and no longer present in the third edition are indicated by "deleted" in the right column.

    Symbols (*, **, +, ++) next to a chapter or section heading indicate a change from the second to the third edition. It is hoped that this comparison table for the two editions will help instructors in making changes in course syllabi designed for the second edition.

<u>Second Edition</u>	<u>Topic</u>	<u>Third Edition</u>

Chapter 1 Introduction

1-A	(4)	Science and Society	1-A	(1)
1-B	(5)	Scientific Method	1-B	(1)
1-C	(6)	Fact and Fiction	1-C	(6)
1-D	(7)	The Limitations of Science	1-D	(6)
1-E	(8)	What is LIfe?*	1-E	(7)
1-F	(10)	Evolution and Natural Selection	1-F	(9)

      * new title: Fundamental Concepts of Biology

Chapter 2 Some Basic Chemistry

2-A	(16)	Chemical Elements of Life	2-A	(16)
2-B	(17)	Structure of Atoms	2-B	(18)
2-C	(19)	Bonds Between Atoms	2-C	(19)
2-D	(20)	Compounds and Molecules	2-D	(22)
2-E	(21)	Chemical Reactions	2-F	(23)
5-A	(67)	Movement of Molecules*	2-E	(23)
2-F	(22)	Water	2-G	(24)
2-G	(24)	Dissociation and the pH Scale	2-H	(27)

      * moved from chapter 5

Chapter 3 Biological Chemistry

3-A	(28)	Properties of Carbon*	deleted	
3-B	(29)	Functional Groups*	deleted	
new		Structure of Organic Molecules	3-A	(31)
3-C	(29)	Carbohydrates	3-B	(34)
3-D	(31)	Lipids	3-C	(38)
3-E	(33)	Proteins	3-D	(42)
3-F	(39)	Nucleic Acids	3-E	(47)
3-G	(41)	Quantitative Comparisons of Classes of Biological Molecules	3-F	(48)
new section		Enzymes**	3-G	(50)
new section		Metabolism	3-H	(54)

          Box: How to Look at Molecular Structures

        Essay: Determine the Amino Acid Sequence of Proteins[+]

      * included in new section 3-A

    ** included in section 3-E in 2/E

    + included in Chapter 10 in 2/E

+ = Chapter 5, Cell Structure and Function in 3/E
* = new heading, Eukaryotic Cells in Chapter 5
** = Sections 5-F to 5-N appear as subtopics in section 4-B
*** = deleted from chapter 4 in 2/E but appears in 3/E in
        chapter 4, Cells and Their Membranes, as Section 4-I

Chapter 5   How Things Enter and Leave Cells*

* = Chapter 4, Cells and Their Membranes in 3/E
** = section 2-E in 3/E
+ = new section 4-D in 3/E which includes materials
      from sections 5-B, 5-C, and 5-D in 2/E
++ = new heading, Membrane Transport of Large Particles
      in 3/E
+++ = section 4-C in 2/E

Chapter 6   Energy and Living Cells

     * = new chapter title, Food as Fuel: Cellular Respiration
         and Fermentation
    ** = new section title, Fermentation

     * = new title, DNA and Genetic Information in 3/E
    ** = 9-E has been deleted as a section in the 3/E but the
         material has been incorporated in sections 9-H and 9-I in
         the 3/E
     + = appears in chapter 10 in 2/E as section 10-H

         * = new chapter title RNA and Protein Synthesis in 3/E
        ** = appears in 3/E as section 9-D
         + = appears in 3/E in chapter 3

Chapter 11   Cell Reproduction*

         * = Chapter 13, Reproduction of Eukaryotic Cells in 3/E
        ** = new heading, Eukaryotic Chromosomes
         + = deleted as section; material incorporated into 13-D
        ++ = appears as section 36-E in 2/E

Chapter 12   Cell Development and Aging*

         * = In the third edition the material from this chapter
             and selected sections from chapter 36 (2/E) are
             found in Chapters 11, Cell Differentiation, and 12,
             Embryonic Development in Animals.
        ** = new heading, Control of Transcription in Prokaryotes
         + = material incorporated into 11-D in 3/E
        ++ = material incorporated into 11-E in 3/E
       +++ = material from section 34-M in 2/E

Chapter 13   Mendelian Genetics*

* = chapter 14, Mendelian Genetics, in 3/E
** = new heading, A Simple Breeding Experiment: The Monohybrid Cross
\+ = material in these sections now as subtopics in section 14-B in 3/E
\++ = new headings, 14-E The Dihybrid Cross: Independent Assortment of Genes, and 14-F Codomance

Chapter 14   Inheritance Patterns and Gene Expression

* = new heading, Phenotypic Expression of Mutations
** = material in section 14-J now in section 13-G, in 3/E

Chapter 15   Population Genetics*

* = chapter 17 in 3/E
** = material incorporated into 17-C
\+ = new heading, What Promotes and Maintains Variability in Populations?

Chapter 16   Natural Selection and Evolution*

* = chapter 25 in 3/E
** = material in section 24-C now presented in separate sections, 25-C to 25-G, in 3/E
+ = material in section 24-I now presented in separate sections, 25-M to 2500.

Chapter 25   Lower Plants*

* = chapter 26 in 3/E

Chapter 26   Higher Plants*

* = chapter 27 in 3/E
** = new heading, Division Bryophyta: Mosses, Liverworts, Hornworts
+ = section 27-D incorporated material from sections 26-D, 26-E, and 26-G in 2/E

9

Alternate chapter sequence for a course with a particular form

    Because there is no general consensus among biologists as to the sequence in which major topics should be presented, each instructor must choose a sequence which suits the needs of the instructor and the students. In this respect the textbook by Arms and Camp is versatile.

    The authors have chosen to emphasize the interdependency and inter-relationships of all organisms in the biosphere. There are several themes running throughout the text, but the authors have written each chapter so that it does not depend heavily on preceding chapters or parts. The various chapters and parts of the textbook can be combined in several ways depending on the instructor's goals and students' interests.

    The textbook can be used in a short course (one semester or two quarters) as well as one in which there is a particular emphasis. Several syllabi are presented in the table below which would be appropriate for a short course or a course with a defined orientation.

Chapter		General Biology (1 semester)	General Biology (2 semesters)	Botany-oriented	Ecology/Evolution (environmental)	Human Biology	Molecular Biology	Zoology
1	Introduction	X	X	X	X	X	X	X
2	Some Basic Chemistry		X	X	X	parts	X	parts
3	Biological Chemistry	parts	X	parts	parts	parts	X	parts
4	Cells and Their Membranes	X	X	parts	parts		X	X
5	Cell Structure and Function	X	X	X	X	X	X	X
6	Energy and Living Cells		parts	parts		parts	X	X
7	Food as Fuel: Cellular Respiration and Fermentation	parts	X	X			X	
8	Photosynthesis	parts	X	X	X		X	
9	DNA and Genetic Information	parts	X	parts	parts	parts	X	parts
10	RNA and Protein Synthesis	parts	X				X	parts
11	Cell Differentiation	parts	X				X	parts
12	Embryonic Development in Animals	X	X		parts	parts	X	X
13	Reproduction of Eukaryotic Cells	X	X	parts	X	parts	X	X

Chapter	General Biology (1 semester)	General Biology (2 semesters)	Botany-oriented	Ecology/Evolution (environmental)	Human Biology	Molecular Biology	Zoology
14 Mendelian Genetics	X	X		parts	X	X	X
15 Inheritance Patterns and Gene Expression	X	X			X		X
16 Evolution and Natural Selection	X	X	X	X	parts		X
17 Population Genetics			X	X			
18 Speciation			X	X	X		X
19 Evolution and Reproduction	X	X		X	X		X
20 Origin of Life			X	X	X	X	
21 Classification of Organisms	parts	X					x
22 Viruses	parts	X	parts	parts	parts	X	X
23 Bacteria	parts	X	X	parts	parts	X	
24 Protista and the Origin of Multicellularity	parts	parts	X	X		X	X
25 Fungi	parts	parts	X	X	parts		
26 Lower Plants		parts	X	X			
27 Higher Plants	parts	parts	X	X			
28 The Lower Invertebrates		parts		parts			X
29 Some Higher Invertebrates	parts	parts	parts	parts	parts		X
30 The Origin of Vertebrates		parts		X			x
31 Vertebrate Anatomy and Evolution	parts	X		X	X		X
32 Animal Nutrition and Digestion	X	X			X	X	X
33 Gas Exchange in Animals	X	X			X	parts	X
Animal Transport Systems	X	X			X	parts	X

Chapter		General Biology (1 semester)	General Biology (2 semesters)	Botany-oriented	Ecology/Evolution (environmental)	Human Biology	Molecular Biology	Zoology
35	Defenses Against Disease	X	X			X	X	X
36	Excretion	X	X			X	parts	X
37	Sexual Reproduction	X	X			X	X	X
38	Neurons	X	X			X	X	X
39	The Vertebrate Nervous System	parts	X			X		X
40	Sense Organs	parts	X			X	X	X
41	Muscles and Skeletons	X	X				X	X
42	Animal Hormones and Chemical Regulation	X	X			X	X	X
43	Behavior	X	X		X	X		X
44	Structure and Growth of Vascular Plants	parts	X	X	X			
45	Transport in Vascular Plants	parts	X	X	X			
46	Soil, Roots, and Plant Nutrition	parts	X	X	X			
47	Reproduction in Flowering Plants	parts	X	X	X			
48	Regulation and Response in Plants	parts	X	X	X			
49	The Biosphere	parts	X	X	X	parts		parts
50	Ecosystems and Communities	parts	X	X	X	parts		parts
51	Populations	parts	X	X	X	parts		parts
52	Evolutionary Ecology		X	X	X			X

Correlation of chapters and topics in Biology (3/E) Karen Arms and Pamela S. Camp (1987, Saunders College Publishing, Philadelphia) with those in other texts.*

* Curtis, Helena. 1983. Biology (4/E). Worth Publishing Co., New York.

Keeton, William T. and James L. Gould. 1986. Biological Science (4/E). W. W. Norton and Co., Inc., New York.

Raven, Peter H. and George B. Johnson. 1986. Biology. Times Mirror/Mosby College Publishing, St. Louis, MO.

Villee, Claude, Solomon, Eldra, and William Davis. 1985. Biology. Saunders College Publishing Co., Philadelphia.

Wallace, Robert A., King, Jack L., and Gerald P. Sanders. 1986. Biology: The Science of Life (2/E). Scott, Foresman and Company, Glenview, Illinois.

Chapter/Topic	Curtis (4/E)	Keeton/Gould (4/E)	Raven/Johnson	Villee/Solomon/Davis	Wallace/King/Sanders (2/E)

1 Introduction
   Scientific method
   limitations of science
   characteristics of living
     organisms
   evolution, natural selection
   adaptation, energy
	Intro.	1	3, 15	1	1

2 Some Basic Chemistry
   chemical elements of life
   structure of atoms, molecules
   types of bonds, chemical
     reactions
   movement of molecules
   structure and properties of
     water
   pH, buffers
	1,2	2	2	2	2

3 Biological Chemistry
   functional groups
   structure, function, properties: carbohydrates, lipids
   proteins, nucleic acid
   enzymes: characteristics,
     method of action, factors
     affecting activity
   metabolism: role of enzymes,
     types of control
	3,8	3	4, 10	3, 7	3, 6

	Curtis (4/E)	Keeton/Gould (4/E)	Raven/Johnson	Villee/Solomon/Davis	Wallace/King/Sanders (2/E)
4 Cells and Their Membranes plasma membrane: structure, properties, function passive, active transport processes endocytosis osmosis, cells as osmotic systems specializations of membrane: tight and gap junctions, desmosomes	6	4	4, 5, 9	5	5
5 Cell Structure and Function methods of studying cells prokaryotic cells: features cellular organelles: structure, function of plant, animal cells cytoskeleton tissues: animal, plant	5, 33	5, 6, 20	5, 6, 7, 42	4	4
6 Energy and Living Cells energy transformations, chemical reactions overview photosynthesis, respiration oxidation, reduction energy intermediates, making ATP chemiosmosis	8	3, 7	10	7	6
7 Food as Fuel: Cellular Respiration and Fermentation coenzymes aerobic degradation of glucose oxidative phosphorylation fermentation alternative food molecules	9	7	11	9	6, 8
8 Photosynthesis chloroplasts: internal structure, function trapping light energy electron flow: cyclic, noncyclic chemiosmotic ATP synthesis carbon fixation control of rate of photosynthesis photorespiration C_4, CAM, sun/shade plants	10	8	12	8	7

	Curtis (4/E)	Keeton/Gould (4/E)	Raven/Johnson	Villee/Solomon/Davis	Wallace/King/Sanders (2/E)
9 DNA and Genetic Information evidence DNA is genetic material DNA: structure, types of replication, repair mutations eukaryotic chromosomes: structure genome: classes of DNA, mobile genetic elements DNA technologies	14, 16, 17, 18	26, 28	14, 15, 16, 17, 18	13, 16	9, 10, 14
10 RNA and Protein Synthesis types, structure, functions formation of RNAs genetic code: features, development transcription, translation	15	27	15, 16, 17	14	10
11 Cell Differentiation genetic information in zygote and adult gene control mechanisms in prokaryotes and eukaryotes: Lac operon, changes in chromatin, X-chromosome inactivation polytene, lampbrush chromosomes Metamorphosis in animals regeneration Cancer: characteristics, causes	15, 17	29, 31	18	15, 44	10
12 Embryonic Development in Animals fertilization, cleavage, gastrulation, neurulation, organogenesis determination, induction, homeotic genes aging	45	31, 32	41	44	37
13 Reproduction of Eukaryotic Cells cell cycle mitosis, meiosis, cytokinesis gametogenesis	7, 12	23	8, 14	10	11

	Curtis (4/E)	Keeton/Gould (4/E)	Raven/Johnson	Villee/Solomon/ Davis	Wallace/King/ Sanders (2/E)

14 Mendelian Genetics
   Mendel's laws, types of crosses
   linkage, mapping
   probability theory
	11, 13	24, 25	13, 17	11	12

15 Inheritance Patterns and Gene Expression
   mutation, lethal genes
   biochemical genetics: PKU
   multiple alleles, polygenes
   sex determination and linkage
   factors affecting gene expression
   counseling, prenatal diagnosis
	13, 18	24, 25	14	11, 12	12, 13

16 Evolution and Natural Selection
   history of theory of evolution
   evidence for evolution
   evolution by means of natural
     selection
	1, 46, 48	1, 33	19, 23	45, 46, 47	16, 17

17 Population Genetics
   Hardy-Weinberg Law: conditions
     formulas
   causes of evolution
   types of selection
   heterozygote advantage
   variation: measurement,
     promotion, maintenance
	47, 48, 49	33	20	45	15, 16

18 Speciation
   definition, characteristics
     formation of species
   isolating mechanisms
   types of speciation
	50	34	21	45	17

19 Evolution and Reproduction
   asexual, sexual reproduction:
    advantages
   origin of sexual reproduction
   roles of males, females;
    sexual dimorphism, mating
    systems
   selfishness, altruism, insect
    societies
	49, 55	22	49	49	39

	Curtis (4/E)	Keeton/Gould (4/E)	Raven/Johnson	Villee/Solomon/Davis	Wallace/King/Sanders (2/E)

20 Origin of Life
  spontaneous generation
  conditions for origin of life
  proposed sequence of events for
    origin of life
  feature, metabolism of early organisms
  early fossils
	4	37	3, 10, 23	47	18

21 Classification of Organisms
  Linnaeus, taxonomy, systematics and
    its tools, taxonomic methods
  five kingdoms: general characteristics
	19	6, 34	21	17	

22 Viruses
  structure, types of evolution of viruses
  lytic, lysogenic cycles
  viral diseases, viruses and cancer
  viroids, prions
	16, 20	28, 38	25	18	18

23 Bacteria
  characteristics, reproduction, types
    of metabolism
  classification, major features of each
    type
  use in food production, bacterial
    diseases, symbiotic bacteria
  origin of mitochondria and plastids
	20	28, 38	26, 27	19	14, 18

24 Protista and Origin of Multicellularity
  types, physiology, method of locomo-
    tion, metabolism
  general features of each phylum
	4, 21	10, 39	27, 1	20	19, 20

25 Fungi
  nutrition, structure, reproduction,
   life histories
  classification, major features of
   each division
  fungal diseases, symbiotic relationships
  fungi as food
  slime molds
	21, 22	10, 39, 41	27, 28	21	20

26 Lower Plants
  classification, major features of divi-
    sions of multicellular algae
  life history, alternation of generation
	21	40	27	22	19

		Curtis (4/E)	Keeton/Gould (4/E)	Raven/Johnson	Villee/Solomon/Davis	Wallace/King/Sanders (2/E)
27	Higher Plants life on land: problems, adaptations, reproduction embryophytes: bryophytes, tracheophytes life histories, characteristics of moss, ferns, pine, flowering plants	23	40	29, 30	23	21
28	The Lower Invertebrates sponges, cnidarians, flatworms, round-worms, rotifers major features of each phylum and important classes symmetry, cephalization, parasitism	24	42	35	24	25
29	Some Higher Invertebrates annelids, bryozoans, molluscs, arthropods major features of each phylum and important classes advantages of coelom, type of embryonic development	25, 26	42	36, 37	25	26
30	The Origin of Vertebrates echinoderms, urochordates, cephalo-chordates, hemichordates, agnathans major features of each phylum and important class relationship to vertebrates	27	42, 43	23, 24, 38	26	26, 27
31	Vertebrate Anatomy and Evolution major features of each vertebrate class and some important orders problems and adaptations to land-living human evolution	27, 56	22, 43	23, 24, 39	26, 47	27
32	Animal Nutrition and Digestion macro, and micronutrients, vitamins, minerals types of digestive systems chemical digestion, absorption, hormonal control, regulation of feeding special adaptations herbivores, carnivores, birds function of liver	34	10, 14	43	33, 34	29

	Curtis (4/E)	Keeton/Gould (4/E)	Raven/Johnson	Villee/Solomon/Davis	Wallace/King/Sanders (2/E)

33 Gas Exchange in Animals
ventilation, respiration; regulation
  of problems, adaptations in gas
  exchange related to habitat
respiratory structures, major features
respiratory pigments; characteristics,
  properties
transport CO_2
swim bladder
	35	7,
		11,
		13
			44	37	30

34 Animal Transport Systems
circulation in invertebrates, vertebrates
circulation in mammals, blood vessels,
  heart cycle, flow, blood pressure
diseases, adjustments of circulatory
  system to exercise
blood, composition, clotting, types
lumphatic system: structure, function
temperature regulation
	36,
	38
		7,
		13
			45	35	31,
					32

35 Defenses Against Disease nonspecific defenses cell-mediated, humoral immunity vaccination, acquired immunity immunoglobulins: structure, types, functions, formation disease states involving immune system	39	13, 30		36	31
36 Excretion metabolic wastes: types, formation osmoregulation in different environ- ments excretory organs of invertebrates nephron: structure, function regulation of kidney function, hormones	37	14	48	38	32

37 Sexual Reproduction
reproductive patterns
reproductive organs: structure, function
physiology sexual intercourse
hormones and reproduction
fertilization, implantation, early
  development
birth control, sexually transmitted
  diseases
	41,
	44,
	45
		17,
		31
			40,
			41
				43	36,
					37

38 Neurons structure, types, function potentials: resting, action, generator synaptic transmission, neurotransmitters durgs and brain	33, 40	18	42, 46	39	34

	Curtis (4/E)	Keeton/Gould (4/E)	Raven/Johnson	Villee/Solomon/Davis	Wallace/King/Sanders (2/E)

39 The Vertebrate Nervous System
  divisions of vertebrate nervous system
  vertebrate brains: functions of parts,
    similarities, differences
  reflex arcs, learning, memory, sleep
  peripheral, autonomic nervous systems
	40, 43	18, 19	46, 48	39, 40	34, 35

40 Sense Organs
  structure, functions, types of
  classification, major features and
  mechanism of functioning of
  mechanoreceptors, photoreceptors,
  chemoreceptors, thermoreceptors,
  electroreceptors
	42	19	47	41	34

41 Muscles and Skeletons
  muscles: properties, types, functions,
  mechanism of contraction, control of
  contraction, molecular structure
  skeleton: parts, composition(bone,
  cartilage)
	33, 42	20	7, 42	6, 32	28

42 Animal Hormones and Chemical Regulation
  hormones: chemical nature, mechanism of
    action, control of production, types
    effects, relationship to nervous
    system
  local chemical messengers, pheromones
  biological rhythms, clocks
	41	16, 21	48	42, 48	33

43 Behavior
  behavior: learned, innate, neuro-
    physiological basis of, develop-
    ment, territorial, mating
  migration
  social behavior: animal societies
	55	21, 22	49	48, 49	38, 39

44 Structure and Growth of Vascular Plants
  primary, secondary, growth roots, shoots
  structural functions of roots, stems,
    leaves
  monocots, dicots
	28, 29	11, 12, 31	31, 32	27, 28	22

45 Transport in Vascular Plants
  xylem, phloem: location, growth,
    structure, function, mechanisms of
    movement of materials in
	30	11, 12	31, 34	27	23

	Curtis (4/E)	Keeton/Gould (4/E)	Raven/Johnson	Villee/Solomon/Davis	Wallace/King/Sanders (2/E)

46 Soil, Roots, and Plant Nutrition
  nutritional requirements, soil
    composition, types
  absorption by roots
  nutritional adaptations
	30	9,
		12,
		36
			34	27,
				30	

47 Reproduction in Flowering Plants
  flowers, formation of pollen,
   mature ovule pollination;
   fertilization; development of seed;
   fruit; dispersal of seed, fruit
   germination
  types of vegetative reproduction
	29	15,
		31,
		33,
		40
			30,
			32
				31	22

48 Regulation and Response in Plants
  hormones: types, chemical nature,
    effects
  flowering; control of; role of
    phytochroma
	31,
	32
		15	33	29	24

49 The Biosphere
  climate, effect on vegetation
  biomes: types, distribution, major
    features
  succession: primary, secondary
	53,
	54
		35,
		36
			50,
			51
				51	40,
					41

50 Ecosystems and Communities
  ecosystem: basic components,
    structure, types of organisms,
    food webs
  energy flow, pyramids, productivity
    (primary, secondary), biogeochemical
    cycles (Cn, N, P)
  lake ecosystems: zones, features,
    properties, pollution effect
  community structure, species diversity
    turnover
	53	35,
		36
			34,
			50,
			51,
			52,
			53
				50	41

51 Populations
  dynamics of populations: growth,
    biotic potential, survivorship,
    carrying capacity, regulation
    of size, competition, predation
  Human population: characteristics,
    effect of agriculture, pollution
	51,
	52,
	56
		22,
		35
			51,
			52
			54
				51,
				52
					42

GENERAL REFERENCES AND CURRENT TITLES LISTED ACCORDING TO PARTS OF TEXTBOOK

Introduction

Gould, Stephen J. 1983. Hen's Teeth and Horse's Toes. W. W. Norton and Co., New York

_____ 1980. The Panda's Thumb. W. W. Norton and Co., New York.

_____ 1981. The Mismeasure of Man. W. W. Norton and Co., New York.

Medawar, P. and J. Medawar. 1983. Aristotle to Zoos: A Philosophical Dictionary of Biology. Harvard Univ. Press, Cambridge, MA.

Thomas, Lewis. 1974. The Lives of a Cell: Notes of a Biology Watcher. Viking Press, New York.

Part I   Cells

Abelson, P. (editor). 1984. Biotechnology and Biological Frontiers. American Association for the Advancement of Science, Washington, D.C.

Alberts, B. et al. 1983. Molecular Biology of the Cell. Garland Pub. Co., New York.

Avers, C. 1981. Cell Biology (2/E). D. Van Nostrand Comapny, New York.

Bloom, W. and D. Fawcett. 1975. A Textbook of Histology (10/E). Saunders Publishing Co., Philadelphia.

deDuve, C. 1984. A Guided Tour of the Living Cell. W. H. Freeman and Co., San Francisco.

Fawcett, D.W. 1981. An Atlas of Fine Structure: The Cell (2/E).

Holtzman, E. and A. Novikoff. 1984. Cells and Organelles (3/E) Saunders College Publishing, Philadelphia.

Karp, G. 1984. Cell Biology (2/E). McGraw-Hill Book Company, New York.

Kessel, R. and R. Kardon. 1979. Tissues and Organs: A Text Atlas of Scanning Electron Microscopy. W. H. Freeman and Co., San Francisco.

Kieffer, G. 1979. Bioethics: A Textbook of Issues. Addison-Wesley Publishing Co., Reading, MA.

Metzler, D. 1977. Biochemistry: The Chemical Reactions of Living Cells. Academic Press, New York.

Shannon, T. (editor). 1981. Bioethics. Paulist Press, Ramsey, NJ.

Stryer, L. 1981. Biochemistry (2/E) W. H. Freeman and Co., San Francisco.

Thomas, L. 1974. The Lives of a Cell: Notes of a Biology Watcher. Bantam Books, Inc., New York.

Wolfe, S. 1981. Biology of the Cell (2/E). Wadsworth Publishing Co., Belmont, CA.

Part II. Information Coding and Transfer

Committee on Science and Technology. 1983. Human Genetic Engineering. Hearings before the Subcommittee on Investigations and Oversight of the Committee on Science and Technology, U.S. House of Representatives. Superintendent of Documents, U.S. Government Printing Office, Washington, D.C. 20402.

Esbjornson, R. (ed). 1984. Manipulation of Life. Nobel Conference XIX. Harper and Row Pub. Co., New York.

Goodenough, U. 1984. Genetics (3/E). Saunders Publishing Co., Philadelphia.

Hartl. D. 1984. Our Uncertain Heritage (2/E) Harper and Row, New York.

Higgins, I. J., Best, D. J., and J. Jones (editors). 1985. Biotechnology: Principles and Applications. Blackwell Scientific Publications, Palo Alto, CA.

Keller, E. F. 1983. A Feeling for the Organism: The Life and Work of Barbara McClintock. W. H. Freeman and Co., San Francisco.

Lewin, B. 1983. Genes. J. Wiley and Sons, Inc., New York.

Lewontin, R. 1984. Human Diversity. W. H. Freeman and Co., San Francisco.

Lygre, D. 1979. Life Manipulation. Walker and Co., New York.

Office of Technology Assessment. 1982. Genetic Technology. A New Frontier. Westview Press, Boulder, CO.

President's Commission for the Study of Ethical Problems in Medicine and Biomedical and Behavioral Research. 1982. Splicing Life. A Report on the Social and Ethical Issues of Genetic Engineering with Human Beings. Superintendent of Documents, U.S. Government Printing Office, Washington, D.C. 20402.

Rothwell, N. 1983. Understanding Genetics (3/E). Oxford University Press, New York.

Stine, G. 1977. Biosocial Genetics. Macmillan Publishing Co., New York.

Watson, J.D., Tooze, J. and D. Jurtz. 1983. Recombinant DNA: A Short Course. W. H. Freeman and Co., San Francisco.

Watson, J.D. and J. Tooze. 1981. The DNA Story. W. H. Freeman and Co., San Francisco.

Part III. Evolution

Lewin, R. 1984. Human Evolution. W. H. Freeman and Co., San Francisco.

Simpson, G. G. 1984. Fossils and the History of Life. W. H. Freeman, Co., San Francisco.

Part IV. Diversity

Margulis, L. and K. Schwartz. 1982. Five Kingdoms: An Illustrated Guide to the Phyla of Life on Earth. W. H. Freeman and Co., San Francisco.

Parker, S. (editor-in-chief). 1982. Synopsis and Classification of Living Organisms. McGraw-Hill Book Co., New York.

Part V. Animal Biology

Barnes, R. 1987. _Invertebrate Zoology._ (5/E). Saunders College Publishing Co., Philadelphia.

Brady, J. (editor). 1982. _Biological Timekeeping_. Cambridge University Press, New York.

Browder, L. 1980. _Developmental Biology_. Saunders College Publishing Co., Philadelphia.

Carlson, B. 1981. _Patten's Foundations of Embryology_ (4/E). McGraw-Hill Book Company, New York.

Dawkins, R. 1976. _The Selfish Gene_. Oxford University Press, New York.

Eckert, R. and D. Randall. 1983. _Animal Physiology: Mechanisms and Adaptations_ (2/E). W. H. Freeman and Co., San Francisco.

Gordon, M., et al. 1982. _Animal Physiology: Principles and Adaptations_. (4/E). Macmillan Co., New York.

Karp, G. and N. Berrill. 1981. _Development (2/E)_. Mc-Graw Hill Book Co., New York.

Kluge, A. et al. 1977. _Chordate Structure and Function_ (2/E). Macmillan Publishing Co., Inc. New York.

Krommenhoek, W., Sebus, J., and G. van Esch. 1980. _Biological Structures_. University Park Press, Baltimore, MD.

McMahon, T. and J. T. Bonner. 1983. _On Size and Life_. W. H. Freeman and Co., San Francisco.

Romer, A. and T. Parsons. 1977. _The Vertebrate Body_ (5/E). Saunders College Publishing Co., Philadelphia.

Rugh, R. 1964. _Vertebrate Embryology: The Dynamics of Development_. Harcourt, Brace and World, Inc., New York.

Schmidt-Nielsen, K. 1979. _Animal Physiology: Adaptation and Environment_ (2/E). Cambridge University Press, New York.

Schmidt-Nielsen, K. 1984. _Scaling: Why is Animal Size so Important?_ Cambridge Univ. Press, New York.

Wilson, M. 1984. _Vertebrate Natural History_. Saunders College Publishing Co., Philadelphia.

Part VI. Plant Biology

Galston, A., Davies, P. and R. Satter, 1980. _The Life of the Green Plant_ (3/E). Prentice-Hall, Inc. Englewood Cliffs, NJ.

Greulach, V. 1983. _Plant Structure and Function_ (2/E). Macmillan Co., New York.

Raven, P., Evert, R., and H. Curtis. 1986. _Biology of Plants_ (4/E) Worth Publishers, Inc., New York.

Wilson, B. 1984. _The Growing Tree_ (revised edition). The University of Massachusetts Press, Amherst, MA.

Part VII. Ecology

Colinvaux, P. 1978. Why Big Fierce Animals are Rare. Princeton University
    Press, Princeton, NJ.

Ehrlich, P. and A. Erhlich. 1981. Extinction. Random House, New York.

Leopold, A. 1970. A Sand County Almanac. Ballantine Books, New York.

Norman, C. 1981. The God that Limps: Science and Technology in the Eighties.
    W. W. Norton and Co., New York.

Owen, J. 1980. Feeding Strategy. University of Chicago Press, Chicago.

Owen, D. 1980. Camouflage and Mimicry. University of Chicago Press, Chicago.

Smith, R. L. 1982. Ecology and Field Biology (3/E). Harper and Row Publish-
    ers, New York.

Wilson, E.D. 1971. The Insect Societies. Harvard University Press, Cambridge,
    MA.

Wilson, E.D. 1975. Sociobiology. Harvard University Press, Cambridge, MA.

REPRINT SERIES, COLLECTIONS AND READERS

Annual Editions Series. In this series are several different volumes each
containing a collection of articles which have appeared in a variety of
journals and magazines and which focus on a particular topic. The series
is published by the Dushkin Publishing Group, Inc., Sluice Dock,
Guilford, CT 06437. Articles contained in the Annual Editions listed
below would be appropriate for both nonmajors and students majoring in
science:

    Biology (4/E)

    Environment

    Health 86/87

    Human Development

    Human Sexuality 86/87

    Taking Sides: Clashing Views on Controversial Bio-Ethical Issues
        (1984)   Edited by Carol Levine

Carolina Biology Readers. Short monographs written by leading scientists
on a variety of subjects including applied biology, cell biology,
insects, evolution, health, biochemistry, reproduction, plants, vertebrates, and human biology. Specific readers are listed with the appropriate
chapter of the textbook. A list of readers can be obtained from Carolina
Biological Supply Company, 2700 York Road, Burlington, NC 27215 or
Box 187, Gladstone, Oregon 97027.

National Science Foundation Mosaic Reader Series. Each reader is assembled
from Mosaic, the publication of the National Science Foundation, and contains
many illustrations, a glossary and index. The following readers are
currently available.

    The Cell: Inter and Intra-Relationships (1983)

    DNA: The Master Molecule (1983)

    Ecology: Impacts and Implications (1983)

Evolution: New Perspectives (1983)

Human Evolution (1983)

Scientific American Readers. Each reader is a collection of articles that have appeared in Scientific American and which deal with a particular topic. Each reader is introduced by a leading scientist in the particular subject area. The following readers would be appropriate for students in an introductory biology course.

Animal Behavior (1975) introduced by T. Eisner and E. O. Wilson

Animal Engineering (1974) introduced by B. Griffin

Animal Societies and Evolution (1981) introduced by H. Topoff

The Biosphere (1970)

Cancer Biology (1985) introduced by Errol Friedberg

Ecology, Evolution, and Population Biology (1974) introduced by E. O. Wilson

Energy and Environment (1980) introduced by R. Siever

Evolution (1978)

Food and Agriculture (1976)

The Fossil Record and Evolution (1982) introduced by L. Laporte

Genetics (1981) introduced by C. Davern

Immunology (1976) introduced by F. Burnet

Industrial Microbiology and the Advent of Genetic Engineering (1981)

Molecules to Living Cells (1980) introduced by P. Hanawalt

Recombinant DNA (1978) introduced by D. Freifelder

Vertebrate Adaptations (1980) introduced by N. Wessels

Vertebrate Physiology (1980) introduced by N. Wessels

JOURNALS AND MAGAZINES

The journals and magazines listed below provide current information on recent research in biological and medical sciences. They are good sources of ideas for lecture and term paper topics, and discussion. In addition many provide reviews of important areas of research and of recently published books.

American Biology Teacher. Journal of the National Association of Biology Teachers, 11250 Roger Bacon Drive, Reston, VA 22090.

American Scientist. Sigma Xi, 155 Whitney Avenue, New Haven, CT 06510.

American Health. American Health Partners, 80 Fifth Avenue, Suite 302, New York, NY 10011.

Audubon. National Audubon Society, 950 Third Avenue, New York, NY
          10022

Bioscience. American Institute of Biological Sciences (AIBS), 1401
          Wilson Boulevard, Arlington, VA 22209.

Biotechnology. Nature Publishing Co., a subsidiary of Macmillan Journals
          of London, 15 East 26th St., NY 10010, or 4 Little Essex St.,
          London WC2R 3LF, U.K.

Discover. Time and Life Building, 541 North Fairbanks Court, Chicago,
          IL 60611.

Hastings Center Report. The Hastings Center Institute of Society,
          Ethics and the Life Sciences, 360 Broadway, Hastings-on-Hudson,
          NY 10706.

Journal of College Science Teaching. National Science Teachers Asso-
          ciation, 1742 Connecticut Avenue, NW, Washington, DC 20009.

Mosaic. National Science Foundation, Washington, D.C. 20550

Natural History. American Museum of Natural History, Central Park West
          at 79th Street, New York, NY 10024.

Nature. Macmillan (Journals) Ltd., Brunel Road, Bosingstoke, Hants,
          England.

Science. American Association for the Advancement of Science. (AAAS),
          1515 Massachusetts Avenue, N.W., Washington, DC 20005.

Science 85. AAAS, 1515 Massachusetts Ave., NW, Washington, DC 20005.

Science Digest. The Hearst Corporation, 959 Eighth Avenue, New York
          NY 10019.

Scientific American. 415 Madison Avenue, New York, NY 10017

Sierra. Sierra Club. 530 Bush Street, San Francisco, CA 94108.

Trends in Biochemical Sciences (TIBS). Elsevier Publications,
          (Cambridge), 68 Hills Road, Cambridge CB2 1LA U.K.

Trends in Neurosciences (TINS). Elsevier Publications (Cambridge), 68
          Hills Road, Cambridge CB2 1LA U.K.

Regular features and general articles on biological topics can also be
found in Newsweek, Time, The New York Times Magazine, The New York Times,
Smithsonian, U.S. News and World Report, National Wildlife, and,
National Geographic.

COMPUTER SOFTWARE

Computer software is available which could be used as a pedogogical
aid in an introductory biology course. Most of the software is written
for Apple II and TRS-80 computers and predominantly covers the topics
of genetics, evolution, and ecology, particularly population dynamics.
There is a limited amount of software which emphasizes the different
physiological systems of animals. New software is being developed for
the Apple and TRS-80 as well as for the Commodore 64 and IBM PC.

New and improved programs are published monthly. Therefore, no attempt will be made to list titles. A list of sources for bioeducational computer software is presented below to which the instructor can write for current catalogues, computer requirements, prices and preview policy.

It is suggested that an instructor not only consider what programs are available, but also how valuable and useful they are for student learning. In 1984 several issues of the American Biology Teacher contain articles on using computers in biological education. The following two articles are recommended: Crovello, T. 1984. "Evaluation of educational software." Vol. 46(3): 173-175, March; and, Crovello, T. 1984. "Computer world turns upside down again." Vol. 46(4): 236-238, April.

Try to personally preview any software before buying it for classroom use. Consult your computer education department or local microcomputer vendor for advice on how to get copies of programs to preview.

Sources of Computer Software

Biolearning Systems, Inc., 420 Lexington Avenue, Suite 2735, New York, NY 10017.

Biology Media, 918 Parker St., Berkeley, CA 94710.

Cambridge Development Lab, 100 Fifth Avenue, Waltham, MA 02154

Carolina Software, Carolina Biological Supply Co., 2700 York Road., Burlington, NC 27215, or PO Box 187, Gladstone, OR 97027

Classroom Consortia Media, 57 Bay St., Staten Island, NY 10301.

Conduit, M310 Oakdale Hall, The University of Iowa, PO Box C, Oakdale, Iowa 52319.

Edutech, 634 Commonwealth Ave., Newton Centre, MA 02159.

E.M.E. Corporation, PO Box 17, Pelham, NY 10803.

Encyclopedia Britannica Educational Corp., 425 North Michigan Ave., Chicago, IL 60611.

Focus Media, Inc., 839 Stewart Ave., Garden City, NY 11530.

Hayden Software Com., 600 Suffolk St., Lowell, MA 01853.

HRM Software, Human Relations Media. 175 Tompkins Ave., Pleasantville, NY 10570.

Human Engineered Software, 150 North Hill Dr., Brisbane, CA 94005.

J and S Software, 140 Reid Ave., Port Washington, NY 11050.

Science Software Systems, Inc., 11899 W. Pico Blvd., West Los Angeles, CA 90064.

AUDIOVISUAL MATERIAL

There is much audiovisual material appropriate for use in an introductory biology course. A partial list of suppliers for slides/ transparencies, filmstrips, film loops, and video cassettes is presented below. The instructor should write to the distributors for current catalogues, preview policy, prices and other information.

BFA Educational Media, 11559 Santa Monica Blvd., Los Angeles, CA 90025
      (BFA Ealing Science Film loops)

Carolina Biological Supply Co., Burlington, NC 27215 or PO Box 187
      Gladstone, Or 97027

Churchill Films, 662 N. Robertson Blvd., Los Angeles, Ca 90069.

Coronet Instructional Films, 66 E.S. Water St., Chicago, IL 60601.

Educational Images, Ltd., PO Box 3456, West Side Station, Elmira, NY
      14905.

Edutek, Inc., 979 Cedarbridge Ave., Brick, NJ 08723.

Encyclopedia Britannica Educ. Corp., 425 N. Michigan Ave., Chicago,
      IL, 60611.

Encyclopedia Britannica Films, Inc., 1150 Wilmette Ave., Wilmette, IL
      60091.

Harper and Row Publ., Inc., 10 E 53rd St., NY, 10022

Hawkhill Assoc., Inc., 125 East Gilman St., Madison, WI 53703

Human Relations Media, 175 Tompkins Ave., Pleasantville, NY 10570

Kalmia Co., Inc., Dept. B7, 21 West Circle, Concord, MA 01742

McGraw-Hill Book Co., Inc., Textbook Film Division, 1221 Avenue of
      the Americas, NY 10020

NBC Educational Enterprises, 30 Rockefeller Plaza, NY 10020

Science and Mankind, Communications Park, Box 2000, Mount Kisco, NY,
      10549.

Scientific Amer. Inc., 415 Madison Avenue, NY, 10017.

LIST OF DISTRIBUTORS FOR FILMS

There are many films for use in an introductory biology course. Films are listed in the appropriate chapter. All films are 16 mm and in color. Inclusion in the chapter does not imply an endorsement of the film. The instructor should write to the distributors listed in this section for current catalogues, rental/purchase costs, preview policy, availability of film on video cassettes, etc. Some films are very popular so that requests for them should be made as early as possible to ensure availability when needed.

American Cancer Society (Consult local chapter for information)

American Heart Association (Consult local chapter for information)

American Medical Assoc., Film Library, 1101 Vermont Ave., NW,
        Washington, D.C. 20005

AMP   Arthur Mokin Productions, 17 West 60th Street, New York NY 10023

AVED   AV-ED Films, 7934 Santa Monica Blvd., Hollywood, CA   90046

BCR   Barbary Coast Releasing, Ltd., 680 Beach, Suite 495, San
                Francisco, CA 94109

BFA   Bailey Film Assoc., Educational Media Dept., 2211 Michigan
                Ave., Santa Monica, CA   90404.

CF   Churchill Films, 622 N. Robertson Blvd., Los Angeles, CA 90069

COR   Coronet Films, 65 E. South Water St., Chicago, IL   60601

CRM   CRM Films, 1011 Camino Del Mar, Del Mar, CA   92014

CRM/Mc   CRM/McGraw-Hill Films, P.O. Box 641, Del Mar, CA   92014

DOC   Document Associates, 880 3rd Ave., New York, NY 10022

EBEC   Encyclopedia Britannica Educational Corp., 1822 Pickwick Ave.,
                Glenview, IL   60025

FI   Films, Inc., 733 Green Bay Rd., Wilmette, IL   60091

HAN   Handel Films, 8730 Sunset Blvd., West Hollywood, CA   90069

IFB   International Film Bureau, 332 S. Michigan Ave., Chicago, IL
                60604

IU   Indiana University, Audiovisual Center, Division of University
                Extension, Bloomington, IN   47401

ME   Milner-Fenwick, Inc., 3800 Liberty Heights Ave., Baltimore,
                MD   21215

MG   Media-Guild, 11526 Sorrento Valley Rd., Suite J., San Diego,
                CA   92121

NGS   National Geographic Society, Educational Services, 17th and
                M Sts., N.W., Washington, D.C.   20012

NIH   National Institutes of Health, 7500 Wisconsin Ave., Bethesda,
                MD   20014

NMAC   National Medical Audiovisual Center, Chamblee, GA   30005

PE   Perennial Education, P.O. Box 236, 1825 Willow Rd., Northfield,
                IL   60093

Planned Parenthood (Contact local chapter for information)

PF   Pyramid Films, P.O. Box 1048, Santa Monica, CA   90406

TLV   Time-Life Video, Time-Life Bldg., New York, NY 10020
         Distribution Center, PO Box 644, Paramus, NJ 07652

UC   University of California, Extension Media Center, 416
        Fourth Street, Berkeley, CA 94720

WNSE   Ward's Natural Science Establ., Learning Aids Division, PO
        Box 1712, Rochester, NY 14603

CHAPTER 1. INTRODUCTION

Outline
I.   Science and Society
II.   Scientific Method
III. It's a Fact
IV.   The Limitations of Science
V.   Fundamental Concepts of Biology
VI.   Evolution and Natural Selection
    A. Adaptations
    B. Energy and Natural Selection

Summary
Scientific knowledge is developed by subjecting problems to the scientific method. First, scientists make observations. Then they formulate alternative hypotheses that might explain the observations, and they test the hypotheses by experiments designed to disprove one or more of the hypotheses, and therefore to strengthen the evidence for those that remain.

Scientific discoveries and theories are useful, but they are always open to question; in science there is no such thing as "proof positive." Time and again in the history of science, widely accepted dogmas have turned out to be wrong, and even today scientists are busily discarding or remodeling some of the cherished "truths" presented in this book. A science editor recently noted that many of his magazine's readers seem to think that what they learned in their science courses was "graven on Sinai." As a science student, you should try to develop a healthy skepticism towards scientific findings, both old and new.

Biology is the science that studies living things. We can group the fundamental concepts of biology under three headings: cellular organization, biological information, and evolution.

Objectives

1. List three steps in the scientific method, and apply them to investigating a sample scientific problem.

2. List eight characteristics of living things.

3. Define evolution, natural selection, selective pressure, adaptation, and energy budget.

What's new or expanded in the Third Edition.

Section 1-B. Scientific Method. More extensive discussion of the scientific method and description of the application of the scientific method to study puddling behavior of yellow sulfur butterflies.

Section 1-F. Evolution and Natural Selection. More extensive coverage of evolutionary theory as presented by Darwin and Wallace.

SUGGESTIONS FOR LECTURE PREPARATION AND ENRICHMENT

The chapter clearly presents the scientific method and several fundamental concepts related to living organisms. Section 1-B - Scientific Method - could be discussed in class. Students might be asked to clearly state the problem, formulate a testable hypothesis, make predictions on the basis of the hypothesis, design and perform experiments, and determine the validity of the hypothesis. Appropriate controls should be pointed out. The scientific method might be applied to a currently controversial subject such as the use of aspartame (Nutrasweet) as an artificial sweetener in food products.

Ancillaries

Several overhead transparencies (OHT) could be used to illustrate some of the basic biological concepts presented on pages 8-9. These include:

OHT # 22 (page 88) a generalized animal cell, and OHT #23 (page 89) a generalized plant cell. The similarities could be pointed out as they illustrate the cell as the fundamental unit of living organisms.

OHT # 24 (page 114) illustrates the flow of matter and energy in living things, and the biological interrelationship of organisms.

OHT # 46 (page 174) presents DNA as the genetic material.

OHT # 62 (page 243) shows cleavage in a frog egg, thus illustrating the concept of living things developing and changing through time.

Supplemental Readings

Franke, Robert. 1983. Ethical questions and biologists. Journal of College Science Teaching, October.

Science 84, November 1984. For this issue editors have chosen 20 discoveries in science, technology, and medicine that they believe rank among this century's most significant historical developments in any field.

Thomas, Lewis. 1984. Medicine's Second Revolution. Science 84 5(9): 93-95. Describes transformations that have occurred in the practice of medicine from an art form to a science based technology.

Films

Biology: The Study of Life (UC, 1975, 18 min.)
Charles Darwin (UC, 1974, 24 min.)
Life? (NMAC, 1976, 14½ min.) Presents common characteristics of living things on both macroscopic and microscopic levels.

Student Activities

Ask students to collect articles on biological topics appearing in newspapers, magazines, etc. or to write a summary of a report seen on television or heard on the radio. These articles and summaries could provide topics for discussion during the next class period or at a later time during the semester. This activity should make students more aware of how the biological sciences affect their lives and how much or little they know about themselves, and their relationship to other living things and the ecosphere. Some of the articles will most likely deal with biomedical research and describe studies which have been done and which support X. These articles could be used for discussing various sides of scientific inquiry including ethics and for pointing out the difference between science and technology.

Ideas for Demonstrations

1. Grow crystals and compare their growth with that of living organisms.

2. Show specimens of living stones (Lithops) which can be purchased from biological supply companies. Ask students which criteria would allow them to distinguish the living stones from morphologically similar pebbles.

Topics for Discussion and Library Research

1. Compare living and nonliving things to determine similiarities and differences; have students point out characteristics unique to living organisms and nonliving things.

2.   Necessary components for valid experiment.

<u>ESSAY QUESTIONS</u>

(obj 2) 1. List and briefly describe five characteristics shared by <u>all</u> living organisms.

(obj 1) 2. Design an experiment to demonstrate the effectiveness of flea collars X, Y, and Z in killing fleas on cats. Outline the procedure to be followed. Be sure to state the hypothesis, and indicate the control(s).

(obj 2) 3. You are walking through a greenhouse and notice some strange looking things. They are soft to touch but you are not certain whether or not they are living. What three criteria would you use to determine whether or not they are living and to which kingdom they belong (if living)?

(obj 3) 4. Define the terms evolution, natural selection and adaptation, and discuss how each concept is related to the other two concepts.

(obj 3) 5. Distinguish the terms "energy income" and "energy budget." Provide two examples for each term, and discuss how they affect the evolutionary success of an individual.

CHAPTER 2. SOME BASIC CHEMISTRY

Outline

I. Chemical Elements of Life
II. Structure of Atoms
III. Bonds between Atoms
IV. Compounds and Molecules
V. Movement of Molecules
VI. Chemical Reactions
VII. Water
VIII. Dissociation and the pH Scale

Summary

More than 100 different chemical elements are known, each with a unique set of chemical properties. About twenty elements are essential to living things. The special properties of these elements are necessary to the processes involved in living, growing, and reproducing.

Living organisms are subject to the same physical and chemical laws that govern nonliving systems. Like nonliving matter, organisms are made up of atoms, which bond in various ways to form compounds. Ionic bonds form when one atom takes one or more electrons given up by another atom, and the resulting ions are attracted to each other by their opposite electric charges. Covalent bonds form when atoms share electron pairs. Hydrogen bonds are much weaker electrical attractions between partial positive and partial negative charges on polarly bonded atoms of different molecules. Chemical reactions rearrange the bonding of atoms, ions, and molecules and so form different compounds. Living organisms constantly carry out a variety of chemical reactions, forming different compounds as required.

Water is the most abundant substance in living things, and is absolutely necessary for life as we know it. The water molecule's structure and hydrogen-bonding ability give water a unique set of properties that make it essential to life: water dissolves polar and ionic substances; it forms interfaces with nonpolar substances; it creeps into small spaces by capillarity; it absorbs heat and disperses it throughout the body; it carries away body heat when it vaporizes from the body surface; and it is denser as a liquid than as a solid. These properties make water vital to the economy of living organisms.

Many substances dissociate when they dissolve in water. The pH of a solution is a measure of its hydrogen ion concentration; the pH value indicates whether a solution is acidic or alkaline. The body fluids of living organisms are maintained at a nearly constant pH by the presence of buffers, chiefly bicarbonate ion.

Objectives

1. Define or recognize the characteristics of the following, and use this knowledge to answer questions about the relationships among them: atom, proton, neutron, electron, isotope, ion, molecule, single bond, double bond, polar, nonpolar, mole, molecular weight, dissociation, acid, base, pH scale; buffer.

2. Recognize examples of ionic, covalent, and hydrogen bonds, and explain the differences between them.

3. Write the correct molecular formulas for water, carbon dioxide oxygen gas, and table salt.

4. List and discuss six reasons why water plays an important role in living systems.

What's new or expanded in the third edition.

Tables 2-2, 2-3, and 2-4 are new. Table 2-2 presents the charge and mass of subatomic particles while table 2-3 lists the valences of the most common elements in living organisms. Table 2-4 lists the strength in KCal/mole of hydrogen bonds and some of the more common ionic and covalent bonds found in biological molecules. On pages 28-29 is a discussion of the chemical properties of buffers and of their importance for living systems.

SUGGESTIONS FOR LECTURE PREPARATION AND ENRICHMENT

Ancillaries

Overhead transparencies (OHT) 1 to 5 illustrate some of the basic concepts in this chapter.

OHT #1 (page 20) diagrams the formation of an ionic bond while OHT # 2 (pages 20, 21) illustrates the covalent bonding between hydrogen atoms and the polar covalent bonding between hydrogen and chlorine, respectively. Ask students to comment on the similarities, differences, and consequences of these two types of covalent bonds, and to compare them with hydrogen bonding diagrammed in OHT # 3.

OHT #4 (page 23) illustrates diffusion. Ask students to comment on factors affecting this physical process.

OHT # 5 (page 28) presents the pH scale on which is pointed out the pH readings of some familiar substances.

Films

Atom in the Hospital (2/E) (HAN, 1979, 21 min.) Outlines use of radiation in medicine.

Student Activities

Have students build models of atoms and molecules, such as O_2, H_2O and CH_4, to illustrate structure as well as chemical bonding between atoms.

Ideas for Demonstrations

1. Models of simple molecules, such as O_2, H_2O and CH_4 to illustrate different types of bonds. Kits can be purchased from biological supply houses, or alternately pipecleaners and styrofoam balls can be used.

2. Density of water. Add ice to water in graduated cylinder. Measure temperature of water at top, middle and bottom of cylinder, when ice is added, after a few minutes have passed, and after the ice melts. Have students explain recorded temperature at the time intervals and relate to spring and fall overturn in lakes and ponds.

Topics for Discussion and Library Research

1. Use of radioisotopes for diagnosis of disease and for biochemical research.

2. Periodic table and atomic structure.

3. Electrons, orbitals, and energy levels--importance for processes of photosynthesis and energy production.

4. Importance of buffers in the body; effectiveness of buffers in commercially prepared products, such as buffered aspirin, or of taking antacids.

ESSAY QUESTIONS

obj 4   1.   List three properties of water and describe how each affects living organisms.

obj 4   2.   List and describe the major types of chemical bonds in a water molecule.

obj 1   3.   Sodium bicarbonate ($NaHCO_3$), a salt, is sometimes taken to relieve acid indigestion. The sodium bicarbonate is mixed in water and then swallowed.
  a)   What happens to the $NaHCO_3$ when it is added to water?
  b)   What chemical reaction occurs in the stomach to relieve the acid indigestion?
  c)   Why does a person belch a few minutes after taking the bicarbonate drink?

obj 1   4.   In biomedical research radioisotopes such as ^{14}C, ^{3}H, and ^{32}P, are used as markers to determine the products of a chemical reaction, the activity of an enzyme, the metabolic pathway of a molecule throughout an organism's body, etc. The radioisotope is substituted for the nonradioactive isotope in the molecule of study. Why is this a valid method for determining the chemical activity of the molecule?

obj 1   5.   Draw and label a general diagram for the structure of an atom and briefly describe each of the components.

obj 1   6.   Distinguish between the members of the following paired terms: acid/base; element/molecule; proton/neutron/electron; energy level/orbital; chemical formula/structural formula.

obj 1   7.   Distinguish between the members of the following paired terms: reactant/product; inorganic/organic; covalent ionic/hydrogen bond; polar/nonpolar; cation/anion/ion.

        8.   For each of the chemical symbols listed below, indicate the name and importance or function in the organism: Ca, Cl, P, K and Fe.

obj 2   9.   Compare ionic, covalent and hydrogen bonds with regards to their strength, polarity, stability, and the effect of water on each.

obj 2,3   10.   Write out the correct molecular formula for water, carbon dioxide, oxygen gas, and table salt, and for each identity the type of chemical bond(s) holding the atoms together.

CHAPTER 3. BIOLOGICAL CHEMISTRY

Outline

I.   Structure of Organic Molecules
     A.   Carbon Skeletons
     B.   Functional Groups
II. Carbohydrates
III. Lipids
     A.   Fatty Acids
     B.   Triacylglycerols
     C.   Phospholipids
     D.   Waxes
     E.   Steroids
IV. Proteins
     A.   Protein Structure
V.   Nucleic Acids
VI. Quantitative Comparisons of Classes of Biological Molecules
VII. Enzymes
     A.   Enzyme-Substrate Complexes
     B.   Factors that Affect Enzyme Activity
VIII. Metabolism
     Box: How to look at Molecular Structures
     Essay: Determining the Amino Acid Sequence of Proteins.

Summary

Living organisms are made up of water, inorganic ions, and organic molecules. Organic molecules are based on carbon, a versatile element able to form molecular skeletons of a myriad of sizes and shapes. We can simplify our study of those that occur in living things by grouping them into four main categories: carbohydrates, lipids, proteins, and nucleic acids.

Carbohydrates and lipids are composed mainly of carbon, hydrogen, and oxygen. Some carbohydrates and lipids are important energy-storage compounds that may be broken down to release energy. Structural poly-saccharides include cellulose, in plants, and chitin, in arthropods. Carbohydrates tend to be polar and associate with water, but lipids are nonpolar and so do not dissolve in water; they are vital components of all biological membranes. Some are also important hormones.

Proteins and nucleic acids play vital roles in directing an organism's growth, activity, and reproduction. Proteins contain the elements carbon, hydrogen, oxygen, nitrogen, and some sulfur; nucleic acids contain carbon, hydrogen, oxygen, nitrogen, and phosphorus. Important proteins include enzymes, structural proteins, hormones, and toxins.

Organic macromolecules are polymers, each made up of many monomeric subunits. A polymer contains a limited number of types of monomers.

Monomers are joined together to form polymers by condensation reactions in which a bond is formed by removing the components of a water molecule from the subunits. Macromolecules are broken down by hydrolysis, the addition of a water molecule between the subunit residues, which thus become separated.

Group	Monomers	joining together breaking apart	Polymers
Carbohydrates	Monosaccharides	$-H_2O$ / $+H_2O$	Polysaccharides
Proteins	Amino Acids	$-H_2O$ / $+H_2O$	Polypeptides
Nucleic acids	Nucleotides	$-H_2O$ / $+H_2O$	DNA, RNA

(The larger lipids are not true polymers)

44

Enzymes are protein catalysts; there are about 2000 kinds of enzymes, each adapted to specific substrates. By lowering the activation energy for the reactions they mediate, enzymes enable organisms to carry out chemical reactions quickly at the relatively low temperatures of their bodies. Enzymatic reactions are organized into the various metabolic pathways that convert one kind of molecule to another, build up or break down polymers, and break down food to release energy. The channelling of substrates into different metabolic pathways is under negative feedback control: allosteric enzymes at the beginnings of metabolic pathways are activated or inactivated according to the organism's metabolic needs. The activity of metabolic enzymes is also affected by substrate concentration, cofactors, inhibitors, pH, and temperature.

Objectives

1. Give or recognize the characteristics of the following, and use this knowledge to answer questions about the relationship among them: organic compound, monomer, polymer, carboxyl group, amino group, carbohydrate, monosaccharide, pentose sugar, hexose sugar, condensation reaction, dehydration synthesis, hydrolysis, disaccharide, polysaccharide, lipid, fatty acid, triacylglycerol, wax, steroid, amino acid, dipeptide, peptide bond, polypeptide, protein, enzyme, substrate, catalyst, equilibrium position, nucleotide, nucleic acid.

2. Classify the following in the appropriate classes of molecules listed in Objective 1, and briefly state their function in living organisms: glucose, cellulose, starch, glycogen, glycerol, cholesterol, enzyme, ATP.

3. List four main classes of biological macromolecules, state the role of each in living organisms, and name the type(s) of subunits from which each is synthesized and the chemical elements typical of each class of molecules.

4. Given a diagram of the structures of two sugars, or two amino acids, or glycerol and a fatty acid, draw and explain a condensation reaction between them, and name the classes of compounds to which the reactant(s) and products belong, or, given the products of such a condensation reaction, draw a diagram of the hydrolysis reaction that each would undergo.

5. Explain the effect of enzyme or substrate concentration, competitive or noncompetitive inhibitors, allosteric interactions, temperature, and pH on the rate of an enzyme-mediated reaction.

6. Define metabolism and briefly describe how metabolic pathways are regulated.

What's new or expanded in the Third Edition

Section 3-A, Structure of Organic Molecules, incorporates material from sections 3-A and 3-B in second edition, and contains additional information on functional groups.

Section 3-B, Carbohydrates, has been expanded and includes more in depth discussion of glycogen, starch, cellulose, and chitin.

In section 3-G, Enzymes, modulators and allosteric interactions are presented as factors affecting enzyme activity.

Section 3-H, Metabolism, discusses the relationship between enzymes and metabolic pathways, their organization, and how they are controlled.

Box 3-1, How to Look At Molecular Structures, provides steps to follow in analyzing structures of molecules such as glucose.

The essay, Determining the Amino Acid Sequence of Proteins, presents information on the rationale and methods used in studying the primary structure of proteins.

In addition to above changes, several figures have been modified and new ones added. Text figure 3-7 (page 37) includes diagrams of molecular structures and electron micrographs of starch and cellulose fibers. Figure 3-16 (page 43) presents the molecular structures of the 20 amino acids found in proteins; and figures 3-20 (page 45) and 3-21 (page 46) illustrate the molecular configuration of the tertiary structure and quaternary structure of proteins.

SUGGESTIONS FOR LECTURE PREPARATION AND ENRICHMENT

Ancillaries

Overhead transparencies (OHT) 6-15 are designed for this chapter.

OHT #6 (page 32) illustrates the different ways by which carbon atoms can bond together. Ask students about the type of bond and how many electrons are shared.

OHT #7 (page 35) illustrates the different molecular forms for glucose. Ask students to compare the various forms, pointing out similarities and differences.

OHT #8 (page 36) diagrams hydrolytic and condensation reactions involving carbohydrates.

OHT # 9 and #10 (pages 39 and 40) present information about fatty acids and phospholipids. Ask students to identify the hydrophilic and hydrophobic parts of fatty acids and phospholipids and to comment on the consequences of this dual nature regarding the cell.

OHTs #19-21 (pages 45, and 46) illustrate the secondary, tertiary and quaternary structures of proteins. Ask students to identify the primary structure and to list the types of bonds important for each structure.

OHTs #14 and 15 (pages 51-53) present information about enzyme activity, illustrate diagrammatically the substrate-enzyme interaction and graphically represent the effect of substrate and enzyme concentration on an enzyme-mediated reaction.

OHTs #43-46 (pages 172-174) illustrate the molecular structure of DNA. Ask students to point out the different types of bonds and the importance of each type of bond for the integrity and function of the molecule.

Correlative Laboratory Exercise

Topic 1, "Biologically Important Molecules."

In this exercise students learn about functional groups which are found on biologically important organic molecules and their role in determining the properties of the molecules. Students will also learn how to perform four simple tests for identifying known carbohydrates (Benedict's test, Iodine test), fats (Sudan III test), and, proteins (Biuret test). This is followed by an exercise in which students test food substances for the presence of simple sugars, starch, fats and amino groups. Finally students are introduced to chromatography, a technique used to separate, in this case, amino acids.

Topic 2 "Enzyme Action"

In this exercise students learn about enzymes and several factors which affect enzyme activity. Students will extract peroxidase from turnips and determine its activity under conditions of varying pH, temperature, concentration of enzyme, substrate concentration and in the presence of inhibitors. Enzyme activity is measured using a spectrophotometer. This exercise provides opportunities for students to gain experience using pipettes and the spectrophotometer.

Supplemental Readings

Karplus, Martin and J. Andrew McCammon. 1986. The dynamics of proteins. Sci. Am., April.

Miller, Jube Ann. 1985. Redesigning molecules nature's way. Science News 128:204-206, Sept. 28.

Student Activities

Have students construct models of four principal biological molecules using pipecleaners and styrofoam balls or kits.

Ideas for Demonstrations

1. Constructed models of biologically important organic molecules, such as glucose, sucrose, glycine, lysine, nucleic acids. Model kits may be purchases from biological supply houses.

2. Perform chemical tests for demonstrating presence of lipids (Sudan III), proteins (Biuret or Lowry), nucleic acids (Dische), and carbohydrates (Benedict's, IKI) in common food substances such as bread, meat, potatoes, etc., or show students the results of such tests conducted on common food substances.

3. Use a slinky-like toy or plastic coil to demonstrate various structural levels of organization for proteins and helical structure of DNA.

Topics for Discussion and Library Research

1. Types of chemical bonds in each kind of molecule.
2. Levels of protein structure and types of bonds important at each structural level.
3. Different types of proteins, their characteristics, and biological importance.

ESSAY QUESTIONS

obj 1 1. Compare proteins, carbohydrates and nucleic acids. Give the subunit structure and a general biological function/role for each.

2. Distinguish among the following paired terms: monomer/polymer; saturated fats/unsaturated fats; polysaccharide/polypeptide; tertiary structure/quaternary structure; and, glycogen/starch.

obj 5 3. Enzyme activity is usually reduced or abolished by the presence of inhibitors, extremes in pH and high temperatures. Discuss how or why each of these factors affects enzyme activity.

obj 6 4. Describe three ways by which the metabolic activities occurring within a cell are controlled and organized in order to proceed in an energy efficient and orderly manner.

obj 1 5. For which of the four biologically important molecules could each of the following isotopes be used as a label?
^{14}C, ^{15}N, ^{35}S, ^{32}P, ^{18}O, ^{3}H.

obj 3 6. Draw a generalized structural formula for an amino acid and indicate which part(s) of the molecule is/are involved in the formation of the peptide bond and which part(s) is responsible for the properties of the amino acid.

obj 3 7. Of the four biologically important molecules which one is the most versatile and why?

obj 4 8. Identify the type or class of molecule represented by each of the following structural formulas, and explain your answer.

```
H - C = O
H - C - OH
HO - C - H
H - C - OH
H - C - OH
H - C - OH
      H
```

(a)

```
    CH3   O    OH
  H       H   H  H
      H       H
     OH      OH
```

(b)

(c)

```
H   O  H H H  H H  H H  H H  H H  H
H-C-O--C-C-C-C-C-C-C-C-C-C-C-C-C-H
H      H H H  H H  H H  H H  H H  H

H   O  H H H  H H  H   H H  H H  H H
H-C-O--C-C-C-C-C-C-C=C-C-C-C-C-C-C-H
H      H H H  H H      H H  H H  H H

H   O  H H H  H H  H   H H  H H  H H
H-C-O--C-C-C-C-C-C-C=C-C-C=C-C-C-C-H
H      H H H  H H      H H  H H  H H
```

(c)

```
H   H  O      H  O       H2CSH  
 N - C - C - N - C - C - N - C - C = O
H    H       H  CH3      H  H     OH
```

(d)

(e)

48

CHAPTER 4 CELLS AND THEIR MEMBRANES

Outline

Summary

Cells must maintain the internal concentrations of all substances at appropriate levels. At the same time, cells must maintain a lively commerce with their environments, taking in new raw materials for their metabolism and expelling waste products.

The plasma membrane regulates what enters or leaves the cell. It is permeable to many types of small molecules and ions, yet sufficiently impermeable to prevent the loss of such materials as nucleic acids, proteins, and polysaccharides.

A biological membrane consists of a fluid lipid bilayer, with various proteins floating in it, some mobile in the bilayer and some anchored to stable cellular structures. Oligosaccharides are attached to some protein and lipid molecules, forming glycoproteins and glycolipids.

This basic structure has two properties crucial to membrane function. First, lipid bilayers spontaneously form closed compartments, thereby keeping the solutions inside and outside the membrane separate. Second, membranes are asymmetrical, with different lipid and protein components in each of the two layers, and with molecules oriented so that they consistently face one membrane surface or the other. For example, active transport molecules are oriented so that they move substances in only one direction.

A membrane's lipid bilayer is freely permeable to water. It also admits small, lipid-soluble molecules, which diffuse through the lipid layers according to their concentration gradients.

Most ions and polar molecules can cross the membrane only with the aid of protein transport molecules. Each protein is specific for a particular solute or a few closely related solutes. Channel proteins form aqueous channels through the membrane; some are gated so that they open in response to a specific stimulus, and most of these gates close spontaneously. The channel proteins, and protein carriers for facilitated diffusion, provide for the diffusion of specific polar molecules and ions down their electrochemical gradients. Other proteins mediate active transport, which can move a solute either with or against its electrochemical gradient. Active transport requires energy, provided either by ATP or by an electrochemical gradient of ions such as Na^+ or H^+. The sodium-potassium pump, powered by ATP, pumps Na^+ out of a cell and K^+ in. This pump is largely responsible for the membrane potential of a cell, and the electrochemical gradient of sodium that it creates also provides energy for the active transport of solutes such as glucose.

When the cell acquires macromolecules or larger particles, the membrane surrounds them and pinches off to become a vesicle or vacuole inside the cell, by the process of endocytosis. Substances can be discharged from many cells by the opposite process of exocytosis.

Cells gain or lose water by osmosis. ⌊The membrane does not control the movement of water molecules directly; rather, it performs active transport of solutes and so creates an osmotic potential difference that will induce osmosis.⌋ The cell wall of a plant cell exerts a pressure that limits the cell's water content. Many protozoans void excess water taken in by osmosis by means of a contractile vacuole.

The plasma membrane may be expanded to provide additional surface area for exchange of substances with the environment. The plasma membranes of adjacent animal cells may interact. Tight junctions seal membranes together and prevent seepage of substances between cells. Intermediary junctions and desmosomes provide mechanical strength by attaching the membranes of adjacent cells. Gap junctions act as "pipes" through animal cell membranes, providing for direct transfer of ions from cell to cell. In plants, direct transfer between cytoplasms of adjacent cells occurs by way of plasmodesmata.

Objectives

From your study of this chapter, you should be able to:

1. Describe the structure of the plasma membrane, and relate its structure to the ability to carry on the processes mentioned in Objective #2.

2. Define and explain the following processes, and state or identify the characteristics that distinguish them from one another: movement of substances through (1) lipid bilayers and (2) protein channels; facilitated diffusion, active transport, endocytosis, exocytosis, osmosis.

3. Name the types of substances that enter the cell by each of the processes listed in Objective #2.

4. List four important features of the sodium-potassium pump and give reasons why it is important to a living cell.

5. Define and use the following terms correctly: homeostasis, permeable, concentration gradient, electrochemical gradient, osmotic potential, osmotic pressure, isotonic, hypertonic, hypotonic, lysis, plasmolysis, turgor.

6. Describe, using the appropriate vocabulary from Objective #5, the effect of placing a plant or animal cell in distilled water or in a concentrated salt solution.

7. Given (1) a description or picture of two solutions separated by a membrane, and (2) the permeability properties of the membrane, predict (a) which solution will have the higher osmotic potential, and (b) the total and net movement of water, solutes, or both in the system.

8. Describe the functions of the central vacuole and the cell wall in the water relations of plant cells.

9. Describe and compare the structures of the following specialized membrane areas, and state their functions: microvilli, tight junctions, intermediary junctions, desmosomes, plasmodesmata, gap junctions.

What's new or expanded in the Third Edition

Information about the plasma membrane and its structure has been expanded and now appears in separate sections (4-A and 4-B) in this edition. Expanded descriptions of the various transport mechanisms are presented as subtopics of section 4-D. Also included in Section 4-D is additional material on active transport systems powered by ATP and by electrochemical gradients, such as a Na^+ gradient. Section 4-E contains new information about receptor-mediated endocytosis in the text and accompanying figure 4-12 (page 71).

Section 4-H, specializations of the Plasma Membrane discusses specializations, such as microvilli and the myelin sheath, in animal cells. The discussion of desmosomes, tight junctions and gap junctions has also been expanded both in written text and in figures.

The chapter includes many new figures which are correlated with material presented in the text. Figure 4-5 (page 63) presents the molecular structures of some of the lipids found in membranes, and in figure 4-7 (page 65) a diagram of the fluid mosaic model of the plasma membrane is presented. Figure 4-8 (page 67) illustrates the different ways by which substances move or are moved through membranes and figure 4-9 (page 68) graphically compares diffusion via carrier proteins and via channel proteins.

Table 4-1 (page 66) presents a comparison of the concentrations of various ions inside and outside a mammalian muscle cell.

SUGGESTIONS FOR LECTURE PREPARATION AND ENRICHMENT

Ancillaries

Overhead transparency (OHT) #4 (page 23) which illustrates diffusion of a solid in a liquid could be shown again.

OHTs #16 and 17 (pages 64 and 65) present the arrangements assumed by phospholipids in an aqueous medium, and of phospholipids and proteins in the plasma membrane. Ask students to comment on the relationship between the properties and structure of the plasma membrane, and the properties and structure of its component molecule, i.e., phospholipids and proteins.

In OHT #18 (page 67) the ways in which substances cross membranes are diagrammed. Ask students to discuss the transport systems in light of membrane structure.

OHTs #19 and 20 (page 73 and 74) illustrate osmotic behavior in animal and plant cells. Ask students to compare these two situations and discuss the different results.

Correlative Laboratory Exercises

Topic 4 Cells and Their Membranes

In this exercise students learn about diffusion, osmosis, dialysis, and the properties of cellular membranes by direct observation of living cells exposed to solutions of varying tonicity and by performing experiments which demonstrate diffusion and osmosis.

Supplemental Readings

Bretscher, Mark. 1985. The molecules of the cell membrane. Sci. Am., October.

Dautry-Varsat, A. and H. Lodish. 1984. How receptors bring proteins and particles into cells. Sci. Am., May.

Miller, J. 1984. Cell communication equipment: Do-it-yourself kit. Science News 125: 236-237.

Owen, J., McIntyre, N., and M. Gillett. 1984. Lipoproteins, cell membranes and cellular functions. TIBS 9: 238-242.

Rothman, J. and J. Lenard. 1984. Membrane traffic in animal cells. TIBS 9: 176-178.

Unwin, N. and R. Henderson. 1984. The structure of proteins in biological membranes. Sci. Am., February.

Ideas for Demonstration

1. Diffusion of solid in liquid. Carefully place a crystal of potassium permanganate ($KMnO_4$) on the bottom of a beaker containing distilled water at the beginning of class period. Have students periodically observe the beaker during the class. Keep beaker to next period.

2. Diffusion of gas in gas. Open a bottle of perfume at beginning of class period. Ask students in back of class to raise hands when able to smell odor. Compare rates of diffusion using different media.

3. Osmosis. Into three dialysis bags pour the same amount of a sugar solution (e.g., 10% corn syrup). Weigh the bags. Put each dialysis bag into a beaker containing a 10%, 20%, or 5% corn syrup solution. At the end of the class period, weigh the bags. Ask students to explain any differences in weights at beginning and end of class period.

4. Osmosis. Fill a dialysis bag with a solution of 25% glucose 0.5% egg albumin and 1% starch. Secure the end of the bag. Place into a beaker containing distilled water to which a small amount of an IKI solution has been added. Let stand for one hour and observe.

5. Slides of electron micrographs of cell membranes and freeze fractured membranes, and slides showing cell functions.

Topics for Discussion and Library Research

1. Discuss the results of demonstrations presented above.

2. Different processes by which materials pass through membranes, and how much each process depends on the membrane being fluid and dynamic.

3. Comparison of plasma membranes of different cells and between plasma membrane and membranes of organelles.

4. Evidence for fluid mosaic membrane structure.

5. Importance of cell junctions and cell communication.

6. Membrane synthesis. See article by Lodish, H. and J. Rothman. 1979. "The assembly of cell membranes." Sci. Am., January.

7. Intracellular membrane traffic. See articles by Geisow, M. J. 1982. "Intracellular membrane traffic." Nature 295: 649-650; Herzog, V. 1981. "Pathways of endocytosis in secretory cells." TIBS 6(12): 319-322, Rothman, J. and J. Lenard. 1984. "Membrane traffic in animal cells." TIBS 9(4): 176-178.

ESSAY QUESTIONS

obj 9 1. List three types of cell junctions and for each describe the general structure, biological function and type of cell or tissue where the junction might be found.

obj 2 2. Compare endocytosis and exocytosis. In your answer describe each process, the requirements, if any, for energy, the selectivity of the process, and how each depends on the membrane being fluid and dynamic.

obj 1 3. Glycophorin is an integral protein found in the membranes of red blood cells. Where in this protein would you expect to find a sequence of hydrophobic or uncharged amino acids? Why?

obj 1   4.   Imagine a cell surrounded by a membrane freely permeable to all substnaces. Would the cell be able to maintain homeostasis? Explain?

obj 6   5.   During surgery a person is given an intravenous aqueous solution containing dissolved sugar and salts. Even though you don't know the exact concentrations of salts and sugar, what can you deduce about the tonicity of the IV solution relative to body fluids? Explain.

obj 6   6.   Red blood cells and <u>Elodea</u> cells are placed in distilled water and in a 10% salt solution. Explain the effect of the different fluids on each type of cell.

obj 7   7.   Three dialysis bags are filled with the same solution. After weighing, each bag is placed into a beaker containing an 0.5%, 2%, or 4% sugar solution. After one hour each bag is weighed. See table below for final weights. What is the concentration of the solution in the dialysis bag? Explain your answer.

	0 Time	1 hour	fluid in beaker
Bag A	10 g	11 g	0.5% sugar
Bag B	10 g	10 g	2.0% sugar
Bag C	10 g	8 g	2.0% sugar

obj 4   8.   A cell is unable to make ATP. What effects will this have on the cell's ability to transport molecules across membranes and to maintain homeostasis.

CHAPTER 5   CELL STRUCTURE AND FUNCTION

<u>Outline</u>

<u>Summary</u>

Each cell must carry out all the processes necessary for life: obtain
food, release energy, eliminate wastes, and divide to reproduce itself.
In addition, each cell of a multicellular organism also carries out
some specialized function as its contribution to the body's overall
economy.

       Important structures found in eukaryotic cells are:
1.   The plasma membrane, a double layer of lipid and protein, which
     regulates the movement of substances into and out of the cell.
2.   The nucleus, containing the genetic material in the form of DNA of
     the chromosomes. DNA and RNA are synthesized in the nucleus. The
     nucleolus is an area in the nucleus where ribosomal subunits are
     synthesized. A nuclear envelope consisting of two membranes, and
     pierced by pores, surrounds the nucleus. The outer membrane is
     continuous with the endoplasmic reticulum.
3.   Ribosomes, the sites of protein synthesis.
4.   Endoplasmic reticulum, a system of membranes which divides the cell
     into compartments and forms surfaces where many chemical reactions
     occur, including synthesis of most of the cell's new membrane.
5.   Golgi complexes, stacks of membranous sacs in which proteins and
     other materials are modified and packages, some for secretion to
     the exterior of the cell.
6.   Lysosomes, sacs of hydrolytic enzymes. Lysosomes fuse with
     vesicles containing food, foreign matter, or worn-out cellular
     structures, which are digested by the lysosomal enzymes.
7.   Peroxisomes, sacs of oxidative enzymes, which detoxify harmful
     substances and perform various metabolic functions.
8.   Mitochondria, complex organelles that produce most of the cell's
     energy supply of ATP.

9. Plastids, found in plant cells and in photosynthetic protists.
    The most important plastids are the chloroplasts, which carry out
    photosynthesis.
10. The cell wall, made largely of cellulose fibers, a porous but
    fairly rigid protective and supportive structure outside the
    plasma membranes of plant cells, fungi, and some protists.
11. Vacuoles, especially large and prominent in plant cells.
12. The cytoskeleton, responsible for shape and movement, is attached
    to the plasma membrane and probably to other organelles. It is
    composed of a variety of protein fibers (listed in order of in-
    creasing diameter):
    a. Microfilaments, composed of actin subunits associated with
        small amounts of myosin. These contractile proteins provide
        the forces necessary for shape changes and movement.
    b. Intermediate filaments, made up of various fibrous proteins,
        probably provide stability and strength.
    c. Microtubules, composed of tubulin subunits, assembled and
        disassembled at need under the direction of organizing
        centers, which include centrioles in the cell center (except
        in higher plants) and basal bodies at the bases of cilia and
        flagella, thread-like projections at the cell surface that
        move the cell itself or move substances past the cell surface.

In multicellular organisms, cells are organized into tissues,
such as epithelium and connective tissue. Several types of tissue may
be organized to form organs, such as kidneys or roots, each with its
own particular function.

The prokaryotic cells of bacteria have cell walls, plasma membranes, cytoplasm, ribosomes, and DNA, but their only internal membrane
system is usually a mesosome, although some also have photosynthetic
membranes.

Objectives

1. Outline how a light microscope, a transmission electron microscope,
    and a scanning electron microscope work.

2. List at least four components of cells that can be seen with a
    light microscope and four that can be seen with an electron micro-
    scope but not with a light microscope.

3. Give at least one function of each of the following structures
    and state whether each would be found in prokaryotic plant, or
    animal cells: *nuclear area, mesosome, *nucleus, *nuclear enve-
    lope, * chromosome, * nucleolus, * ribosome, * endoplasmic
    reticulum, *Golgi complex, lysosome, peroxisome, *mitochondrion,
    plastid, *chloroplast, *cell wall, *vacuole, cytoskeleton, micro-
    tubules, *cilium or flagellum, centriole, intermediate filaments,
    microfilament.

4. Given a photograph taken using a light microscope or trans-
    mission electron microscope, identify the plasma membrane, cyto-
    plasm, and any structures marked *in Objective 3.

5. Describe the main differences between a eukaryotic and a prokaryotic
    cell.

What's new or expanded in the Third Edition

    Sections 5-B, Cell and Tissue Culture, and 5-C, Cell Fractionation
are new. Section 5-J, Lysosomes, Peroxisomes, and Glyoxysomes, contain
additional information on the latter two organelles. Section 5-0,
the cytoskeleton, discusses the cytoskeleton, its organization and
the three types of filaments (microtubules, microfilaments intermediate filaments) in greater detail. The discussions of the cell
nucleus and lysosomes, are also expanded. Several figures have been
added such as figure 5-1 which is a comparison of the light microscope

with the two types of electron microscopes, figure 5-8 which diagram-matically represents the structure of the nuclear envelope, and figure 5-10 which shows the movement of transport vesicles from the ER to another membrane. Table 5-5 which presents the common features of eukaryotic cells should be a useful summary for students.

SUGGESTIONS FOR LECTURE PREPARATION AND ENRICHMENT

Ancillaries

The following overhead transparencies (OHT) would enhance the presentation of material in this chapter.

OHT #17 (page 65) introduces the student to the structure of the plasma membrane.

In OHT #21 (page 84) three types of microscopes are compared--the light microscope, the transmission EM, and the scanning EM. Ask students to point out similarities and differences, and to comment on which type of microscope would be used to reveal a named cellular organelle or feature.

OHTs # 22 and 23 (pages 88, 89) illustrate generalized animal and plant cells respectively. Ask students to identify designated organelles and their functions in each type of cell and to compare both types of cells.

OHTs # 29 and 34 (pages 130, 145) show the internal structures of a mitochondrion and a chloroplast. Ask students to point out simi-larities and differences.

Correlative Laboratory Exercices

Topic 3, Cells and the Microscope
Topic 5, Cell Structure and Function

In Topic 3 students learn about the operating principles, the com-ponent parts and how to use correctly the compound microscope and stereomicroscope. Students gain experience by viewing prepared slides, measuring objects using objectives of varying magnification, and by making their own slides of living organisms.

From the exercises in topic 5 students will become more familiar with prokaryotic and eukaryotic cells which exist as single celled organisms or as parts of tissues in multicellular organisms. Plant and animal cells are studied.

SUPPLEMENTAL READINGS

Birchmeier, W. 1984. Cytoskeleton structure and function. Trends in Biological Sciences (TIBS) 9: 192-194.

Carolina Biology Readers:

Cook, G. M. W. 1980. The Golgi (2/E)

John, B. and K. Lewis. 1980. Somatic Cell Division (2/E)

Jordan, E. G. 1978. The Nucleolus (2/E)

Nachmias, V. 1984. Microfilaments

Satir, P. 1983. Cilia and Related Organelles

deDuve, C. 1983. Microbodies in the living cell. Sci. Am., May.

Goodman, S. 1984. The bones of cell. (the cytoskeleton) New Scientist 104 (1424): 44-47, 4 October.

Rothman, James. 1985. The compartmental organization of the Golgi apparatus. Sci. Am., September.

Shulman, R. 1983. NMR spectroscopy of living cells. Sci. Am. January.

Tartakoff, A. M. 1982. Simplifying the complex Golgi. TIBS $\underline{7}$:
174-177.

Silberner, Joanne. 1985. Touch-me-nots. Science News $\underline{127}$: 58,
January 26. An examination of the causes of epidermolysis bullosa, a disease characterized by a lack of cohesion between or
within the layers of the skin.

Weber, Klaus and Mary Osborn. 1985. The molecules of the cell matrix.
Sci. Am., October.

Films

The Cell: A Functioning Structure. Parts I, II (CRM, 1972, 30 min.
each) Covers structure and functions of cellular organelles.

Man, The Incredible Machine (NGS, 1975, 16 min.) Focuses on human physiological systems.

Student Activities

1. After students have viewed OHTs and slides of cells and
organelles, have students generate a table comparing plants
and animal cells, and eukaryotic and prokaryotic cells.

2. Have students read chapters entitled "The lives of a cell"
and "Organelles as organisms" in Thomas, Lewis, 1974.
The Lives of a Cell: Notes of a Biology Watcher. Bantam
Books, Inc., New York. Then ask students to write a short
essay on the types of symbiotic relationships existing between
cells and the organism and between cells and their subcellular
organelles.

Ideas for Demonstrations

1. Pass around or set up a display of electron micrographs of
cells, and subcellular organelles. See book by Fawcett, D.W.
1981. The Cell (2/E), Saunders Publ. Co., Philadelphia, PA.

2. Set up microscopes with stained slides of different cell types
such as blood cells, neurons, bacteria, protozoans, plant
cells (Elodea), epithelial cells from the cheek, or of different tissue types.

3. Surface area to volume ratio. Using pipe cleaners and styrofoam balls have student construct cubes with linear dimensions
from 1-8. Have them calculate volume and total surface area
for each cube. Have students determine the point at which
the total surface area becomes a limiting factor for the size
of cube if the cube represents a cell.

4. Bring in actual tissues from chickens. Skin represents
epithelial tissue; tendons--dense connective tissue; ligaments
--elastic connective tissue; tissue around muscles, under skin
and surrounding organs--loose connective tissue; fat--adipose
tissue; muscle-muscle tissue; bone and cartilage; nerves and
blood.

Topics for Discussion and Library Research

1. Relation between cell volume and surface area; constancy of
cell size even though varied shapes; size limitations.

2. Evolution of cells. See articles by Schopf, J.W. 1978.
"The evolution of the earliest cells." Sci. Am. Sept;
Valentine, J.W. 1978. "The evolution of multicellular plants
and animals." Sci. Am., Sept; Vidal, G. 1984. "The oldest
eukaryotic cells." Sci. Am., Feb.

3. Movement of substances throughout the cell.

4. Relation between cell shape and function; effect on function of changing shape.

5. Methods for studying cells: differential centrifugation, immuno-fluorescence, autoradiography, different types of microscopy.

6. Relation between structure and function in cellular organelles; effect on function of changing structure; a lysosome with a double membrane or a mitochondrion with a single membrane.

ESSAY QUESTIONS

obj 3 1. Eukaryotic cells contain a number of membrane bound organelles. List and describe the structure and function of <u>five</u> of these organelles.

obj 5 2. Describe <u>four</u> differences between eukaryotic and prokaryotic cells and <u>one</u> difference between animal and plant cells.

obj 3 3. Distinguish between the members of the following paired terms: smooth/rough endoplasmic reticulum; scanning/transmission electron microscope; magnification/resolving power; prokaryotic/eukaryotic cell; microtubule/microfilament.

obj 3 4. Distinguish between the members of the following paired terms: nucleus/nucleolus; chromatin/chromosomes; light/electron microscope; cilia/flagella; vesicle/vacuole.

obj 5 5. Draw a typical plant cell and label ten structures or organelles.

obj 5 6. Draw a typical animal cell and label ten structures or organelles.

obj 5 7. List five different types of cells found in your body. For these cells discuss two similarities and two differences.

obj 1 8. Compare the light microscope with the two types of electron microscopes regarding degree of magnification and resolving power, nature of lenses, advantages, and disadvantages.

obj 2, 3 9. For each of the following organelles or structures describe the appearance when viewed with a light microscope, a transmission EM, and a scanning EM:
   a) nucleus and nuclear envelope
   b) mitochondrion
   c) ribosome

10. Subcellular organelles can be separated from each other using differential centrifugation. To accomplish this cells are first broken up by one of a variety of homogenization procedures, such as sonication or grinding with a pestle. The homogenate is then fractionated using differential centrifugation which depends on the principle that particles of different sizes will travel at differnt rates towards the bottom of a centrifuge tube when centrifugal force is applied. The cellular homogenate is spun in a centrifuge at different speeds for varying periods of time to separate the subcellular organelles. This procedure is reflected in the flow chart below:

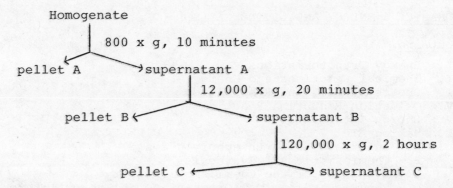

Homogenate

800 x g, 10 minutes

pellet A   →supernatant A

12,000 x g, 20 minutes

pellet B←   →supernatant B

120,000 x g, 2 hours

pellet C←   →supernatant C

After the fractions are collected, they are analyzed biochemi-
cally and cytochemically to determine which type of organelle
is present. Consider the following: A piece of liver is homo-
genized and fractionated according to the scheme above. Given
the information below, identify which organelles would most likely
be present in the designated pellet or supernatant fraction.

Pellet A contains DNA and RNA and when observed with an
electron microscope contains large membrane bound fragments.

Pellet B contains membrane bound particles some of which
can produce ATP and some of which are capable of destroying other
organelles.

Pellet C contains small membrane fragments some of which
function in lipid metabolism.

Supernatant C contains small particles capable of synthesi-
zing polypeptides.

CHAPTER 6 ENERGY AND LIVING CELLS

Outline

I.   Energy Transformations
II. Chemical Reactions and Energy
III. Photosynthesis and Respiration
IV. Oxidation-Reduction Reaction
V.   Energy Intermediates
VI. Making ATP
    A. Substrate Level Phosphorylation
    B. Chemiosmotic ATP Synthesis
    C. Evidence for the Chemiosmotic Theory
    D. The Electrochemical Gradient as an Energy Intermediate

Box: Free Energy, Heat Flow, and Entropy: The Gibbs Free Energy
      Equation

Summary

Living organisms require energy in order to maintain their chemical composition, move, repair damage, grow, and reproduce. Energy cannot be created or destroyed, but each time energy is converted from one form to another, some free energy is degraded into an unusable form. To remain alive, organisms must constantly acquire fresh supplies of energy.

The central energy-processing pathways of life are photosynthesis and respiration. In photosynthesis, the sun's energy is captured and stored in the chemical bonds of food molecules, which can later be broken down during respiration to release the trapped energy. The ultimate task of both photosynthesis and respiration is to produce energy intermediates to drive endergonic reactions.

The most common energy intermediate is ATP. Although some ATP is formed by substrate-level phosphorylation, most is believed to be made by chemiosmosis, using an electrochemical potential gradient as an energy source.

Chemiosmosis is carried out by molecules associated with respiratory and photosynthetic membranes. Electron transport systems in these membranes carry out a series of redox reactions, establishing an electrochemical potential gradient, with H^+ ions trapped on one side of an H^+-impermeable membrane. This gradient is used to make ATP, probably by allowing H^+ to pass through the membrane, down its concentration gradient, by way of protein channels associated with ATP synthetase enzymes. ATP synthetase uses the energy of the H^+ gradient to make ATP. The chemiosmotic theory is supported by experimental findings that ATP synthesis occurs in the presence of pH gradients across intact membranes, and that destroying the gradient or the membrane virtually halts ATP formation.

The electrochemical potential gradient itself serves as an energy intermediate for some energy-requiring reactions.

Objectives

1. In addition to the terms mentioned in the other objectives, use or interpret the following terms correctly:

potential energy	autotroph
free energy	heterotroph
entropy	ADP
	P_i

2. State the first and second laws of thermodynamics, and explain how living organisms carry out endergonic chemical reactions.

3. List the basic starting materials and end products of photosynthesis and respiration, and describe the roles of photosynthesis and respiration in the energy economy of the living world.

4. Recognize examples of oxidation and reduction reactions. Given such reactions, identify which substances are oxidized and which reduced as a result of the reaction.

5. Discuss the role of ATP in the energy economy of living organisms.

6. Distinguish between substrate-level phosphorylation and chemiosmotic phosphorylation.

7. Describe the chemiosmotic theory of ATP synthesis, including the role of the electron transport system, the membrane housing this system, the electrochemical gradient, and ATP synthetase.

What's new or exapnded in the Third Edition

Section 6-A, Energy Transformation, has been expanded and includes additional information on the qualitative relationship between free energy, heat flow, and entropy. Box 6-1 which is also new gives the quantitative relationship between free energy, heat flow, and entropy.

In section 6-B the changes in free energy during exergonic and endergonic reactions are represented graphically. (page 113)

Sections 6-D, Oxidation-Reduction, Reactions, and 6-E, Energy Intermediates, have been expanded and now exist as separate entities rather than subsections of 6-C in the 2/E.

SUGGESTIONS FOR LECTURE PREPARATION AND ENRICHMENT

Ancillaries

Overhead transparency (OHT) # 24 (page 114) illustrates the flow of energy and matter through living organisms. Ask students to point out the interrelationship between photosynthesis and respiration and to compare the two processes.

OHT #25 (page 119) shows diagrammatically the basic scheme of chemiosmotic ATP synthesis as it occurs in mitochondria and bacteria. OHT # 29 (page 130) presents mitochondrial structure. Ask students to identify where the electrochemical gradient is established.

OHT #26 (page 120) illustrates a demonstration of chemiosmotic ATP synthesis in chloroplasts. Ask students which would happen to ATP synthesis if the pH of the medium were pH 4 and the inside of the chloroplast were pH 8.5.

Student Activities

Have students write a short essay on the implications of the following two quotes regarding the cell, organism, and ecosphere. The quotes are from G. Tyler Miller, Jr. (see Miller, G. Tyler, Jr. 1982. Living in the Environment (3/E). Wadsworth Publ. Co., Belmont, CA, pg. 42). First law of energy: "Regarding energy quantity, you can't get something for nothing--you can only break even. Second law of energy (law of energy degradation): "Regarding energy quality, you can't break even."

Topics for Discussion and Library Research
1. Laws of thermodynamics and entropy.
2. ATP hydrolysis and production.

ESSAY QUESTIONS

obj 1 1. Distinguish among the following paired terms: endergonic/ exergonic; first law of thermodynamics/second law of thermodynamics; potential energy/kinetic energy; activation energy/free energy; autotroph/heterotroph.

obj 2 2. Are living organisms contradictions to the first and second law of thermodynamics? Explain.

obj 2 3. A majority of the chemical reactions occurring in a cell are endergonic. Describe two ways by which these reactions can occur in a cell.

obj 2, 4. Consider the flow of energy: the sun--plants--herbivore--
3 carnivore--bacteria. Is the amount of energy available to the bacteria greater than/less than/equal to the amount of radiant energy converted to chemical energy by the plants? Explain your answer.

obj 5 5. Describe the chemical structure of ATP and discuss its function in cellular metabolism.

obj 2, 6. Does ATP functioning as the energy currency in the cell violate
5 either of the laws of thermodynamics? Explain.

obj 6 7. Compare substrate level phosphorylation and chemiosmotic phosphorylation regarding reactants, products, location, and involvement of mitochondria.

obj 7 8. If the inner membrane of the mitochondrion were freely permeable to H^+, how would chemiosmotic ATP synthesis be affected?

CHAPTER 7 FOOD AS FUEL: CELLULAR RESPIRATION AND FERMENTATION

Outline

I. Coenzymes
II. Breakdown of Glucose Under Aerobic Conditions
    A. Glycolysis
    B. Into the Mitochondrion
    C. Citric Acid Cycle
    D. Oxidative Phosphorylation
    E. The Energy Yield of Glucose

III. Fermentation
IV. Alternative Food Molecules

    Essay: Pasteur and Yeasts

Summary

Cellular respiration is the process by which cells extract free energy from the energy stored in the chemical bonds of food molecules (usually glucose) and use this energy to regenerate their supply of ATP.

During glycolysis, glucose is broken down anaerobically to two molecules of pyruvate, and NAD^+ is reduced to $NADH + H^+$. Glycolysis also yields ATP by substrate-level phosphorylation.

Each pyruvate formed during glycolysis loses a carbon dioxide to become an acetyl group that combines with coenzyme A. Acetyl CoA enters the citric acid cycle by combining with the 4-carbon compound oxaloacetate. During one turn of the cycle, the equivalents of the two carbon atoms of the acetyl group are oxidized to carbon dioxide. ATP is produced by substrate-level phosphorylation, and NAD^+ and FAD are reduced to $NADH + H^+$ and $FADH_2$. Oxaloacetate and coenzyme A are regenerated and can go through the cycle again.

Oxidative phosphorylation produces most of the ATP derived from respiration. $NADH + H^+$ and $FADH_2$ from glycolysis and the citric acid cycle pass pairs of hydrogen atoms to the electron transport chain. The electron transport chain forms an electrochemical gradient of hydrogen ions that can be used to phosphorylate ADP to ATP. At the end of the chain, the electrons combine with oxygen to form water.

Neither glycolysis nor the citric acid cycle requires oxygen directly. However, in a cell that is short of the final electron acceptor, oxygen, most of the NAD^+ in the cell will be tied up as NADH, unable to release its electrons to the electron transport chain. Some cells have an adaptation that permits them to continue to produce ATP from glycolysis under such anaerobic conditions: pyruvate accepts electrons from $NADH + H^+$ forming ethanol or lactate. This releases NAD^+ so that glycolysis can continue. No such mechanism exists for the acid cycle, which therefore cannot function under anaerobic conditions.

Many other metabolic pathways feed into glycolysis, the citric acid cycle, and the electron transport chain, enabling cells to use many organic compounds other than glucose as food sources to generate usable energy in the form of ATP.

Objectives

1. Recognize examples of coenzymes: explain their function in living organisms.

2. Explain why most organisms need oxygen and state how carbon dioxide

and water are produced as waste products of cellular respiration.

3. Name the starting materials and the important end products of:
   a. glycolysis
   b. the citric acid cycle
   c. oxidative phosphorylation

4. Explain the functions of the three processes listed in Objective 3 in the scheme of cellular respiration.

5. State where in the cell glycolysis, the citric acid cycle and oxidative phosphorylation occur in eukaryotes and in prokaryotes.

6. Explain the importance of the electron transport system to the cell.

7. Describe how mitochondria carry out ATP synthesis.

8. Compare and contrast the process of alcoholic fermentation by a wine yeast with the process of lactate, fermentation by a muscle.

9. Explain how the ability to undergo fermentation and to acquire an oxygen debt, is a useful adaptation for a muscle.

10. Compare respiration and fermentation with respect to the amount of ATP regenerated by each process.

11. Explain why we get fat when we eat more food than we need.

What's new or expanded in the Third Edition

Tables 7-1, Coenzymes used in Respiration, and 7-2, Summary of the Breakdown of Glucose Under Aerobic Conditions, are new and should be very useful to students. Figure 7-10 which shows a possible electron transport sequence in the inner mitochondrial membrane is also new as is the subsection on the energy yield of glucose (page 135).

SUGGESTIONS FOR LECTURE PREPARATION AND ENRICHMENT

Ancillaries

Several overhead transparencies (OHT) could be used to enhance the presentation of this somewhat difficult material. These include: OHTs #27 (page 126) and #28 (page 129) which present summaries of the breakdown of glucose under aerobic conditions and of glycolysis respectively. Ask students to list reactants and products, and amount of energy generated by each process.

PHT #29 (page 130) illustrates mitochondrial structure. OHT #30 (page 132) presents the reactions of the citric acid cycle. Ask students to summarize the reactants and products, and the number of CO_2, NADH, H^+, and ATP molecules generated each time acetyl CoA enters the cycle.

OHT #31 (page 134) presents a simplified scheme of oxidative phosphorylation in mitochondria. Ask students where the electrochemical gradient forms, where the citric acid cycle is located, and to identify the source of NADH and H^+ ions.

OHT # 32 (page 138) illustrates the relationship between respiration and fermentation in muscle. Ask students to identify oxidation and reduction reactions, reactants and products, to comment on which process provides more energy, and to discuss the roles played by each process during muscle contraction.

In OHT #33 (page 139) an overview of metabolism is diagrammed. The various routes by which dietary protein, fat and carbohydrate, are degraded and converted into intermediates in metabolic pathways are illustrated.

Correlative Laboratory Exercise

Topic 6 Cell Respiration and Fermentation

In this exercise students will study both aerobic and anaerobic processes. Fermentation by yeasts will be determined by measuring the amount of carbon dioxide given off under conditions in which different media are used. Respiration in plants and animals will also be determined by measuring the amount of carbon dioxide released using a pH indicator. Students will investigate the electron transport chain by determining the activity of cytochrome oxidase under various experimental conditions.

Supplemental Readings

Brunoir, M. and M. Wilson. 1982. Cytochrome oxidase. TIBS 7: 295-299.

Carolina Biology Readers:

   Chappell, J. B. 1979. The Energetics of Mitochondria (2/E)

   Nicholls, P. 1982. The Biology of Oxygen

   Nicholls, P. 1984. Cytochromes and Cell Respiration (2/E)

Kolata, Gina. 1985. How do proteins find mitochondria? Science 228: 1517-1518, June 28.

Neupert, W. and G. Schatz. 1981. How proteins are transported into mitochondria. TIBS 6: 1-4.

Srere, P. 1982. The structure of the mitochondrial inner membrane-matrix compartment. TIBS 7: 375-378.

Student Activities

Have students comment on the following situation. A "living" muscle is removed from the leg of a pithed frog, and placed in an isotonic saline solution in a closed container without oxygen. When stimulated, the muscle contracts for a time and then stops. However if the container is opened, the muscle regains the ability to contract when stimulated.

Ideas for Demonstration

   1. Set up display of electron micrographs of mitochondria.

   2. Respiration in animals and plants. The following exercise is adapted from Topic 8 in Eberhard, C. 1982. Biology Laboratory--A Manual to accompany Biology by Arms and Camp. Into each of six 100mL beaks pour 25 mL of a 0.005% phenolphthalein solution adjusted to pH 10. Into beakers #1 and 2, put one goldfish; beaker #3--two snails; beaker #4 and 5--five cm of Elodea; beaker #6--no organism. Cover tops of beakers 1, 2, 3, 4 and 6 with foil. Place beaker #2 on ice. Completely cover beaker 5. AT 10 minute intervals note change in color of solutions in beakers. After 30 minutes remove organisms and add HCl (0.0025M) drop by drop until solution is colorless. Count number of drops. The number of drops of HCl added is inversely related to the amount of CO_2 produced by the organism. The amount of CO_2 produced by the organism in mM/mL/hr can be calculated using the following equation:

$$\frac{[mL\ HCl\ (control)-mL\ HCl\ (expt)]\ x\ 2.5\ \ MHCl/mL}{volume\ of\ organism\ (mL)\ x\ time\ (hr)}$$

The volume of the organism can be determined by displacement of water.

<u>Topics for Discussion and Library Research</u>

1. Results of demonstration above. Discuss why the phenolphthalein solution changed color, which organism had the highest metabolic rate, and the effect, if any, of temperature on respiration.

2. Comparison of catabolic and anabolic reactions--similarities and differences.

3. Energy yield from aerobic respiration compared with anaerobic processes.

4. Interrelatedness of metabolic pathways and common intermediary molecules such as acetylCoA.

5. Chemiosmotic phosphorylation.

6. Relation of structure and function in mitochondria.

7. Regulation of cellular respiration.

<u>ESSAY QUESTIONS</u>

obj 7   1. If the inner mitochondrial membrane were permeable to hydrogen ions, what effect would this have on the production of ATP?

obj 7   2. When added to mitochondria certain ion-transporting chemicals, such as dinitrophenol, and the antibiotic valinomycin, act as uncouplers. They prevent phosphorylation of ADP, but do not interfere with the passage of electrons down the transport chain to oxygen. Describe how these uncouplers might act to prevent the synthesis of ATP.

obj 6   3. Electrons from NADH and $FADH_2$ are passed through a series of carriers making up the electron transport system and are finally accepted by oxygen. Explain why electrons are transferred in this manner rather than being passed directly to oxygen.

         4. Distinguish between the following paired terms: NAD+/NADH; oxidative phosphorylation/substrate level phosphorylation; ATP-ADP translocase/F_0-F_1 ATPase; anaerobic/aerobic; cristae/matrix.

obj 2   5. An animal is injected with a solution of glucose in which one of the carbon atoms is radioactively labeled. Where in the animal's body would you expect to find the labeled carbon at the end of cellular respiration?

obj 10   6. Give two reasons why aerobic respiration is more energy efficient than anaerobic respiration.

obj 10   7. Compare aerobic with anaerobic respiration regarding the fate of the hydrogen atoms removed from the fuel molecule.

obj 1   8. NAD+ and NADP+ play similar roles in cellular metabolism. Discuss these roles.

obj 3   9. Fill in the table below.

	cellular location	initial reactants	end products	number of NADH/1 molecule glucose	number of ATP/1 molecule glucose
glycolysis					
citric acid cycle					

CHAPTER 8   PHOTOSYNTHESIS

Outline

Summary

     Photosynthesis is the process in which green plants store the
energy of sunlight by converting carbon dioxide and water into organic
compounds. These organic compounds are used in turn, by plants and
by the animals that eat plants, to build cells and to power other
energy-requiring processes. Respiration is, in many ways, the reverse
of photosynthesis, since it breaks down the end products of photosynthesis and releases their stored energy. By the same token, respiratory
end products, carbon dioxide and water, which are compounds with very
little energy, can be recycled by green plants in photosynthesis. Since
energy cannot be recycled, however, the sunlight that drives photosynthesis is the ultimate source of energy for nearly all life on earth.

Photosynthesis may be considered in three parts:

1. The energy of sunlight is trapped by molecules of chlorophyll and
    other photosynthetic pigments in the thylakoid membranes of
    chloroplasts initiating a flow of electrons through the membrane's
    electron transport chain.

2. The flow of electrons reduces NADP$^+$ to NADPH + H$^+$ and creates the
    H$^+$ reservoir used by ATP synthetase enzymes to phosphorylate ADP
    to ATP. Oxygen from water is released as a by-product. The NADPH
    + H$^+$ and ATP are released into the stroma of chloroplasts, where
    their energy is used to fix carbon dioxide.

3. During the C$_3$ cycle carbon dioxide becomes attached to a 5-carbon
    sugar ribulose bisphosphate, which then breaks to yield two 3-
    carbon phosphoglycerate molecules; these are then phosphorylated by
    ATP and reduced by hydrogens from NADPH + H$^+$ to make phosphogly-
    ceraldehyde. The resulting ADP and NADP$^+$ are recycled. The 3-
    carbon PGAL molecules may be made into structural or energy-storing
    molecules, or may be processed, with the use of more ATP, to make
    more ribulose for carbon fixation. In C$_4$ and CAM plants, carbon
    dioxide is temporarily added to a 3-carbon molecule, from which it
    is later removed and re-fixed by the C$_3$ pathway.

A photosynthesizing plant captures light energy in two parts of the
reaction sequence. In each case, the light energy boosts an electron to

a high energy level, and the energy so transferred is then channeled into increasingly more permanent forms of energy storage:

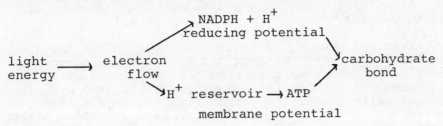

$$\text{light energy} \longrightarrow \text{electron flow} \nearrow \begin{array}{l}\text{NADPH} + \text{H}^+ \\ \text{reducing potential}\end{array} \searrow \text{carbohydrate bond}$$

$$\searrow \text{H}^+ \text{ reservoir} \longrightarrow \text{ATP} \nearrow$$

$$\text{membrane potential}$$

Objectives

From your study of this chapter, you should be able to:

1. Name or recognize the necessary raw materials of photosynthesis and the important end products.

2. Describe or sketch the structure of a chloroplast; explain where the following are to be found and the importance of their location to their roles in photosynthesis: chlorophyll, electron transport system, ATP synthetase enzymes, hydrogen ion reservoir, C_3 cycle enzymes.

3. Name the three main groups of photosynthetic pigments and state the functions they perform.

4. State which colors of light are most effective in promoting photosynthesis, and explain why.

5. Name the raw materials and end products of the electron transport reactions, chemiosmotic ATP synthesis, and the C_3 cycle. Predict how altering light intensity or temperature will affect each.

6. State what drives carbon fixation and explain what happens in the C_3 cycle.

7. Summarize the important steps in energy transfer during photosynthesis.

What's new or expanded in the Third Edition

The essay, Experimental Milestones in Photosynthesis presents chronologically in text and in a table the important discoveries which helped scientists understand the photosynthetic process. Carbon fixation in a C_4 leaf is illustrated in figure 8-19 (page 161).

SUGGESTIONS FOR LECTURE PREPARATION AND ENRICHMENT

Ancillaries

Overhead Transparency (OHT) # 34 (page 145) shows chloroplast structure. OHT #35 (page 147) graphically presents the absorption spectra for the three chlorophylls, and the carotenoids and phycobilins. Ask students why there are different pigments in a leaf, where the pigments are located in the leaf, and to discuss the relationship between type of pigment and leaf color.

OHTs # 36, 37, and 38 (pages 151, 153, and 155) illustrate diagrammatically various reactions involving the thylakoid membranes. In OHT #36 a summary of the major reactions occurring in photosynthesis is presented. OHT #37 shows the Z scheme path of electrons through carriers in the membranes while OHT #38 presents a summary of the events of electron flow in thylakoid membranes. Ask students to compare electron transport occurring in the mitochondria to that occurring in the thylakoid membranes. Ask students to list similarities and differences.

Reshow OHT #31 (page 134) which illustrates oxidative phosphorylation. OHT #39 (page 155) illustrates cyclic electron flow involving photosystem I. Ask students to compare with noncyclic flow of electrons presented in OHT #37.

The Calvin Cycle or C_3 cycle is presented in OHT #40 (page 157) Ask students to identify reactants and products and to relate spatially and temporally to reactions involving thylakoid membranes. OHT # 41 (page 160) presents interpretive drawings of a C_3 and a C_4 leaf while OHT #42 (page 161) illustrates carbon fixation in a C_4 leaf. Ask students to compare carbon fixation and correlate with leaf structure in C_3 and C_4 plants.

Correlative Laboratory Exercise

Topic 7 Photosynthesis

In this exercise students perform several different activities each of which is designed to demonstrate a feature of photosynthesis. Students will use paper chromatography to separate photosynthetic pigments, and a spectrophotometer to generate an absorption spectrum for chlorophyll. The effect of light on photosynthesis will be determined by measuring oxygen production of Elodea under conditions of different light intensities. Even though light itself is not required for carbon fixation, the products of the light dependent reactions, ATP and NADPH, are necessary. Students will perform an experiment designed to demonstrate the above. This series of activities will not only help students gain a deeper understanding of this complex process, but also give them an opportunity to develop their laboratory techniques, and to use the spectrophotometer.

Supplemental Readings

Anderson, J. and B. Anderson. 1982. The architecture of the photosynthetic membrane: lateral and transverse organization. TIBS 7: 288-292.

Bjorkman, Olle and Joseph Berry. 1973. High efficiency photosynthesis. Sci. Am., October.

Govindjee and Rajni Govindjee. 1974. The primary events of photosynthesis. Sci. Am., December.

Miller, Kenneth. 1979. The photosynthetic membrane. Sci. Am., October.

Films

Photosynthesis (3/E) (EBEC, 1981, 20 min.)

Plants Make Food (2/E) (CF, 1981, 13 min.) Covers photosynthesis and energy stored in plants using animation and live action.

Student Activities

Not too long ago the slogan, "Have you thanked a green plant today?" appeared on bumper stickers. Have students write a short essay in which they provide reasons for responding positively to the question.

Ideas for Demonstrations

1. Light activation of chlorophyll. Prepare a chlorophyll extract and pour into a test tube. From the side shine a light (or use sunlight) on the chlorophyll. The photons of light will excite the electrons in the chlorophyll molecules. As the electrons return to their ground level, they emit a red light which can be observed.

2. Prepared slides of cross sections through leaves from a mono-cot, such as corn or grass, and dicot.

3. Set up a display of electron micrographs of chloroplasts and thylakoid membranes.

4. Paper or thin-layer chromatogram of pigments extracted from spinach leaves.

Topics for Discussion and Library Research

1. Structure/function relationship of chloroplast.

2. Comparison of cyclic and noncyclic photophosphorylation.

3. Action spectrum and absorption spectrum-differences.

4. Pathways for CO_2 fixation, C_3 and C_4.

5. Organization of photosystems in the thylakoid membrane.

6. Comparison of C_3 and C_4 plants--advantages and disadvantages.

ESSAY QUESTIONS

obj 1   1. A photosynthesizing plant is given water containing ^3H rather than the normally occurring isotope of hydrogen. After one hour where would you expect to find the ^3H? Explain your answer.

obj 5   2. Isolated chloroplasts are placed in a solution with an acid pH. After one hour the pH of the stroma and thylakoid space is measured and found to be the same. Will these chloroplasts be able to make ATP? Explain your answer.

obj 5   3. Compare cyclic and noncyclic photophosphorylation regarding source of electrons, types of molecules produced, relationship to events of the Calvin cycle, and involvement of photosystems I and II.

obj 6   4. Compare C_3 plants with those possessing the C_4 pathway regarding the anatomical structure of the leaf, the advantages and disadvantages of having just the C_3 pathway.

5. Distinguish between the following paired terms: cyclic photo-phosphorylation/noncyclic photophosphorylation; C_3 pathway/ C_4 pathway; thylakoid/granum; photosystem I/photosystem II; photolysis/photosynthesis.

CHAPTER 9   DNA AND GENETIC INFORMATION

Summary

     The evidence that DNA is the genetic material in all organisms,
from bacteria to oak trees, came from several lines of inquiry:

     1.   DNA is the substance that transfers genetic information from
          one cell to another during bacterial transformation.

     2.   When a phage takes over the genetic machinery of a bacterium,
          only its genetic material, DNA, enters the cell; its protein
          coat remains outside.

     3.   In most species, all of the body cells of individuals of the
          same species contain the same amount of DNA (with minor
          exceptions); reproductive cells contain half this amount of
          DNA. The cells of members of different species contain
          different amounts of DNA.

     4.   The DNA of all members of any species has the same ratio of
          nitrogenous bases.

     The DNA molecule is a double helix, with two antiparallel strands
of a sugar-phosphate backbone forming the sides of a twisted ladder.
The strands are connected by crosswise "rungs" consisting of the base-
pairs adenine and thymine or guanine and cytosine, with each base
hydrogen-bonded to its complement on the opposite strand.

     DNA is replicated semi-conservatively. The two strands of the
double helix are separated by DNA helicases which disrupt the hydrogen
bonds between base pairs. Each strand then serves as the template for
the formation of a complementary strand of DNA by DNA polymerase. Several
enzymes cooperate in DNA replication. Enzymes proofread the newly
formed DNA and correct errors of replication. Damaged DNA is also
repaired. These mechanisms ensure that the nucleotide sequence of DNA
is very stable and that mutations are rare. The circular DNA of a
prokaryotic cell is replicated at two replication forks, starting
from one replication origin. Replication of linear eukaryotic chromosomes

starts at many origins and produces replication bubbles which elongate until they meet.

Mutations are inheritable changes in the DNA. X-rays, ultra-violet radiation, and various chemicals are among the mutagens that may cause loss or duplication of parts of the DNA, or changes in the sequence of nucleotides, which are passed on in future replications of the DNA.

A prokaryotic cell's genetic material consists of a circular, double-helical DNA molecule. Sometimes one or more plasmids are also present. Mitochondria and plastids also contain circular molecules of DNA not complexed to histones. A eukaryotic cell nucleus houses many chromosomes, each containing a linear molecule of DNA. Eukaryotic chromatin consists of about equal amounts of DNA and proteins. The DNA is wound around structural histone proteins and supercoiled into many loops. Interconversion of DNA forms (such as B-DNA and "left-handed" Z-DNA) is believed to be one of the ways genes are turned on and off.

The eukaryotic genome contains much repetitive DNA and noncoding DNA. The function of most of this DNA is unknown. Some of it may be structural, and some may be the result of the activities of transposable elements, which move around in the genome sporadically and may multiply divide, or delete other genes as they do so. Genomes of prokaryotes and of many eukaryotes contain mobile elements which may move themselves and genes attached to them from one part of the genome to another.

Tools of genetic engineering such as hybridization techniques, restriction endonucleases, and cloning and sequencing techniques, have permitted many advances in our understanding of genome structure and gene function. Recombinant DNA experiments have introduced artificial genes and the genes of various higher organisms into bacterial cells, which then produce the protein encoded by the gene. Genetic engineering techniques have also succeeded in making gene transplants into cells of higher organisms, and both plants and animals containing transplanted genes have been produced. The use of such techniques poses new moral problems for society.

Objectives

1. Describe and explain the evidence that DNA is the genetic material, using these studies as evidence: (a) bacterial transformation; (b) infection of bacteria by bacteriophages; (c) the quantity of DNA in body cells and in reproductive cells of a species; (d) comparison of the base composition of DNA in cells from members of the same and different species.

2. Describe the structure of a nucleotide.

3. Describe the structure of a molecule of DNA, and explain why the number of adenine bases in the molecule equals the number of thymine bases and the number of guanine bases equals the number of cytocine bases.

4. Explain the meaning of the terms 3' end and 5' in relation to a DNA molecule.

5. Describe the experiments of Meselson and Stahl and explain how they provided evidence that DNA is replicated in a semi-conserva-tive fashion.

6. Briefly describe the replication of DNA, mentioning the importance of the following structural features of the molecule: (a) existence of two DNA strands in the helix; (b) covalent bonding between sugar and phosphate groups of each strand's backbone; (c) hydrogen bonding of nitrogenous bases on opposite strands.

7. Define mutation, list some kinds of mutations, and explain the importance of mutations.

8. Compare and contrast the structures of a eukaryotic chromosome and prokaryotic DNA.

9. Define the following terms, and use them correctly: histones, genome, transposable elements, noncoding DNA, restriction endo-nucleases.

10. Briefly describe the techniques of nucleic acid hybridization and DNA cloning and give a possible use of each.

11. Briefly describe how recombinant DNA is made, and list some applications of this technology.

What's new or expanded in the Third Edition

Chapter 9 in the third edition contains much new information and many new figures. In section 9-B, The Structure of DNA, there are several new figures (9-3, 9-4, 9-5, and 9-6) which illustrate different features of the structure of DNA.

Section 9-C, DNA Replication, includes new material and figures on replication in both prokaryotes and eukaryotes. In figure 9-11 (page 179) both types of replication are presented together for purposes of comparison. Replication bubbles are illustrated in figure 9-12 (page 179). Within 9-C is a new subsection on DNA repair.

Section 9-D, Mutations, presents a discussion of the different types of mutations (Table 9-2) and comparison of somatic and germ cell mutations. Mutation is also discussed from an evolutionary perspective.

Section 9-F, Structure of Eukaryotic Chromosomes, is greatly expanded and includes new material on the different structural levels of organization in chromosomes. The discussion is accompanied by three new figures (9-14, 9-15, 9-16) showing nucleosomes and levels of chromatin packing. Also included is a short description and a diagram of the B and Z forms of DNA.

Section 9-G, Structure of the Genome, contains new material in mobile genetic elements and discusses McClintock's contributions to our knowledge of transposons and these movable pieces of DNA. Within the section are new figures illustrating the effects of mobile genetic elements in corn and the insertion of a bacteriophage (virus) into the DNA of a bacterial cell.

In section 9-H, Molecular Technology, the techniques of nucleic acid hybridization and cloning DNA sequences are discussed in addition to bacterial restriction enzymes.

Section 9-I, Recombinant DNA, has also been expanded and presents a discussion of the pros and cons of this new technology.

In the essay, Determining the Nucleotide Sequence of DNA, the Maxam and Gelbert method is briefly presented.

SUGGESTIONS FOR LECTURE PREPARATION AND ENRICHMENT

Ancillaries

Overhead transparencies (OHT) #s 43-46 (pages 172-174) illustrate various features of the structure of DNA. Ask students to list the important features of DNA and to identify the different types of chemical bonds, and their locations.

74

OHT #47 (page 175) presents diagrammatically the alternative hypotheses of DNA replication tested by Meselson and Stahl. OHT # 48 (page 177) and OHT # 49 (page 178) illustrate the action of DNA polymerase as it replicates one strand of the DNA double helix, and the nature of DNA replication as it occurs on both strands of the DNA double helix. Ask students to relate the events of replication with the results obtained by Meselson and Stahl. Ask students to describe differences in the replication of the two antiparallel strands of the DNA double helix and to comment on the limiting factors affecting the replication process. In OHT #50 (page 179) replication occurring in prokaryotes and eukaryotes is presented. Ask students to compare replication process in each of these types of cells.

OHT #51 (page 183) illustrates diagrammatically the various levels of packaging chromatin in an eukaryotic cells. Ask students why packaging occurs.

OHT # 52 (page 189) shows a typical recombinant DNA experiment. Ask students to identify the features of properties of DNA upon which this technique is based.

Correlative Laboratory Exercise

Topic 8 DNA, RNA, and Protein Synthesis

Supplemental Readings

Genes and cancer (Also see Chapter 11)

Benowitz, Steven. 1985. Retinoblastoma: Unmasking a cancer. Science News 127: 10-12, January 5. A discussion of Retinoblastoma, a heritable eye cancer, and the first such cancer to be linked to a damaged recessive gene that is expressed in the absence of its normal dominant allele.

Bishop, J. M. 1982. Oncogenes. Sci. Am., March.

D'Eustachio, P. 1984. Gene mapping and oncogenes. American Scientist 72(1): 32-41.

Hunter, T. 1984. The proteins of oncogenes. Sci. Am., August.

Rothenberg, Randall. 1985. Cashing in on Biotech. Science Digest 93 (3):50-55, March. Biotechnology is used to develop anticancer drugs.

Weinberg, R. 1983. A molecular basis of cancer. Sci. Am., November.

Genetic engineering

Beutler, E. 1981. Future trends: Enzyme replacement therapy. TIBS 6: 95-97.

Chinnici, Madeline. 1985. The promise of gene therapy. Science Digest. 93(5): 48-52, May.

Geiger, J. 1984. Genetic engineering: An introduction to two special American Biology Teacher issues. American Biology Teacher 46 (7): 365-372.

Kolata, Gina. 1985. Clotting protein cloned. Science 228: 1415-1416, June 21.

Miller, J. 1984. Diagnostic DNA. Science News 126: 104-107.

Tucker, Jonathan. 1985. Biotechnology goes to sea. High Technology, February. Marine organisms through biotechnology may be altered genetically to provide pharmaceuticals, foods, fuels, and other useful substances and to make them more resistant to heavy metal pollutants, etc.

Tompkins, John S. 1986. Capitalizing on life. Science Digest 94(6): 32, June.

Gene Transfer

Anderson, W. French. 1985. Beating nature's odd, Science 85 6 (9): 49-50, November.

Brinster, R. L. and R. Palmiter. 1982. Induction of foreign genes in animals. TIBS 7: 438-440.

Chilton, M. D. 1983. A vector for introducing new genes into plants. Sci. Am., June.

Itakura, K. 1982. Chemical synthesis of genes. TIBS 7: 442-445.

Marx, Jean. 1985. Making mutant mice by gene transfer. Science 228: 1516-1517, June 28.

Miller, Julie A. 1985. Zapping DNA into plant cells. Science News 128: 22, July 13. A short report about using a new technology, called electroporation or electrotransformation, to introduce DNA into plant cells.

Sidebottom, E. and N. Ringertz. 1984. Experimental Cell Fusion. Carolina Biology Reader.

Jumping genes and genes in pieces

Berg, C. and D. Berg. 1984. Jumping genes: The transposable DNA's of bacteria. American Biology Teacher 46(8): 431-439.

Gilbert, Walter. 1985. Genes-in-pieces revisited. Science 228: 823-824, May 17.

Morse, G. 1984. Genetic engineering and the jumping gene. Science News 125: 264-268.

Concerns about genetic engineering

Brill, W. J. 1985. Safety concerns and genetic engineering in plants. Science 227: 381-384, January 25.

Culliton, Barbara. 1985. Gene therapy guidelines revised. Science 228: 561-562, May 3.

Hall, Stephen. 1985. Biologist in the Boardroom. Science 85 6(1): 42-50, Jan/Feb. Story of Walter Gilbert, a Nobel prize winning molecular biologist, and his switch from distinguished research scientist and professor at Harvard to chief executive and scientist at Biogen, a Swiss-based biotechnology company.

Judson, Horace, F. 1985. Who shall play god? Science Digest 93(5): 52-55, May.

Maranto, G. 1984. Attack on the gene splicers. Discover 5(8): 16-25, August.

Maranto, Gina. 1986. Genetic engineering: Hype, hubris, and haste. Discover 7(6): 50-64, June.

Miller, J. 1984. Clergy ponder the new genetics. Science News 125: 188-190.

Miller, Julie A. 1985. Lessons from Asilomar. Science News 127: 122-126. A retrospective look at the historic conference on the risks of gene-splicing research held ten years ago at Asilomar.

Revkin, Andrew. 1985. Jeremy Rifkin: Devil's advocate. Science Digest 93(5) 55, May.

DNA structure and replication

Baltimore, David. 1984. The Brain of a Cell. Science 84 5(9):149-151. November. The story of the discovery of DNA and of the beginning of molecular biology.

Denhardt, D. 1983. Replication of DNA. Carolina Biology Reader.

Federoff, N. 1984. Transposable genetic elements in maize. Sci. Am., June.

Grivell, L. 1983. Mitochondrial DNA. Sci. Am., March.

Krider, H., 1984. Revolting developments in our understanding of the organization of the eukaryotic genome. American Biology Teacher 46(4): 373-383.

Moore, G. 1984. The c-value paradox. Bioscience 34: 425-430, July/August.

Vique, C. 1984. Oswald Avery and DNA. American Biology Teacher 46(4) 207-211.

Weinberg, Robert. 1985. The molecules of life. Sci. Am., October.

Weisburd, S. 1984. Dissecting the dance in DNA. Science News 125: 362-364.

Films

Chemistry of Heredity I: Identification of Genetic Material and DNA Structure (MF, 1979, 15 min.). Presents historical approach to identification of DNA as heredity material.

The Gene Engineers (NOVA) (TLC, 1977, 57 min.) Covers controversy surrounding genetic engineering from the perspectives of scientists and society.

Life: Patent Pending (TLV, 1982, 57 min.) Focuses on industrial applications and political implications of recombinant DNA technology.

Living Cell: DNA (EBEC, 1976, 20 min.) Covers molecular structure of DNA, DNA replication, protein synthesis.

Student Activities

A vital key in the development of recombinant DNA technology was the discovery of restriction endonuclease and their exploitation as chemical scalpels by D. Nathans, W. Arber, and H. O. Smith. The importance of these enzymes as tools in recombinant DNA technology lies in their specificity for a particular substrate. Each enzyme attacks a specific sequence of nucleotides in the DNA double helix. Some restriction endonucleases attack symmetrical (palindromic) sequences composed of four to seven nucleotides while other enzymes cleave asymmetrical sequences of four to five nucleotides long. The enzyme cleaves the DNA into pieces called restriction fragments.

Below are two nucleotide sequences of DNA and a list of restriction endonucleases and their recognition sequences. Have students, either in class or as homework, determine which restriction endonuclease will cleave both pieces of DNA and have them indicate the sites of attack and number of fragments.

DNA sequences:

1) CCAGTCGTTAACGAATTCGTCGACGTCGAC
    GGTCAGCAATTGCTTAAGCAGCTGCAGCTG

2) ACGGGTTAACCCAATGGATCCCAAGTTAACGGTAC
    TGCCCAATTGGGTTACCTAGGGTTCAATTGCCATG

Restriction endonuclease*	Recognition site**
Eco RI	G/AATTC
Bam HI	G/GATCC
Hpa I	GTT/AAC
Sal I	G/TCGAC

  * Each enzyme recognizes a symmetrical or palindromic
    sequence
 ** The / indicates the site of cleavage

Ideas for Demonstrations

1. Palindromes and restriction enzymes. Show students catalogs
    from biochemical suppliers for these enzymes.

2. Southern blot of DNA on nitrocellulose

3. Gel showing ethidiumbromide stained fragments of DNA.

4. Crhomosomal mutations. Chromosomal mutations such as
    translocations, duplications, and deficiencies can be demon-
    strated using karyotypes of humans. Carolina Biology Supply
    Company has biophoto sheets showing a D/G translocation and
    a deletion.

5. Point Mutations. A simple sentence such as "the guests are
    now here" can be used to show the effects of base substitu-
    tion and addition or deletion of a letter or space on the
    message."The guests are now here" becomes the guests are not
    here (base substitution) or the guests are nowhere (deletion),
    or these guests are now there (addition). Nonsense and missence
    mutations can also be created by substituting a period or an
    Z for the w in now, respectively.

6. Model of DNA to show three dimenstional structure.

7. Electron micrographs of DNA isolated from bacterial cells.

Topics for Discussion and Library Research

1. Chromosome replication

2. Evidence for semi-conservative replication of DNA

3. Different forms of DNA and their significance

4. Different classes of DNA, their nature and significance, and
   information content

5. Mutagens. The Ames test for determining the mutagenicity of
   substances could be presented along with a list of some of the
   mutagens found in common foods and in materials frequently used.
   The relationship between mutagenicity and carcinogenicity can
   also be explained. Two interesting and informative references
   are: Ames, B. 1983. "Dietary carcinogens and anticarcinogens."
   Science 221: 1256-1264; and, Devoret, R. 1979. "Bacterial tests
   for potential carcinogens." Sci. Am., August.

6. Genetic engineering-ethical implications

7. Patenting life forms

8. Recombinant RNA technology

9. Gene transfer-Super mouse

10. Gene therapy

11. Genetics of cancer. The following articles could be assigned and discussed in class, or provide subjects for term papers:

Benowitz, S. 1985. Retinoblastoma: Unmasking a cancer. Science News 127: 10-12.

Cooper, G. 1983. Cellular transforming genes. Science 218: 801-806.

Fox, J. L. 1983. Research in genetic basis of cancer heating up. Chemical and Engineering News, March 14.

Murphree, A. L. and W. Benedict. 1984. Retinoblastoma: Clues to human oncogenesis. Science 223: 1028-1033.

Yunis, J. 1983. The chromosomal basis of human neoplasia. Science 221: 227-236.

12. Different orders of chromatin packing in eukaryotic chromosomes

ESSAY QUESTIONS

1. Distinguish among the following paired terms: DNA ligase/restriction endonuclease; plasmid/phage; oncogene/protooncogene; palindrome/recognition site.

2. Identify the importance of each of the following components which are used to make recombinant DNA: restriction endonuclease, DNA ligase, palindrome, plasmid, and recognition site.

3. Describe three different sources for a gene used to make a recombinant DNA molecule.

4. Describe three properties of DNA that make it possible for DNA molecules from different sources to be combined and to function.

5. When a mature mRNA molecule is hybridized to the sense strand of DNA containing information for the mRNA, loops of DNA are seen between regions of complementarity. What do these loops represent?

obj 11 6. Outline the sequence of steps followed in producing a recombinant DNA molecule from human DNA and plasmid DNA.

7. List and describe three different methods of introducing human genes into the host cell.

8. You have gone through the procedure for introducing human gene X into a bacterial host cell. Describe two ways by which you could determine that gene X is present and active in the host cell.

9. Distinguish between oncogenes and proto-oncogenes, and describe a method that could be used to detect an oncogene in a cell.

obj 11 10. A large, prestigious university in your city wants to conduct research using recombinant DNA technology to produce an organism capable of metabolizing dioxin and PCB's into harmless substances. You have been asked to represent your community's interests on a committee composed of scientists, politicians, and citizens, which was set up to decide whether or not the research should be done. Outline a rational argument either for or against the university doing this research. Include biological and ethical reasons.

obj 8   11. Suggest a reason why the genetic material is packaged into chromosomes in eukaryotic cells.

         12. Describe three properties that must be possessed by the genetic material regardless of its chemical nature.

obj 1   13. Identify the contribution of each of the following scientists in determining the nature of the genetic material or its molecular structure: Avery, Hershey and Chase, Chargaff, Pauling, and Franklin.

obj 6   14. List and briefly describe the function of five molecules required for the replication of DNA.

obj 6   15. Identify the function of each of the following molecules involved in DNA replication: DNA polymerase, dTTp and DNA template.

         16. For the sequence of DNA below, write the complementary strand and indicate, using P and OH for the phosphate and hydroxyl groups, respectively, their location on both chains

5' C G G A T C T 3'
   - - - - - -

CHAPTER 10 RNA AND PROTEIN SYNTHESIS

Outline

Essay: Proteins as Evolutionary Puzzle Pieces

Summary

Proteins are essential molecules of both cell structure and cell metabolism. Every cell must be able to form exact copies of its various proteins as needed. Some of the cell's DNA carries the information specifying the order in which amino acids must be joined to produce these proteins. This information directs the fabrication of proteins by an intricate process involving the cooperation of many RNA and protein molecules in association with ribosomes.

RNA is transcribed from the cell's DNA, and thus the nucleotide sequence of RNA is complementary to the nucleotide sequence in DNA. The three main types of RNA in a cell are messenger RNA, whose base sequence is translated into the sequence of amino acids in a polypeptide chain; ribosomal RNA, which makes up part of the structure of ribosomes; and transfer RNA, which carries amino acids to the ribosome for protein synthesis and brings them into their proper position in the polypeptide chain.

Messenger RNA in prokaryotes can be translated by ribosomes as soon as it is synthesized. Eukaryote mRNA, on the other hand, must be processed before it can be translated. A cap and tail are added, and introns (of largely unknown function) are spliced out, to produce a mature mRNA molecule.

A sequence of three nucleotides in mRNA codes for each amino acid. The code is degenerate in that most amino acids are coded for by more than one codon. The code has no "punctuation marks" except for codons that code for the beginning and end of the polypeptide chain. Mutations are changes in DNA that are passed on when the DNA replicates; they are also passed to RNA transcribed from the DNA, and changes in mRNA may result in changes in the protein produced.

During protein synthesis, the code carried by the sequence of nucleotide bases in messenger RNA is translated into the sequence of amino acids in a polypeptide. The mRNA attaches to a ribosome, and transfer RNAs carrying amino acids attach to the mRNA-ribosome complex by means of base-pairing between the mRNA codons and the tRNA anticodons. Each tRNA in turn donates its amino acid to the growing polypeptide chain. As each successive peptide bond is formed between the growing polypeptide and the newly arrived amino acid, the ribosome moves along the mRNA. This brings the next codon onto the ribosome, where it can bind the anticodon of the tRNA carrying the next amino acid. When a Stop codon reaches the ribosome, the completed polypeptide is released and processed into a finished protein.

Objectives

1. List three differences between DNA and RNA.

2. Describe the genetic code and explain why it must be a triplet code.

3. Given a DNA coding strand and a table of codons, determine the complementary mRNA strand, the codons and anticodons that would be involved in peptide formation from that mRNA sequence, and the amino acid sequence that would be translated.

4. Describe the role of DNA, mRNA, tRNA, ribosomes, and amino acids in protein synthesis.

5. Sketch a transfer RNA molecule and indicate where the anticodon and aminoacyl attachment sites are.

6. Describe the initiation of protein synthesis, and the three steps in elongation of a polypeptide.

What's new or expanded in the Third Edition

Section 10-A, Overview of Protein Synthesis, introduces students to the molecules playing important roles in protein synthesis. The differences in protein synthesis between prokaryotes and eukaryotes are discussed in a subsection of 10-A.

Transcription of mRNA and its posttranscriptional processing are discussed in section 10-E, Messenger RNA, and illustrated in figure 10-6 (page 203). The discussion of introns has been expanded and includes new material on the role of small ribonucleoprotein particles in the processing of mRNA. Figure 10-7 (page 205) shows introns of a chick egg white protein gene as revealed by hybridization.

Section 10-F, Ribosomal RNA and Ribosomes, has been expanded and includes new material on the formation of rRNAs, and on the synthesis and assembly of eukaryotic ribosomes which is represented in figure 10-8 (page 207).

In section 10-G, Transfer RNA, is a new figure (10-10, page 209) illustrating the molecule's three-dimensional shape.

Associated with section 10-4, Protein Synthesis, are four new figures (10-12, page 210, 10-13-10-15, page 211) which represent initiation, elongation, and termination of protein synthesis, and an electron micrograph showing simultaneous transcription and translation of E. coli genes.

SUGGESTIONS FOR LECTURE PREPARATION AND ENRICHMENT

Ancillaries

Overhead transparency (OHT) # 53 (page 197) summarizes information flow during protein synthesis. Ask students to identify the location of each process in the eukaryotic cell.

Transcription and processing of RNA to produce mature mRNA are shown in OHT #54 (page 203). Ask students to list the various types of posttranscriptional processing presented in the figure.

The synthesis and assembly of eukaryotic ribosomes is shown in OHT # 55 (page 207). Ask students to compare with same process occurring in prokaryotes, and to speculate on driving force for assembly.

Transfer RNA is shown in OHT #56 (page 209). Ask students to

82

compare its structure with that of the other types of RNAs, and to speculate on the importance of its three-dimensional shape in translation.

OHTs #57-59 (pages 210, 211) illustrate the three steps in protein synthesis: initiation, elongation, and termination. Ask them to list requirements for each step, to compare the three steps with each other, and to compare protein synthesis with transcription and replication.

Correlative Laboratory Exercise

Topic 8 DNA, RNA, and Protein

Supplemental Readings

Darnell, J., Jr. 1983. The processing of RNA. Sci. Am., October.

Darnell, James E., Jr. 1985. RNA. Sci. Am., October.

Doolittle, Russell. 1985. Proteins. Sci. Am., October.

Hofstadter, D. 1982. Metamagical themas. Sci. Am., March, An amusing, interesting, provocative article about the genetic code.

Lawn, Richard and Gordon Vehar. 1986. The molecular genetics of hemophilia. Sci. Am., March.

Nomura, M. 1984. The control of ribosome synthesis. Sci. Am., January.

Films

Chemistry of Heredity II: Protein Synthesis. (MF, 1979, 9 min.) Deals with genetic code and information transfer.

Ideas for Demonstrations

1. Genetic code. From a master chart or handouts point out the degeneracy, redundancy, and the flexibility of the 3rd position of the genetic code.

Topics for Discussion and Library Research

1. Translation from "Nucleotidian" to "Aminoacidian." The article by Hofstadter (Hofstadter, D. 1982. Metamagical Themas (Is the genetic code an arbitrary one, or will another code work as well?)   Sci. Am., March) could be the basis of discussion about the functions of each of the molecules involved in translation and the events and problems of this process.

2. Comparison of transcription and translation. Both involve specific enzymes and hydrogen bonding between complementary nucleotides, proceed in 5' to 3' direction, have initiation and termination signals, are endergonic reactions.

3. Comparison of transcription and translation in eukaryotes and prokaryotes.

ESSAY QUESTIONS

1. Distinguish between members of the following paired terms: intron/exon; transcription/translation; codon/anticodon/triplet; tRNA/mRNA/rRNA; plus strand/minus strand.

2. Identify the function of each of the following molecules/structures in translation: A-site, small ribosomal subunit, UAA, tRNA, and AUG.

3. Describe three similarities between the processes of transcription and translation.

obj 6   4. Compare initiation, elongation, and termination steps of protein synthesis regarding involvement of the subunits of the ribosome, other factors, specific codons, source of energy.

obj 4   5. Compare the four types of RNA regarding formation of mature RNA, size, three dimenstional structure, and role in protein synthesis.

CHAPTER 11 CELL DIFFERENTIATION

Outline

Summary

During embryonic development, cells come to differ from one another
as different genes are switched on and off in different cells. A single differentiated plant cell will develop into a mature plant. Simi-
larly, nuclear transplantation experiments show that the nucleus of a
differentiated animal cell will support development of an adult. These
experiments led to the generalization that all the cells of an adult contain the same genome as the zygote from which they are all descended.
(Somatic mutations and the loss of chromosomes from somatic cells in
some animals are exceptions to this rule).

In prokaryotes, transcription of particular genes is switched on
and off when repressor or activator proteins, produced by the action of
regulatory genes, bind or release the operator region of an operon.
Inducer and inhibitor substances, which are often food molecules, control the binding of regulatory proteins to operators.

Gene activity can also be induced in eukaryotes, but transcription
during differentiation is usually controlled by changes in chromosome
structure that are inherited by a cell's progeny at cell division.
Methylation of DNA, and changes in histones and their binding to DNA
are examples of such changes.

Evidence that specific genes are switched on and off as cells
differentiate comes from studies such as those on X chromosome inactivation, the changes in polytene chromosomes in some flies, and
lampbrush chromosomes in amphibian oocytes.

Various signals inside and outside an organism cause some of the
changes in gene activity that constitute differentiation. The
germination of some plants is controlled by light, the genes needed for
molting in insects are switched on by the hormone ecdysone, and trophic
factors from nerves are needed for limb regeneration. Amphibian
metamorphosis, molting and metamorphosis in insects, and the regeneration of lost organs, are convenient, non-embryonic systems for the
study of differentiation.

One of the most important influences on gene activity in early embryonic development is the egg cytoplasm, which controls many activities of any nucleus that lies within it. Different areas of the egg cytoplasm cause differential gene activity in nuclei in different parts of the egg.

Cancer is a condition that develops when various mechanisms that control cell division, differentiation, and adhesion do not function normally. Genetic changes induced or caused by viral genes are responsible for some cancers. Others are caused by substances that cause somatic mutations. Genes that determine susceptibility to some forms of cancer are inherited. In many cases two separate events, such as viral infection and exposure to an environmental carcinogen, are needed before a cancer develops.

Objectives

1. Use the following terms in context: differentiation, nuclear transplantation, gene transcription, operon, zygote, somatic cells, germ cells, chromosome puffs, lampbrush chromosome, Barr body.

2. Describe how food molecules induce the synthesis of specific enzymes in prokaryotes.

3. Describe what is known of the regulation of transcription in eukaryotes.

4. List two systems other than embryonic development of a plant or animal in which cells undergo differentiation.

5. Describe two kinds of evidence that all the cells of an adult contain the same genetic material.

6. Describe the structure of a polytene chromosome; state where such chromosomes are found and why they are useful in studies of genetic activity.

7. Describe X chromosome inactivation and its effect on gene activity in the cells of a female mammal.

8. Given two examples of situations in which a hormone is a stimulus to differentiation.

9. Explain the selective advantage to animals of going through metamorphosis at some stage in the life history; describe how metamorphosis takes place and what factors control it.

What's new or expanded in the Third Edition

In section 11-B, students are introduced to the different levels at which gene expression may be controlled.

Section 11-C, Control of Transcription in Prokaryotes, contains a more detailed description of the lac operon, and inducible and repressible systems. In figure 11-5 (page 222) gene regulation in prokaryotes is summarized.

Section 11-D, Control of Transcription in Eukaryotes contains additional material in gene regulatory substances, such as the 5S transcription factor and enhancer protein. Figure 11-6 (page 223) shows the two stages believed to be involved in activation of a eukaryotic gene. Euchromatin is shown in figure 11-8 (page 225). Figure 11-12 (page 228) shows a lampbrush chromosome from a newt oocyte.

In section 11-E metamorphosis in insects is illustrated in greater detail in figure 11-14 (page 231).

In section 11-G, the characteristics of cancerous cells are described. Also included in an extended discussion of the causes of cancer and of cancers which appear to be associated with certain genes, called oncogenes, and oncogenic viruses. Table 11-2 (page 236) lists some substances known to be carcinogenic.

SUGGESTIONS FOR LECTURE PREPARATION AND ENRICHMENT

Ancillaries

Overhead transparency (OHT) #60 (page 221) illustrates regulation of the lac operon in E. coli while OHT #61 (page 222) shows four ways in which different combinations of regulator proteins and ligands can affect gene expression. Ask students to describe conditions under which each type of regulation might operate.

Correlative Laboratory Exercise

Topic 8 DNA, RNA, and Protein Synthesis

In this exercise students study the lac operon in prokaryotes and demonstrate the effect of inducer on the activity of genes in this operon.

Supplemental Readings (Also see Chapter 9)

Bennett, Dawn. 1985. Drugs that fight cancer naturally. Science News 128: 58-60.

Cairns, John. 1985. The treatment of diseases and the war against cancer. Sci. Am., November.

Carolina Biology Reader
Pardee, A. and G. Prem veer Reddy. 1982. Cancer: Fundamental Ideas.

Chisholm, R. 1982. Methylation and developmental regulation of gene expression. TIBS 7: 421-422.

DiBernardino, M.A., Hoffner, N., and L. Etkin. 1984. Activation of dormant genes in specialized cells. Science 224: 946-951.

Felsenfeld, Gary. 1985. DNA, Sci. Am., October.

Hammer, Signe, Dorfman, Andrea, and Amy Wilbur. 1985. To conquer cancer. Science Digest 93(8): 31, August. Examination of cancer on molecular level, its prevention, and cures.

Kolata, G. 1982. Fetal hemoglobin genes turned on in adults. Science 218: 1295-1296.

Kolata, G. 1984. New clues to gene regulation. Science 224: 558-589.

Langone, John. 1986. Special Report: Cancer. Discover 7(3):36-35, March.

Mohandas, T., Sparkes, R., and L. Shapiro. 1981. Reactivation of an inactive human X chromosome: Evidence for X inactivation by DNA methylation. Science 211: 393-396.

Sachs, Leo. 1986. Growth, differentiation and reversal of malignancy Sci. Am., January.

Selkirk, J. and M. Macleod. 1982. Chemical carcinogenesis: Nature's metabolic mistake. Bioscience 32: 601-606, July/August.

Films

Cancer: The Wayward Cell (DOC, 1976, 26 min.).

Ideas for Demonstrations

    1. Jacob-Monod model for operon.

    2. Hormone stimulation of gene transcription in Diptera. Culture salivary glands isolated from Drosphila and expose to ecdysone to reveal puffing in regions of polytene chromosomes.

Topics for Discussion and Library Research

    1. The operon

    2. Transposons and their role in gene regulation

    3. Equivalence of nuclei in terms of amount of genetic material

    4. Extranuclear inheritance

ESSAY QUESTIONS

    1. Distinguish among the following paired terms: repression/induction; repressor/inducer; regulatory gene/structural gene; operator/operon.

obj 2 2. A key feature of an inducible enzyme system is that the repressor must react with an inducer before the operon can be transcribed. How is this different from a repressible enzyme system?

obj 3 3. In a certain strain of E. coli the operator site of an operon containing the structural genes for enzymes X, Y, and Z, has been deleted as a result of a mutation. Enzymes X, Y and Z are inducible under specific conditions. What is the effect of this deletion of the operator site on the production of these enzymes? Explain your answer.

obj 2 4. Compare an inducible enzyme system with a repressible enzyme system with respect to how each controls the genes responsible for the production of the enzymes.

    5. In both prokaryotes and eukaryotes the same genetic code is used, and the mechanics of the processes of transcription and translation are essentially the same. Yet they do not employ the same system of gene control. Suggest three reasons for why you would expect eukaryotes to have a different type of genetic control system compared with prokaryotes.

    6. Give a description for a frameshift mutation and explain why a frame shift mutation does not lead to the incorrect expression of all of the genes in the chromosome.

obj 1, 6 7. Compare polytene and lampbrush chromosomes regarding where they are found, and what they reveal about gene regulation and expression.

obj 7 8. Why is a mammalian male more likely to show the effects of an X-linked gene compared with a mammalian female?

obj 5 9. Describe two types of experiments which demonstrate that differentiation in most cases does not involve a loss of genetic material.

obj 3 10. Describe four different levels at which gene regulation could occur in eukaryotic cells.

    11. Describe three characteristics of cancerous cells.

CHAPTER 12 EMBRYONIC DEVELOPMENT IN ANIMALS

Outline

Summary

An animal starts life as a zygote, which must undergo embryonic development before it becomes self-sufficient. Development involves several different processes: differential gene activity in different cells so that they differentiate into various types of cells in the adult; growth of the embryo; and changes in the shape of the body as a whole and of the organs that form within it.

Fertilization contributes male chromosomes to the egg, activates protein synthesis in the egg; and induces cell division. The first stage of development is cleavage, when the embryo divides rapidly into ever-smaller cells to form a hollow blastula. Cleavage is controlled by the genes of the mother, not of the embryo, by way of messenger RNA laid down in the cytoplasm as the egg was formed. Cleavage looks very different in different animals. The amount of yolk in the egg is one factor that determines how cleavage occurs.

Cleavage is followed by gastrulation. A hybrid embryo with maternal and paternal chromosomes that are fatally incompatible will die at this stage, showing that the embryo's genes have become active. The cells rearrange themselves into layers surrounding the archenteron cavity. The three germ layers of the gastrula are the ectoderm, which will develop into the skin and other external structures as well as the nervous system; the mesoderm, which forms internal organs such as the kidneys, heart, and blood vessels; and the endoderm; which forms the digestive tract and organs associated with it. A split in the mesoderm will eventually form the coelom.

The next stage is neurulation. In vertebrates and sea urchins the neurectoderm rolls up to form the neural tube, from which the brain and the rest of the nervous system will develop. Changes in microfilaments and other elements of the cytoskeleton permit cells to move and change shape during neurulation and other developmental stages. Organogenesis produces all the organs of the body by a complicated series of call interactions.

Studies in which parts of an embryo are transplanted into new positions reveal that the way a cell will develop may be determined before the cell differentiates into a specialized cell. Determination is inherited by all the descendants of a determined cell, showing that it involves a relatively permanent genetic change. Experiments in Drosphila show that determination involves the switching on and off of control genes that regulate the activity of many structural genes. The embryo is divided into compartments and the control genes specify which compartment a cell will occupy and the type of cell into which it will differentiate within that compartment. The full determination

of a cell's destiny is built up over time as several different
control genes are switched on and off within the cell. A cell's determination follows from its position in the embryo.

Some of the influences that cause determination are known. Hormones
influence the determination of some cells. In addition, various substances in the egg cytoplasm become encased within the cells of the
morula during cleavage and partly determine the fate of the cells they
lie in. Experiments on embryonic induction have shown that interactions
with other cells cause at least partial determination of some groups of
cells.

Aging is an important part of development after birth. We understand very little about aging. It is possible that aging has many
causes whose interactions are complex and difficult to disentangle or,
less likely, that there is some major key to the process of aging that
has yet to be discovered.

Objectives

1. Describe the process of fertilization and state its function and
   importance.

2. Name the four main stages into which embryonic development is
   divided and list definitive features of each.

3. Describe evidence that cleavage is controlled by factors in the egg
   cytoplasm and that the genes of the zygote do not become important
   in development until gastrulation.

4. List or recognize body parts formed from each of the primary germ
   layers (ectoderm, mesoderm, and endoderm).

5. Use the following words and phrases correctly: zygote, cleavage,
   morula, blastocoel, blastula, gastrula, gastrulation, neurula,
   neurulation, organogenesis, differentiation, determination, embryonic
   induction.

6. Describe an experiment that shows the difference between differentiation and determination.

7. Outline what is known about determination.

What's new or expanded in the third edition

This chapter is new and incorporates material from chapters 12
and 36 in the second edition in addition to presenting new information
on determination, pattern formation, and embryonic induction.

Figures 12-6 (page 242) and 12-8 (page 243) illustrate cleavage
in an insect embryo and a frog egg. Section 12-F, Determination and
Induction, contains new material on determination and development
in Drosophila. Figures 12-17 and 12-18 (page 24) show the life
history and development from egg to adult of Drosophila. In the latter
figure the imaginal discs, from which adult structures are derived,
are indicated. The homeotic genes controlling development are also
discussed.

Pattern formation is discussed in section 12-6. The relationship
between a cell's position in the embryo and its developmental fate
is also discussed. Determination in the development of chick limbs
is described in this section and illustrated in figure 12-23 (page 253).

Theories about aging are presented in section 12-I in this edition.

SUGGESTIONS FOR LECTURE PREPARATION AND ENRICHMENT

Ancillaries

Overhead transparencies (OHT) #62 and 63 (pages 243 and 245) show cleavage and gastrulation in the development of the frog. Ask students to comment on the changes occurring in the amount of surface area and size of each cell, and to describe differences in cleavage patterns as a result of the amount of yolk.

The fate of the germ layers in a vertebrate embryo at the end of gastrulation is shown in OHT #64 (page 245) while the beginning of neurulation is shown in OHT #65 (page 246). Organogenesis in a chick embryo is shown in OHT #66 (page 247). Ask students to compare figures in OHT #65 and 66 regarding location and fate of the cells in the germ layers.

Correlative Laboratory Exercise

Topic 9 Embryonic Development in Animals

Fertilization, and early embryonic events, such as cleavage and gastrulation are studied using living sea urchins. Living chick embryos at 33, 48, 72, and 96 hour stages are also examined to study the development of the organs and organ systems.

Supplemental Readings

Bayer, Ronald. 1982. Women, work, and reproductive hazards. The Hastings Center Report 12(5):14-19, August.

Carolina Biology Readings

Edwards, R. G. 1981. Test-Tube Babies

Chisholm, R. 1982. Gene amplification during development. TIBS 7: 161-162.

Edelman, G. 1984. Cell-adhesion molecules: A molecular basis for animal form. Sci. Am., April.

Edelman, G. 1984. Cell surface modulation and marker multiplicity in neural patterning. TIBS 7: 78-84.

Fellman, Bruce. 1985. Antler answers. Science 85 6(2):88, March. Description of experiments designed to study factors affecting the growth and development of antlers in fallow deer.

Gehring, Walter. 1985. The molecular basis of development. Sci. Am., October.

Gold, Michael. 1985. The babymakers. Science 85 6(3):26-38, April. A discussion of infertility and in vitro fertilization (where, when, how, why it's done.)

Goodman, C. and M. Bastiana. 1984. How embryonic nerve cells recognize one another. Sci. Am., December.

Grobstein, C., et. al., 1983. External human fertilization: An evaluation of policy. Science, October 14.

Hall, Stephen. 1985. The Fate of the Egg. Science 85 6(9):40-48.

Hynes, Richard. 1986. Fibronections. Sci. Am., June.

Mapletoft, R. 1984. Embryo transfer technology for the enhancement of animal reproduction. Biotechnology 2(2):149-160.

Maranto, G. 1984. Clones on the range. Discover 5(8): 34-38.

Maranto, G. 1984. Choosing your baby's sex. Discover 5(10):24-27.

Maranto, G. 1984. Aging. Discover 5(12):17-21.

Ruddick, William and William Wilcox. 1982. Operating on the fetus. The Hastings Center Report 12(5): 10-13, August.

Films

The Beginning of Life (PF, 1975, 26 min.) Deals with oogenesis, spermatogenesis, fertilization and implantation.

Chick Embryology (NGS, 1974, 12 min.) Presents development of chick from one day to hatching.

Developmental Biology (COR, 1981, 17 min.) Covers reproduction and embryonic development in Xenopus from the molecular, cellular, and organismal perspectives.

The Fabric of Life (MG, 1981, 24 min.) Explores genetic control of differentiation and morphogenesis, nuclear transplantation.

The Feminine Mistake (PF, 1978, 24 min.) Deals with physiological effects of smoking on various parts of the body, such as the skin, hair, lungs, circulatory system, and on the fetus.

Human Reproduction (CRM/Mc, 1981. 20 min.) Presents reproductive systems of male and female, fertilization, development and birth.

Life Span: How Long Do We Live? (MF, 1975, 12½ min.) Examines differences in life spans of various organisms.

Ideas for Demonstration

1. Preserved or living specimens of representative vertebrate embryos, such as chick, amphibian, sea urchin, mouse or rat.

2. Placentas. Preserved specimens are available from biological supply houses.

3. Embryos in utero. Preserved pregnant uteri can be purchased from biological supply companies, and dissected to show relationship of embryo to the placenta.

Topics of Discussion and Library Research

1. Effect of teratogens on human development.

2. Aging and programmed senescence. See articles by: Maranto, G., 1984. "Aging: Can we slow it down?" Discover 5(12):17-21; Greenwald, I. and A. Martinez-Arias. 1984. "Programmed cell death in invertebrates." Trends in Neurosciences, June; Hayflick, L. 1980. The "cell biology of human aging." Sci. Am. January; Diamond, J. 1984. "Big-bang reproduction." Discover 5(10):52-56.

3. Birth process

4. The placenta. See article by: Beaconsfield, P., Birdwood, G., and R. Beaconsfield, 1980. "The placenta." Sci. Am. August.

5. In vitro fertilization. See articles by: Grobstein, C. 1979. "External human fertilization." Sci. Am., June; Edwards, R. and R. Fowler, 1970. "Human embryos in the laboratory." Sci. Am., December.

6. Reproductive technologies such as in vitro fertilization, embryo transfer, nuclear transplantation in mammals, cloning. See articles by: Seidel, G. et al. 1981. "Superovulation and embryo transfer in cattle." Science 211: 351-358; Cherfas, J. 1984. "Test-tube babies in the zoo." New Scientist, December 6; Mapletoft, R. 1984. "Embryo transfer technology for the enhancement of animal reproduction." Biotechnology, February.

ESSAY QUESTIONS

obj 4   1.   Identify the three germ layers and at least two adult structures developed from each.

obj 1   2.   Describe two consequences of fertilization.

obj 2   3.   Describe the distinguishing features of each of the four main stages into which embryonic development is divided.

        4.   Describe the process of aging, and indicate which cell types tend to age more rapidly than others.

        5.   In animals three developmental processes are important. Identify these processes and given an example of each as to human development.

obj 5   6.   Distinguish between the members of the following paired terms: blastocoel/archenteron; spiral cleavage/radial cleavage; ectoderm/endoderm; coelom/gastrocoel; neurula/morula.

        7.   Discuss the relationship between the pattern of cleavage and the amount and distribution of yolk in the egg.

obj 5, 8.   Arrange the following three developmental processes in a temporal
7,8   sequence, define each process, and relate each to changes occurring in the genes regarding their activity or expression : differentiation, induction, determination.

CHAPTER 13   REPRODUCTION OF EURKARYOTIC CELLS

Outline

I.   Eukaryotic Chromosomes
    A.   Haploid and Diploid Chromosome Numbers
II.   The Cell Cycle
III.   Mitosis
    A.   Prophase
    B.   Metaphase
    C.   Anaphase
    D.   Telophase
IV.   Cytokinesis
    A.   Syncytia and Coenocytes
V.   Meiosis
VI.   Gamete Formation in Animals
VII.   Genetic Recombination
    A.   Nondisjunction and Translocation

Essay: Radiation and Cell Division

Summary

Cells are the reproductive units of life. New cells are produced as existing cells divide in two. Cell divisions are of two kinds: mitotic division, in which a cell of any ploidy gives rise to two daughter cells with chromosome complements identical to that of the parent; and meiotic division, in which a diploid cell divides twice, forming four haploid daughter cells.

The period from one nuclear division to the next is known as the cell cycle; it can be divided into G_1, and S period (when DNA synthesis occurs), G_2, and mitosis. The length of the cell cycle varies from as little as 15 minutes in some early embryos to several days or weeks. The initiation of DNA synthesis (S) is the key event committing the cell to undergo division, but little is known about how this synthesis, or the length of different phases of the cell cycle, is controlled.

Mitosis is a nuclear division in which precise events ensure that the two daughter nuclei inherit chromosomes identical to those of the parent nucleus. During prophase of mitosis, the replicated chromosomes, each consisting of two sister chromatids, condense and become visible under the light microscope. The nucleolus and nuclear membrane disperse, and microtubules are assembled to form the mitotic spindle. In metaphase, all of the sets of sister chromatids are lined up at the equator of the spindle, with their kinetochore fibers attached to the polar fibers of the spindle. During anaphase, each centromere splits into two, releasing the sister chromatids from one another and allowing them to travel to the opposite poles of the spindle. During telophase, the chromosomes at each pole form a nucleus as the nuclear membrane and nucleolus reform, and the chromosomes unravel from their condensed form. Mitosis is usually accompanied by cytokinesis, the division of the cytoplasm and its components to form two separate cells. In animal cells, a band of microfilaments pinches the cell in two. Cytokinesis in plants involves the assembly of a partition between the two daughter cells, which then build their cell walls on either side. Mitosis without cytokinesis forms a syncytium or a coenocyte, containing many nuclei within one membrane.

Meiosis is the series of two nuclear divisions that produce four haploid nuclei from a diploid nucleus. Meiosis halves the number of chromosomes in a cell in such a way that each daughter nucleus receives one member of each pair of homologous chromosomes. Thus meiosis prevents the chromosome number from doubling in each generation of organisms that reproduce sexually. Meiosis also results in genetic recombination, both by forming new chromosome combinations and by synapsis and crossing over, in which homologous chromosomes exchange genetic information. Additional genetic variety results from the random combination of gametes at fertilization.

Synapsis and crossing over occur during prophase I of meiosis. At metaphase I, the tetrads of homologous sister chromatids line up at the spindle equator in such a way that homologous chromosomes are separated during anaphase. Each of the two resulting nuclei contains one member of each pair of homologous chromosomes. Not until the second division do the centromeres divide, permitting sister chromatids to move into different nuclei. Translocation or nondisjunction during meiosis results in cells with too much or too little genetic material.

Gamete formation in animals involves both meiosis and differentiation to form specialized reproductive cells. Each spermatocyte gives rise to four sperm, the male gametes, which are stripped down to the bare necessities: half a set of genetic material and the locomotory apparatus to deliver it to the egg. Oogenesis involves unequal cytokinesis, producing only one, large egg swollen with material destined to support the early embryo, and tiny polar bodies, containing little more than the excess chromosomes being shed from the forming egg.

Objectives

1. Define the following terms and be able to use them in context: haploid, diploid, tetraploid, somatic cell, germ cell, fertilization, zygote, interphase, sister chromatids, homologous chromosomes, centromere, kinetochore, mitotic spindle, cytokinesis, tetrad, chiasma, synapsis.

2. Define and describe the four stages in the cell cycle.

3. State how you would recognize a cell in prophase, metaphase, anaphase, or telophase of mitosis.

4. State why substances that interfere with microtubule function or formation interfere with cell division; name one such substance and state how it is useful to plant breeders.

5. Explain how cytokinesis occurs in animal cells and in plant cells.

6. Define syncytium or coenocyte and give an example of how such a structure can be formed.

7. Describe the respective functions of mitotic and meiotic nuclear divisions in the life history of an organism.

8. Compare and contrast what happens to the chromosomes during mitosis with what happens to them in meiosis.

9. Compare and contrast the processes of spermatogenesis and oogenesis in animals.

10. Describe synapsis, crossing over, and the reassortment of chromosomes during meiosis, and explain their biological importance.

11. Describe nondisjunction and translocation of chromosomes.

What's new or expanded in the third edition

Table 13-1 (page 259) lists the haploid and diploid chromosome numbers of some common organisms.

Section 13-B, The Cell Cycle, has been expanded and includes new material on experimental work being done to determine factors affecting the cell cycle in general and transition points in the cell cycle. The effect of contact inhibition is also discussed. Figure 13-5 (page 260) illustrates a typical cell cycle, and provides information about activities occurring during each period.

Section 13-C, Mitosis, has been expanded and includes more details and new figures showing various stages in mitosis.

Section 13-D, Cytokinesis, is new and presents information on division of the cytoplasm and its contents in both animals and plants. Section 13-F, Gamete Formation in Animals, is also new and provides details of spermatogenesis and oogenesis in animals. These two processes are represented diagrammatically in several new figures. Table 13-2 which provides a comparison of mitosis and meiosis should be useful to students.

Section 13-G, Genetic Recombination, has been expanded and includes information on nondisjunction and translocation.

SUGGESTIONS FOR LECTURE PREPARATION AND ENRICHMENT

Ancillaries

In overhead transparency (OHT) #67 (page 260) the periods of the cell cycle are shown diagrammatically. Ask students to indicate key transition points.

Mitosis is illustrated diagrammatically in OHTs #68 and 69 (pages 262, 263). Meiosis is shown diagrammatically in OHTs #71 and 72 (pages 268, 269). Ask students to compare mitosis and meiosis particularly concerning the events of prophase, metaphase, and anaphase.

OHT #70 (page 267) shows cytokinesis in a plant cell. Ask students to compare with that occurring in an animal cell.

In OHTs #73 and 74 (pages 271, and 272) spermatogenesis and oogenesis are shown diagrammatically. Ask students to compare these two processes concerning the number of cells produced from one parent cell, the location, the temporal sequence, and the size of daughter cells.

Genetic recombination is shown in OHT #75 (page 274). Ask students to list two other ways by which new gene combinations are produced in progeny.

Correlative Laboratory Exercises

Topic 10 Reproduction in Eukaryotic Cells

IN this exercise students study prepared slides showing mitosis in animal and plant cells, and meiosis in animals. Using pipecleaners and styrofoam balls students construct chromosomes which are then used to illustrate the events occurring in meiosis.

Supplemental Readings

John, B. and K. Lewis, 1984. The Meiotic Mechanism (2/E) Caroline Biology Reader

McIntosh, J.R. 1984. Mechanisms of mitosis. TIBS 9: 195-198.

Films

Mitosis (2/E) (EBEC, 1980, 14 min.) Covers cell cycle using animation
and time lapse photography.

Student Activities

Have students simulate chromosomal behavior in meiosis and mitosis
using chromosomes constructed of colored pipecleaners and styrofoam
balls. Have them demonstrate, in particular, the events of prophase I--
i.e., chromosomal pairing and crossing over and recombination.

If the class size is small, students themselves could act as
chromosomes, and simulate chromosomal behavior during prophase I and
the other stages of meiosis and mitosis.

Ideas for Demonstrations

1. Events of meiosis. From styrofoam balls and pipecleaners
   of varying lengths and colors, chromosomes can be constructed
   and used to demonstrate the events of meiosis, such as
   synapsis, crossing over, anaphase I, II.

2. Oogenesis in Ascaris and mammalian spermatogenesis. Set up
   slides of prepared specimens for student viewing.

3. Karyotypes of different organisms to show differences in numbers, sizes, and shapes of chromosomes.

Topics for Discussion and Library Research

1. Comparison of mitosis and meiosis.

2. Comparison of spermatogenesis and oogenesis.

3. Different orders of chromatin packing for eukaryotic chromosomes: alpha helix--nucleosome--25nm fiber-looped domains--
   radical looped fibers.

4. Models of recombination.

ESSAY QUESTIONS

obj 10   1. Compare the events of meiosis I with those of meiosis II regard-
            ing chromosomal behavior.

         2. Compare spermatogenesis and oogenesis regarding the number and
            characteristics of the end products, cytokinesis, and continuity
            of the process.

         3. Distinguish among the following paired terms: chromatid/
            chromatin; haploid/diploid; meiosis/mitosis; spermatogenesis/
            oogenesis; and, primary oocyte/secondary oocyte.

obj 8   4. Describe three differences between meiosis and mitosis.

obj 9   5. Describe one distinguishing characteristic of each of the
            following stages in oogenesis: prophase I, anaphase II,
            telophase II, metaphase I, anaphase I.

         6. Suggest a reason why the genetic material is packaged into
            chromosomes.

obj 9   7. Describe two similarities and two differences between a mature
            sperm and a mature ovum.

obj 2   8. Identify the four stages of a typical cell cycle and describe at least one characteristic of each stage.

obj 10 9. During which stages of meiosis would you expect to see pairs of homologous chromosomes, single diploid chromosomes, and haploid chromosomes?

10. An organism has a haploid chromosome number of 10.

   a. How many chromosome pairs are present in prophase I?
   b. How many chromatids are present in Metaphase II?
   c. How many chromosomes are present in the gamete?
   d. How many chromosomes are present in the first polar body?

CHAPTER 14   MENDELIAN GENETICS

Outline

Summary

The experiments of Gregor Mendel were the foundation of the modern science of genetics--the study of the patterns of inheritance of genetic traits. Mendel succeeded in discovering the rules of inheritance largely because of his shrewd choice of an experimental organism, the garden pea plant; his painstaking breeding of large numbers (hundreds) of plants; and his use of mathematics to analyze his results. We can summarize Mendel's conclusions in modern terms in this way.

1. Genetically based traits are determined by discrete units, called genes, which are passed from parent to offspring during reproduction.

2. A plant or animal contains pairs of genes that determine its genetic characteristics.

3. Genes for a trait may occur in different allelic forms, and one allele of a gene (dominant) may hide the presence of another allele (recessive) with which it is paired in a heterozygous individual.

4. During meiosis, the two members of each gene pair separate from one another and pass into different cells (law of segregation).

5. At fertilization, each offspring receives a pair of genes for each characteristic, one member of each pair from the gamete of each parent.

6. The genes from each parent remain distinct in the offspring and may reappear in the phenotype of later generations even if they are masked by the phenomenon of dominance in some individuals in intervening generations.

7. During meiosis, the genes of one pair assort independently of genes of other pairs, so long as they are located on different chromosomes (law of independent assortment).

The behavior of genetically determines traits in breeding experiments is paralleled by the behavior of the chromosomes during meiosis. This parallelism provides part of the evidence that genes are carried on chromosomes. Genes located on the same chromosome are linked and are inherited together except when they are separated by crossing over during meiosis.

The laws of probability can be used to calculate the likelihood that the offspring of given parents will inherit a particular set of alleles.

Objectives

1. Define and use the following terms: parental (P_1) generation, first filial (F_1) generation, second filial (F_2) generation, dominant, recessive, alleles, homozygous, heterozygous, monohybrid cross, dihybrid cross, segregation, independent assortment, co-dominance or incomplete dominance, homologous chromosomes, locus, linkage groups, crossing over, crossover values, map distance.

2. Give reasons for Mendel's success in elucidating the laws governing the inheritance of genetic characters, where others had failed.

3. Define and compare the terms phenotype and genotype and their relationship to the terms dominant and recessive.

4. Use a Punnett square to illustrate a monohybrid or independently assorting dihybrid cross, use a "branching" diagram to illustrate a dihybrid cross; and work out the genotypic and phenotypic ratios expected from such crosses.

5. Explain what is meant by a test cross, and discuss its significance as a genetic tool. Design a test cross to determine the genotype of an organism with a dominant phenotype.

6. Correlate the pattern of inheritance of genetic characteristics in breeding experiments with the behavior of the chromosomes during meiosis and fertilization.

7. Given data from problem situations, identify linkage phenomena and calculate map distances between linked genes.

8. Explain the biological significance of tetrad formation and crossing over during meiosis.

9. Use the rules of probability to solve genetics problems such as those at the end of this chapter.

10. In your own words, state the rules of inheritance that were Mendel's most important contribution to genetics.

What's new or expanded in the third edition

In figure 14-5 (page 285) the law of segregation is illustrated through the behavior of the chromosomes in meiosis. Section 14-C, Predicting the Outcome of a Genetic Cross, is new and should allay students' fears of genetics problems. In figure 14-12 (page 293) a dihybrid cross involving linked loci is diagrammed.

SUGGESTIONS FOR LECTURE PREPARATION AND ENRICHMENT

Ancillaries

In overhead transparency (OHT) #76 (page 284) a monohybrid cross showing the inheritance of genes for flower color in peas is diagrammed. OHT #77 (page 285) illustrates the law of segregation as it reflects the events of meiosis. Ask students to predict probability of certain gametes forming regarding genes for flower color.

Independent assortment of members of two gene pairs during gamete formation is shown in OHT #78 (page 289). Ask students to predict the probability of a certain gamete if one of the parents is heterozygous for one gene pair.

Codominance is illustrated in OHT #79 (page 291) while a dihybrid cross involving linked loci is shown in OHT #80 (page 293). Ask students to predict offspring if crossing over occurs between the linked genes.

Correlative Laboratory Exercises

Topic 10 Mendelian Genetics

Topic 12 Human Genetics

In topic 11 students use fruit flies (<u>Drosophila melanogaster</u>) to demonstrate Mendel's laws and study patterns of inheritance. Before setting up the designated crosses, students become familiar with the flys' physical characteristics and techniques for handling them, and the stages in their life cycle. The progeny in the F_1 and F_2 generations are analyzed to determine the pattern of inheritance of the gene(s) being studied. In this exercise students have an opportunity to analyze their data using a statistical test which is outlined in appendix B of the laboratory manual.

Topic 12 should be very interesting for students because they have an opportunity to determine their own genotype for some physical genetic traits, such as bent little finger, widow's peak, and attached ear lobes. They can also determine their own blood type for the ABO series and Rh factor using an antibody-antigen test. Also included is an activity in which students generate a human karyotype by cutting chromosomes out of a copy of a chromosomal squash preparation and arranging these chromosomes on an analysis chart.

Supplemental Reading

John, B. and K. Lewis. 1984. <u>The Meiotic Mechanism</u> (2/E). Carolina Biology Reader.

Films

<u>Chromosomal Basis of Heredity</u> (MP, 1979, 16 min). Uses animation to describe cell division, mitosis and meiosis, and Mendelian inheritance.

<u>Gregor Mendel</u> (UC, 1974, 24 min.)

Ideas for Demonstrations

1. Mendel's Laws of segregation and independent assortment. These laws can be illustrated using chromosomes constructed of styrofoam balls and pipecleaners of varying lengths and colors.

2. Probability. This can be demonstrated by flipping coins.

3. Effect of crosses. Carolina Biological Supply Company has material such as ears of corn, pea mounts, which is useful for demonstrating the effects of crosses and basic principles of heredity.

Topics for Discussion and Library Research

1. Human gene mapping and the current status of the human gene map.

obj 6 1. Relate Mendel's laws of segregation and independent assortment to specific events or stages in meiosis.

obj 1 2. Distinguish among the following paired terms: genotype/ phenotype; homozygous/heterozygous; gene/allele; dominant/ recessive/codominant; monohybrid/dihybrid.

CHAPTER 15 INHERITANCE PATTERNS AND GENE EXPRESSION

Outline

Essay: Genetics of Cats and Dogs

Summary

Genes express themselves by coding for the sequence of amino
acids in polypeptides or proteins: structural proteins, blood
proteins, enzymes, etc. The severity of a mutation depends on how
much it affects the protein encoded by the gene. Some mutations
result in lethal alleles, which cause premature death. Most
familiar lethal alleles are recessive, and cause death only in the
homozygous condition.

Changes in less vital proteins may cause metabolic disorders
(inborn errors of metabolism), as exemplified by albinism and phenylketonuria.

Several different alleles of a gene may exist in a population
as a result of different mutations in different individuals. Such
multiple alleles are found in the human ABO blood group and in cell
surface proteins. Polygenic characters are determined by multiple
loci, that is, the interaction of several different gene pairs;
these polygenic characters show a wide range of phenotypes.

In most familiar organisms, sex is determined by one sex being
homozygous and the other heterozygous for an entire pair of chromosomes, the sex chromosomes. In humans and most other mammals, and in
Drosophila, females have the sex chromosome combination XX and males
are XY, whereas in birds females are ZW and males ZZ. Traits
carried on nonhomologous portions of the sex chromosome are said to
be sex-linked. Sex-influenced characters are carried on the
autosomes (usually), but depend on the balance of sex hormones for
their expression, and hence are more common in one sex than the other.

An individual's phenotype depends on what mix of genes it has,
how these genes are influenced by the products of other genes (enzymes,
enzyme products such as hormones or pigments, or non-enzyme proteins),
and what factors it encounters in its external environment. External
factors influencing gene expression include nutrition, light, and
temperature.

Objectives

1. Explain how mutations may affect the protein encoded by a gene,
   and how this is related to phenotypic expression of mutant alleles.

2. Given data from an appropriate breeding experiment, recognize the

1 : 2 : 1 and 2 : 1 ratios characteristic of lethal alleles, and demonstrate knowledge of the inheritance patterns expected from parents carrying lethal alleles by working out crosses correctly.

3. State the possible genotypes of people with blood types A, B, AB, and O, and use your knowledge of these genotypes to solve problems.

4. Explain what is meant by the term multiple alleles, and how this differs from multiple loci; give or recognize examples of each.

5. State the pattern of sex determination (sex chromosome complement of each sex) and inheritance of sex-linked genes for mammals, birds, and Drosophila, and use this information in working out sex-linkage problems.

6. Demonstrate your knowledge of the inheritance patterns of sex-linked characteristics by answering relevant problems correctly; recognize the phenomenon of sex linkage when presented with data showing these patterns.

7. Explain the difference between sex-linked and sex-influenced characteristics, and give examples of each.

8. List at least five factors that may affect the expression of a particular gene in an organism.

9. Describe the inheritance pattern found in the human genetic disorders hemophilia, red-green colorblindness, sickle-cell anemia, Tay-Sachs disease, and phenylketonuria.

What's new or expanded in the third edition

Section 15-F, Sex Determination, contains new material on sex differentiation in human embryos. In figure, 15-9, (page 310) sex differentiation is presented diagrammatically.

Section 15-G, Sex Linkage, contains new material on the inheritance of the gene for hemophilia in the descendants of Queen Victoria of England. A pedigree is shown in figure 15-12 (page 313).

In Section 15-I, additional factors affecting gene expression are described.

Section J, Genetic Counseling and Amniocentesis, provides new material on different techniques currently used to determine the genetic health of a fetus.

SUGGESTIONS FOR LECTURE PREPARATION AND ENRICHMENT

Ancillaries

Overhead transparency (OHT) #81 (page 309) diagrammatically shows sex determination systems in mammals and in birds. OHT #82 (page 312) illustrates the inheritance of a sex-linked gene for colorblindness in two generations. Ask students to relate sex determination to the inheritance of genes on the X chromosome and to predict the probability of a female heterozygous for an X-linked gene producing a gamete with the abnormal gene.

Correlative Laboratory Exercise

Topic 12 Human Genetics

In this exercise students determine their own genotypes for several physical traits as well as for their own blood groups. They

will also analyze human karyotypes to determine whether they represent normal or abnormal genetic conditions.

Supplemental Readings

Baum, Rudy, 1985. Chromosome-specific human gene libraries made
   available. Chemical and Engineering News 63 (9): 24-25,
   March 4. Using high speed flow sorters it is possible to isolate
   individual human chromosomes.

Brown, William. 1984. Hybrid Vim and Vigor. Science 84 5(9):
   77-78. November. Outlines George Shull's experiments with
   inbreeding and crossbreeding corn which resulted in hybrid corn.

Croce, Carol and George Klein. 1985. Chromosome translocations and
   human cancer. Sci. Am., March.

Dixon, Bernard. 1984. Of different bloods. Science 84 5:65-69; November. Chronicles Landsteiner's discovery of blood groups (ABO,
   MN, and Rh). Includes discussion of nonmedical applications of
   blood typing.

Frances, M. and D. Duksin. 1983. Heritable disorders of collagen
   metabolism. TIBS 8: 231-234.

Siwolop, Sara and Mayo Mohs. 1985. The war on Down Syndrome. Discover 6 (2):66-69 February. A discussion of efforts being made
   to uncover the underlying cause of the defects such as mental
   retardation, and congenital heart disorders which are associated
   with this syndrome.

Winchester, B. 1982. Animal models of human genetic diseases. TIBS
   7:71-74.

Films

Chromosomal Errors (MF, 1977, 10 min.) Discusses certain syndromes
   associated with chromosomal abnormalities, amniocentesis, and
   genetic counseling.

Genetic Defects: The Broken Code (IU, 1976, 90 min.) Discusses
   transmission, characteristics and detection of genetic diseases,
   such as cystic fibrosis, Huntington's disease, and combined
   immunodeficiency disease as well as genetic counseling for these
   diseases.

Sickle Cell Fundamentals (NIH, 1978, 30 min.) Explains molecular and
   genetic aspects of this disease.

The Sickle Cell Story (MF, 1977, 16 min.) Deals with scientific and
   human aspects of this disease; describes historical background
   and physiology of this disease.

Student Activities

1. For homework have students construct a family pedigree for
    an easily identifiable and simply inherited, genetic trait
    such as bent little finger, tongue rolling, attached ear
    lobes, ability to taste PTC, sodium benzoate, thiourea, etc.
    Papers for taste testing are available from biological supply
    houses.

2. Select three to five easily identifiable, and simply inherited genetic traits. Have students in the class survey
a large portion of the student body to determine the number
of students exhibiting the particular genetic trait. E.g.,
have students observe others for the presence of widow's peak.
Once the numbers are tabulated for each trait ask students to
try to correlate numbers with mode of inheritance. E.g., the
gene for widow's peak is inherited in an autosomal dominant
pattern, yet from this writer's experiences, the gene is not
that common in a random population. For variety, have students do taste testing or observe sex-linked or sex-influenced
characteristics whose genes are located on autosomes, such as
baldness, but whose expression is affected by the sex of the
individual.

3. Have students construct human karyotypes. Biophoto sheets
of human chromosomes are available from Carolina Biological
Supply Company.

Ideas for Demonstrations

1. Human karyotypes, normal and abnormal. Carolina Biological
Supply Company has biophoto sheets which are produced from
photographs of metaphase chromosome spreads. The chromosomes
can be cut from a biophoto sheet and organized as a karyotype.
Represented on biophoto sheets are several human chromosomal
conditions including normal male and female, Down Syndrome, etc.

2. Karyotypes of different organisms particularly other primates
to show differences and similarities compared with humans.

3. Human karyotypes demonstrating different staining techniques
(quinacrine mustard, Giemsa) which are used to reveal chromosomal bands or the centromere.

4. Genetic counseling. Ask a genetic counselor to conduct a mock
session.

Topics for Discussion and Library Research

1. Penetrance and expressity

2. Human gene mapping and current status of human gene map

3. Sex linkage and sex determination

4. Lethal genes

5. X chromosome inactivation

6. Genetic counseling. Discuss benefits, limitations, reasons
for a couple to seek counseling.

7. Problems with eugenic practices.

8. Association of genetic diseases and particular ethnic racial,
or religious group. Discuss reasons for association.

9. Genetic disease found in certain isolated populations, such
as Dunkers, Menonites, etc.

10. Amniocentesis, ultrasound and chorionic villi analysis as
prenatal diagnostic techniques. Discuss risks, benefits,
limitations.

11. Nondisjunction in meiosis.

12. Types of aneuploidies, chromosomal rearrangements. Discuss
nature, origin, incidence of chromosomal abnormality.

13. The Blue people of Troublesome Creek. See article by:
    Trost, C. 1982. "The blue people of Troublesome Creek."
    Science 82 3(9):34-40. These people have an inborn error of
    metabolism affecting the conversion of methemoglobin to
    hemoglobin. They lack the enzyme diaphorase from their red
    blood cells so methemoglobin accumulates making their blood
    blue.

ESSAY QUESTIONS

obj 5   1. Discuss why human males are more likely to suffer from sex-
            linked diseases than females.

obj 4   2. Suppose human eye color is determined by four pairs of genes,
            all of which are equivalent, i.e., the genes of one pair do
            not result in the production of more pigment than the genes of
            any other pair. A person with eight dominant genes, AABBCCDD,
            would have the darkest eye color, a person with four dominant
            genes would have an intermediate color like hazel, and a person
            with all eight recessive genes would have the lightest eye
            color. Two people with the genotypes AaBbCcDd and AaBbCcDd and
            hazel colored eyes plan to start a family. Could they have
            children with very darkly colored eyes? very lightly colored
            eyes? What eye color would their children most likely have?
            Explain your answer.

obj 4,   3. Discuss how you could determine whether a particular phenotype
   8   is due to polygenes, multiple alleles, incomplete dominance,
            or the environment.

obj 5   4. A normal woman and normal man have a short daughter with hemo-
            philia. Excluding the possibility of a new mutation in the
            daughter, suggest a plausible reason for the daughter's hemo-
            philia.

         5. Describe using labeled diagrams how the   chromosomal ab-
            normalities associated with Klinefelter and Down syndromes
            might occur.

         6. Describe the technique of amniocentesis and indicate which
            general types of genetic abnormalities can be diagnosed using
            this procedure.

obj 8   7. Describe three factors that may affect the expression of a gene
            in an organism.

         8. You are a genetic counselor. A couple with a child afflicted
            with congenital heart disease seeks information from you about
            the possibility of having another affected child. What three
            questions might you ask these parents and why?

CHAPTER 16   EVOLUTION AND NATURAL SELECTION

Outline

I.   History of the Theory of Evolution
   A.   Lamarckism
   B.   Darwin and Wallace
II.   The Evidence for Evolution
   A.   The Evidence drom Artificial Selection
   B.   The Evidence from the Fossil Record
   C.   The Evidence from Comparative Anatomy
   D.   The Evidence from Embryology
   E.   The Evidence from Biogeography
III.   Evolution by Means of Natural Selection
   A.   The Peppered Moth
   B.   Tolerance of Toxic Metals by Plants
IV.   Genetic Contribution to Future Generations
V.   Adaptations
   A.   Oak Trees and Caterpillars
   B.   Resistance to Pesticides and Antibiotics

Essay: Charles Darwin

Summary

The theory of evolution asserts that species are not unchangeable, but arise by descent and modification from pre-existing forms. Members of any species of organism differ from one another, and some of their differences are inherited. Natural selection is the differential reproduction of genetically different individuals in each generation: it leads to evolution, a change in the gene pool of a population from one generation to the next.

The theory of evolution by means of natural selection was put forward in 1858 by Darwin and Wallace. Their thinking was stimulated by the writings of Lyell and Malthus, and by observations they made during their own travels. Many nineteenth-century biologists came to realize that artificial selection by human farmers and breeders had produced rapid evolution in domesticated plants and animals. They also recognized the compelling logical arguments for the process of evolution based on observations of the fossil record and biogeography, which provided information on the distribution of organisms through time and space. Comparative anatomy and embryology also provided evidence that various structures in ancestral organisms had been modified in their descendants and had become adapted to different functions, or had even been lost when a new way of life rendered them unnecessary. However, the evolution of wild populations by means of natural selection was not convincingly shown until the twentieth century, when Kettlewell showed that predation by birds was the selective force that led to the evolution of melanic populations of the peppered moth in polluted areas of England.

The anatomical, physiological, and behavioral traits that survive the process of natural selection may be thought of as adaptations that fit an organism to live and reproduce in its particular environment. Adaptations are many and various. The only consistent effect of selection is that it ensures that the genetic contribution of a "successful" individual to future generations is as large as possible.

Objectives

1.   Define evolution in your own words.

2.   Describe Lamarck's theory of how evolution occurs, and explain why Lysenko believed in this theory.

3. Describe the roles of Darwin and Wallace in formulating the theory of evolution and state why their theory was more convincing than the descriptions of evolution put forward by their predecessors.

4. Define artificial selection; homologous, analogous, and vestigial structures; adaptive radiation, and endemic species, and give or recognize examples of each.

5. Explain how the following provide evidence for the occurrence of evolution, and give or recognize examples in each category; artificial selection, the fossil record, comparative anatomy, embryology and biogeography.

6. List or recognize conditions that favor fossilization and conditions that make it unlikely that an organism will be fossilized.

7. State the four observations leading to the conclusion that evolution occurs under the influence of natural selection.

8. Define natural selection, and state what it means to be evolutionarily successful. Outline how an adaptation may be selected for, mentioning the role played by each of the following: gene, genetic variation, gene frequency, natural selection, and population.

9. Describe Kettlewell's experiments with Biston betularia, and explain how they demonstrated that industrial melanism in this moth has evolved under the influence of natural selection.

10. Describe Lack's experiments with Swiss starlings, and state what these experiments tell us about the effect of natural selection.

11. Explain why selection does not produce a population of identical, perfectly adapted organisms.

What's new or expanded in the third edition

Section 16-B, The Evidence for Evolution, is new and provides information on the various lines of evidence supporting evolution. The evidence comes from the practice of artificial selection, the fossil record, studies of comparative anatomy and embryology, and from biogeography.

In section 16-C an example of natural selection related to a plant's tolerance to toxic metals is discussed.

SUGGESTIONS FOR LECTURE PREPARATION AND ENRICHMENT

Ancillaries

Overhead transparency (PHT) #83 (page 333) shows homologous structures in the forelimbs of various vertebrates. Ask students to comment on the different shapes and sizes of the homologous bones.

OHT #84 (page 336) illustrates the zoogeographic regions of the world, proposed by Wallace. OHT #85 (page 337) shows Wallace's line, a proposed "boundary" to mammalian migration.

Supplemental Readings

Bioscience: June, 1982 issue on Darwin and Evolution

Hiam, A. 1982. Airborne models and flying mimics. Natural History 91 (4): 42-49.

Lewis, Roger. 1985. Why do inbred mice evolve so quickly? Science 228: 1187, June 7.

"Masters of mimicry." Discover 6(6):56-63 June, 1985. Photographic
    essay of mimicry in insects.

Natural History: December 1982 issue devoted to Hawaii: Showcase of
    evolution.

Sidhu, G. 1984. Genetics of plant and animal parasitic systems.
    Bioscience 34(6): 368-374, June.

Stebbins, G. Ledyard and Francisco Ayala. 1985. The evolution of
    Darwinism. Scientific American, July.

Sibley, Charles. 1986. Reconstructing bird phylogeny by comparing
    DNA's. Sci. Am., February.

Wilson, Allan, 1985. The molecular basis of evolution. Sci. Am.,
    October.

Films

Colors in Nature (EBEC, 1980, 12 min.) Examines adaptive value of
    coloration for a variety of organisms.

Now You See Me, Now You Don't (AMP, 1977, 26 min.) Explores protective
    strategies of insects, including mimicry, camouflage, and release
    of noxious substances.

The World of Darkness (NGS, 1973, 25 min.) Examines adaptations of
    animals living in darkness and emphasizes the bat.

Ideas for Demonstrations

1. Mimicry in Butterflies. Display mounts are available from
    biological supply companies.

2. Protective coloration. Slide sets are available from biologi-
    cal supply companies.

3. Preserved specimens of representative vertebrate embryos
    to illustrate evolutionary relatedness.

Topics for Discussion and Library Research

1. Dating methods.

2. Biogeography

3. Homology and analogy

4. Evolutionary relationships and DNA. See article by: Lewin, R.
    1984. "DNA reveals surprises in human family tree." Science 226:
    1179-1182.

5. Mimicry, protective coloration

6. Natural Selection and artificial selection

7. Development of resistant organisms

8. Symbiosis. See article by: Moore, J. 1984. "Parasites
    that change the behavior of their hosts." Sci. Am., May.

9. Coevolution. See article by: Gilbert, L. 1982. "Coevolu-
    tion of a butterfly and a vine." Sci. Am., August.

10. Charles Darwin. See June, 1982 issue of Bioscience.

ESSAY QUESTIONS

obj 5 1. Evidence for evolution has come from several disciplines including anatomy, biochemistry, paleontology, and embryology. Which of these would be most accurate in determining evolutionary relationships and why?

2. How is "success" measured in evolutionary terms?

3. Describe three types of evidence from living organisms in support of evolution.

4. From the fossil record it appears that the horseshoe crab has changed very little over the past 200×10^6 years. As a evolutionist, provide a reasonable explanation for the status of this invertebrate.

obj 8 5. Explain how natural selection acting against a phenotype in one generation can affect the genotype of the next generation.

6. Can natural selection act against genetic variation if the genes are not expressed as phenotypes? Explain.

CHAPTER 17   POPULATION GENETICS

Summary

     Although natural selection acts on individual phenotypes, only
populations can evolve. This is because the population is the smallest
unit with a gene pool in which the frequency of alleles can change, and
thus evolve.

     The Hardy-Weinberg Law describes the frequencies of different
genotypes in a population and states that the proportions of different
alleles and genotypes will remain the same as long as: (a) mating is
random with respect to genotype; (b) there is no net mutation; (c)
there is no gene flow; (d) the population is large; and (e) there is no
selection for or against the traits being considered. Under these
conditions, evolution will not occur. The Hardy-Weinberg equation can,
therefore, be used to give a measure of these evolutionary forces when
they do affect a population.

     Populations of the same species in different geographical areas
tend to form a cline, in which adjacent populations differ from one
another along a gradient of some environmental factor. Adaptations
to local areas increase this difference; gene flow between adjacent
populations decreases it.

     Genetic drift may be an important cause of evolution in small
populations that are not subject to strong selective pressures.

     The gene pool of a population evolves so that each genotype becomes
a coadapted gene complex. Genes are often expressed differently when
they are inserted into the gene complex of another population. Dominance
and recessiveness of alleles may be a result of modifier genes that have
evolved in the same coadapted gene complex. Heterozygote advantage may
be a result of evolution of dominance and recessiveness. Heterozygote
advantage also contributes to a population's genetic load.

     Genetic variation in natural populations can be measured by
methods such as nucleotide sequencing, measuring the variation of phenotypic characters, and electrophoresis of proteins.

     Genetic polymorphism is important in maintaining genetic variation
in populations. Factors that tend to increase the variation within a
population include mutation, polymorphism maintained by heterozygote
advantage or by other factors, disruptive selection, gene flow between
populations, sexual reproduction, and relaxation of selective pressure.

Factors that may decrease variation in a gene pool include gene fixation, and the selective pressures that adapt a population precisely to local conditions.

Selection may be thought of as acting on alleles, complexes of coadapted genes, individuals, or even groups of related individuals, all as a result of the expression of genes in the phenotype.

Objectives

1. Define and use in context: gene pool, evolution, cline, gene flow, genetic drift, founder effect, coadapted gene complex, heterozygote advantage.

2. State, and explain the significane of, the Hardy-Weinberg Law.

3. State and explain the five situations in which the Hardy-Weinberg Law is invalid.

4. Given the necessary data, use the Hardy-Weinberg equation to determine the frequencies of two alleles, and of the genotypes they produce in a population.

5. Explain why selection is unlikely ever to eliminate a lethal recessive allele from a large population of diploid organisms.

6. Explain why genetic drift is most likely to cause evolution in a small population.

7. Differentiate between stabilizing, directional, and disruptive selection, and give or recognize examples of selective pressures that may cause each.

8. Explain how dominance can evolve.

9. Give one reason for heterozygote advantage and explain the relationship between heterozygote advantage and genetic load.

10. Define polymorphism and discuss three ways it can be maintained.

11. Explain why a rapidly expanding population is more variable genetically than one whose size is constant.

12. List three factors that tend to increase and three that tend to decrease genetic variation in a population, and state how each acts.

What's new or expanded in the third edition

The discussion of heterozygosity (section 17-C) has been expanded and includes material on the effects of inbreeding on heterozygosity, and on hybrid vigor. In section 17-E the discussion of polymorphism and the distribution of ABO blood groups in the human population has been expanded. Figure 17-13 (page 366) shows the geographical distribution of the B allele of the human ABO blood group system in various European populations.

SUGGESTIONS FOR LECTURE PREPARATION AND ENRICHMENT

Ancillaries

Overhead transparency #86 (page 359) illustrates the effect of different types of selection on a polygenic character in a population. Ask students to comment on which type(s) of selection would eventually result in changes in gene frequencies in the population.

Correlative Laboratory Exercise

Topic 13   Evolution and Population Genetics

In this exercise students get practical experience concerning the Hardy-Weinberg Law. The frequencies of genes for taster/ nontaster with regards to PTC and sodium benzoate are determined for a population using Hardy-Weinberg formula. The effect of natural selection on the frequency of a gene is also studied using colored beans to represent genotypes and gene pools.

Supplemental Readings

Carolina Biology Readers:

   Ayala, F. 1983. Genetic Variation and Evolution.

O'Brien, S. J. et al. 1985. Genetic basis for species vulnerability in the cheetah. Science 227:1428-1434, March 22.

Ryden, Hope. 1985. The swift and the savage. Science Digest 93 (5): 56, May. Story about the cheetah, its life style and natural and evolutionary history.

Films

Genetic Polymorphisms and Evolution (MF, 1976, 16 min.) Examines reasons for polymorphisms for coloration in Biston betularia, the British moth, and sickle cell hemoglobin in humans.

Student Activities

   1. Have students determine their ability to taste phenylthio- carbamide (PTC) and/or sodium benzoate. Test and control papers are available from biological supply companies.
       Tabulate the results for the class. Then have students determine the frequencies for the dominant gene (taster) and recessive gene.

   2. Have students study a larger population, i.e., the student body dormitory and ethnic group, etc. as to ability to taste PTC and/ or sodium benzoate. Tabulate results and determine frequencies for larger group. Compare results of class and larger popula- tion. Have students explain differences using concepts pre- sented in this chapter.

   3. Demonstration of Hardy-Weinberg Law using different colored beads/beans/cat food, etc. Divide students into groups and assign each group a gene frequency for the recessive allele. E.g., assign to one group a recessive gene frequency of 0.3, and to another group a recessive gene frequency of 0.1. Have each group follow the directions below:
       a) Create a gene pool of 100 beads using one color, to represent dominant gene, and the other color the recessive gene, according to given frequencies.
       b) Put beads in containers and remove pairs until all beads are matched.
       c) Record number of each kind of pair in Table A below.
       d) Return beads to container and repeat #b and c above.
       e) Repeat for two more generations
       f) Determine frequency of each gene in each generation
       g) Explain any differences in gene frequency from one generation to the next.

   4. Demonstration of natural selection on gene frequencies using colored beads. Divide students into groups and assign each group

a gene frequency for the recessive allele. Have each group follow the directions below.

   a) Create a gene pool of 100 beads using one color to represent dominant allele and a second color to represent recessive allele according to given frequencies. The recessive gene is lethal.

   b) Put beads in a container and remove pairs until all beads are matched.

   c) Record number of each kind of pair in Table B below.

   d) From the paired sets, remove all the sets that represent the homozygous genotype, a lethal genotype.

   e) For the remaining beads determine the percentage of the dominant gene:

$$\frac{\text{\# dominant beads}}{\text{total \# beads}} \times 100 = \text{\% dominant beads/genes}$$

Record dominant gene frequency in Table B.

   f) Restore the population to 100 beads. Add the appropriate number of each kind of bead to reflect the calculated percentage for 100 beads. E. g. If you calculated the dominant gene frequency as 78% (see e above), and the original starting frequency was 70% then you add 8 beads. You also have to add enough of the recessive beads to make 100.

   g) From this new gene pool, remove pairs of beads until all are matched.

   h) Record number of each kind of pair in Table B below.

   i) From the paired sets, remove all the pairs representing homozygous recessive genotype.

   j) Calculate percentage of dominant genes in remaining beads. See 4e above.

   k) Follow steps f-j for another two generations, paying particular attention to step f.

   l) Graph the frequency for each gene for each generation (Generation on abscissa, frequency on ordinate).

   m) Will the curve ever cross the abscissa? Explain.

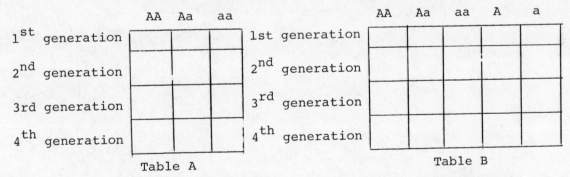

Table A   Table B

This exercise could also be used to demonstrate the effect of genetic drift and, gene flow on gene frequency, and the bottleneck and founder effects.

<u>ESSAY QUESTIONS</u>

obj 7 1. Distinguish between stabilizing selection, directional selection, and disruptive selection and give the evolutionary significance of each.

obj 3 2. List and describe four major agents which can affect or change the frequencies of genes in a population.

obj 6 3. An investigator is studying populations of turtles living at 5 different ponds in an area about one acre. Among the turtles

which belong to the same species, the investigator identifies
five patterns in shell coloration corresponding to the five
populations. The turtles rarely move between ponds and each
population has about 15 members. The investigator decides that
the five populations provide evidence for genetic drift. Is this
conclusion justified? Is there another explanation?

obj 8   4. If some alleles are dominant and others are recessive, why don't
the recessive ones eventually disappear, and why aren't the dominant always present in most of the organisms in a population?

obj 6   5. Compare gene flow and genetic drift and explain how each affects
gene frequency.

obj 12   6. What are the genetic disadvantages and advantages of too little
or no genetic diversity, or too much variation in a population?

obj 2   7. State the implication of the Hardy-Weinberg Law and the five
conditions under which it operates.

         8. Define fitness and adaptation from an evolutionary sense.

obj 4   9. The gene for free earlobes (E) is dominant over the gene for
attached earlobes (e). One quarter of a population of 1000
individuals has attached earlobes.
             a) What is the frequency of E in the population?
             b) What is the frequency of e in the population?
             c) How many people are heterozygous for this gene?

CHAPTER 18   SPECIATION

Outline

I. Morphological Species
II. Biological Species
III. Isolating Mechanisms
    A. Prezygotic Isolation
    B. Postzygotic Isolation
    C. Selection for Prezygotic Isolation
    D. Function of Isolating Mechanisms
IV. Speciation
    A. Allopatric Speciation
    B. Pleistocene Glaciations
    C. Sympatric Speciation
    D. Parapatric Speciation
    E. Selection Against Hybrids
V. How Quickly Do New Species Form?

Essay: Continental Drift.

Summary

A species is a group of interbreeding organisms that is reproductive-
ly isolated from other such groups. This reproductive isolation protects
a coadapted gene pool that gives rise to a limited numberof phenotypes;
it is clearly legitimate to classify organisms by these phenotypes (i.e.
morphologically) because they reflect something that is real in reproductive terms: the coadapted genes of an interbreeding group of organisms
Such morphological classification is generally more practical
than classification by ability or inability to interbreed. Organisms do
not fit tidily into morphological or reproductive definitions of species.

Reproductive isolation betweenspecies may be due to prezygotic or
postzygotic mechanisms. Of the two, prezygotic mechanisms are more
auvantageous because they prevent the waste of gametes and energy that
are expected before postzygotic mechanisms can come into play.

Allopatric speciation occurs when two populations of a species
become separated so that there is no gene flow between them. Each
evolves under the influence of local selective pressures, and they may
become so different that they are considered different species. Whether
they actually are "good" species or not will be determined only when
the two populations again become sympatric. Sympatry will have three
possible outcomes: introgressive hybridization may occur and the two
populations become one; the hybrids may be at a selective disadvantage so
that reproductive isolation between the two will increase; or they may
already be separate species and not interbreed at all.

Sympatric speciation usually occurs as a result of polyploidy. It
might also theoretically, arise in a polymorphic population in which
hybrids between the morphs were at a selective disadvantage, but no
such situation has even been conclusively demonstrated in nature. Mutation in one or a few genes may also suffice to create reproductive isolation, and hence speciation, by creating different morphs in sympatric
populations.

Parapatric speciation may occur as two adjacent populations develop
reproductive isolation from each other. A sharp boundary or contrast in
some environmental factor may act as the selective pressure favoring
isolation of the two morphs, each of which is better adapted to environmental conditions on its own side of the "boundary."

In light of recent evidence, the traditional concept of speciation
as a result of gradual and continuous change in the gene pool is being

replaced. It now seems likely that most species form in small, more-or-less isolated local populations. Such a population may diverge very rapidly from the parent population and, in the unlikely case that it does not become extinct, form a new, rapidly evolving species.

Objectives

1. List the advantages and disadvantages of basing classification on morphological characters.

2. Give a biological definition of a species.

3. List the advantages and disadvantages of the biological species concept.

4. List and describe seven categories of reproductive isolation: classify each as prezygotic or postzygotic.

5. Distinguish between allopatric, sympatric, and parapatric modes of speciation, and describe how they work. List or recognize examples of each type.

6. List and explain three possible outcomes when two separate populations become sympatric.

What's new or exapnded in the third edition

Section 18-E, How Quickly Do New Species Form?, has been expanded and includes new material on punctuated equilibrium which provides an explanation for the sudden appearance of a new species.

SUGGESTIONS FOR LECTURE PREPARATION AND ENRICHMENT

Supplemental Readings
Carolina Biology Readers:

Ayala, F. 1983. The Origin of Species

Cavalli-Sforza, L. L. 1983. The Genetics of Human Races

Colbert, E. 1983. An Outline of Vertebrate Evolution

Nelson, G. and N. Platnick. 1984. Biogeography

Tarling, D. H. 1980. Continental Drift and Biological Evolution

Flessa, K. 1980. Biological effects of plate tectonics and continental drift. Bioscience 30(8): 518-524, August.

Gilbert, L. 1982. Coevolution of a butterfly and a vine. Sci. Am., August.

Wilson, Edward O. 1985. In praise of sharks. Discover 6(7): 40-53. July. A discussion of the adaptive radiation and evolution of sharks.

Topics for Discussion and Library Research

1. Definition of a species

2. Genetic isolates such as the Amish, Menonites, Dunkers, island groups.

3. Plate tektonics and continental drift. See article by: Flessa, K. 1980. "Biological effects of plate tektonics and continental drift." Bioscience 30(8): 518-524; Courtillot, V. and G. Vink. 1983. "How Continents break up." Sci. Am., July .

ESSAY QUESTIONS

1. Distinguish between microevolution and macroevolution, and speculate on which type of evolution might be associated with the concept of punctuated equilibrium.

2. Contrast LaMarck's theory of evolution with Darwin and Wallace's theory and the theory of punctuated equilibrium.

obj 5 3. Distinguish between allopatric, parapatric, and sympatric, speciation.

obj 4 4. List and describe two prezygotic isolating mechanisms and two postzygotic isolating mechanisms, and explain which type is most effective.

5. Many of the marsupials of Australia have morphologically similar placental counterparts in other parts of the world. Suggest a reason for this close resemblance between marsupials and placental mammals.

CHAPTER 19   EVOLUTION AND REPRODUCTION

Outline

Summary

All species have a certain amount of genetic variation among their
members as a result of mutation. The amount of such variation is slight,
and members of species that reproduce asexually are, therefore, genetically
very similar to one another. Members of sexual species are much more
variable because genes are reshuffled during meiosis, and form new
combinations at fertilization. Asexual reproduction uses energy more
efficiently than sexual reproduction and is common in species that occur
in many places in the world and are adaptable to changing conditions.
For more localized and specialized species, the energy wasted in sexual
reproduction is worthwhile because at least some of the genetically different individuals in a sexually reproducing species can usually survive
and evolve in changed conditions.

Sexual reproduction probably originated as the accidental fusion of
two asexual reproductive cells. The advantage of having one gamete
stuffed with a food supply for the new individual selected for the evolution of oogamy, the most common form of sexual reproduction today.
Adaptations such as specific mating seasons, environmentally determined
sex, and hermaphrodism help to overcome the difficulties encountered when
two individuals must act in concert to achieve reproduction.

The sexual system of species is determined by the amount of energy
each sex puts into producing and rearing offspring and by ecological
factors such as the distribution of food, prevalence of predators, etc.
Because eggs take more energy to produce than do sperm, females are
usually more selective than males in their choice of mate. Sexual
dimorphism may arise when the selective pressures on the two sexes conflict, or when males and females have different roles in reproduction.
Sexual dimorphism tends to be greater in polygamous species. In monoga-
mous species, the members of both sexes must choose their mates with
discrimination, and the roles and behavior of the two sexes are more
similar.

An allele that makes an individual perform altruistic behaviors
detrimental to itself can be selected for when the behavior enhances
the survival of other copies of the allele in the individual's relatives,
allowing that allele to spread through the population. Altruistic behavior
is most likely to arise in species in which closely related individuals
spend much time together.

Objectives

1. Define isogamy, oogamy, hermaphrodism, polygamy, polyandry, polyggyny,
monogamy.

2. State the advantages and disadvantages of sexual reproduction contrasted with asexual reproduction.

3. Discuss the advantages enjoyed by organisms that combine sexual and asexual reproduction in the life history.

4. Give at least one advantage of oogamy and of hermaphrodism.

5. Give some reasons why selective pressures acting on a female may be different from those acting on a male and describe some resulting differences between the two sexes in a species.

6. Give evidence for the theory that female choice almost invariably exists in mating systems.

7. Describe what is meant by altruistic behavior and kin selection, and explain how alleles for altruistic behavior may spread through a population.

What's new or expanded in the third edition

In section 19-E polygyny and polyandry are discussed separately and in greater detail.

SUGGESTIONS FOR LECTURE PREPARATION AND ENRICHMENT

Ancillaries

The life history of Ulothrix, an alga, and sexual reproduction in Oedogonium, a filamentous alga, are shown in overhead transparencies #87 (page 396) and #88 (page 397). Ask student to compare gamete sizes in both types of algae.

Supplemental Readings

Borgia, Gerald. 1986. Sexual selection in Bowerbirds. Sci. Am., June. Evolution of sex. See article by: Maranto, G. and S. Brownlee, 1984. "Why Sex?" The Evolution of Human Sexuality. Oxford Univ. Press, New York.

Ideas for Demonstration

1. 2"x2" slides showing sexual differences or dimorphism in vertebrates.

Topics for Discussion and Library Research

1. Parthenogenesis
2. Evolution of sex and asexual dimorphism
3. Mating systems; advantages, disadvantages
4. Altruistic behavior, kin selection
5. Social insects
6. Vertebrate societies
7. Courtship behavior

ESSAY QUESTIONS

1. Natural selection has favored mechanisms promoting sexual reproduction. Describe three such mechanisms which increase the likelihood for a successful sexual encounter.

2. What do you think is the relationship between the degree of pair bonding and parental care, and the number of offspring produced? Explain from an evolutionary perspective.

obj 7　3.　What is altruistic behavior? How can the existence of this type
of behavior be explained from an evolutionary perspective?

obj 2　4.　Compare asexual and sexual reproduction regarding advantages,
and disadvantages, and discuss conditions under which one type
would be favored over the other type of reproduction.

CHAPTER 20   ORIGIN OF LIFE

Outline

Summary

Until the nineteenth century, people believed that living organisms
were constantly being formed from nonliving substances when conditions
were favorable. Pasteur and Tyndall destroyed the belief that organisms
are formed spontaneously on earth under present-day conditions. However,
most scientists today believe that life originally arose spontaneously.

The conditions under which life began, however, were very different
from those on earth today. Evidence from geology and astronomy suggests
that the primitive earth probably had a mildly reducing atmosphere,
composed of the gases in today's atmosphere with the exception of oxygen.
Such an atmosphere would have been conducive to the formation and stabi-
lization of organic compounds, which gradually polymerized, formed macro-
molecular aggregates, and evolved systems of metabolism, information
transfer, and reproduction, eventually becoming living organisms.

Some important events during the early history of life were the
evolution of photosynthesis and respiration, and the acquisition of
intracellular organelles, mitosis, and meiosis and fertilization. Organisms have changed their environment from an earth of barren water
and rock under a somewhat reducing atmosphere to one of teeming oceans
and verdant landscapes in an oxidizing atmosphere. Each environmental
change caused by organisms exerted selective pressures to adapt to the
new environment, which in turn changed the environment even more. Thus
living organisms and their environment have shaped each other during
the evolution of life on earth.

Five questins about the origin of life have tentatively been
answered:

1.   How did enzymes arise without previous enzymes to make them?
2.   How did cells come into existence without cells to make them?
3.   How did membranes originate?
4.   How did informational macromolecules arise before the complex
     genetic code?
5.   How did reproduction begin?

Objectives

1.   Recognize what is meant by the terms spontaneous generation,
information (as applied to biological molecules), and emergent properties.

2.   Give two reasons why it is unlikely that spontaneous generation
could occur under the conditions that exist on earth today.

3. Discuss the importance of time in the theory of the origin of life presented in this chapter.

4. Compare the environment in which life is believed to have arisen with the present environment on earth.

5. Trace the steps by which life may have originated on earth, from the formation of organic monomers through the rise of eukaryotic organisms.

6. State what evidence we have that these steps were possible, describing the experimental work of Miller, Fox, and Oparin.

7. List (a) kinds of places and (b) sources of energy, on the prebiotic earth, that could have been important in the formation of organic molecules and prebiotic systems.

8. Explain why proteins and nucleic acids would have had to evolve together.

9. Describe the order and steps by which fermentation, respiration, and photosynthesis may have evolved.

10. Compare fermentation and respiration and describe their significance for the origin and evolution of life.

11. State the significance of the evolution of the first autotrophs for the evolution of early life.

12. Describe changes in the environment that resulted from the presence of living organisms, and explain how the evolution of modern organisms was dependent on the change to modern environmental conditions.

What's new or expanded in the third edition

Section 20-F, Formation of Aggregates, has been expanded and includes a description of the criteria that define a cell. Section 20-L contains information on fossils of bacteria and blue green bacteria, which are thought to be 3.4 to 3.6 billion years old.

SUGGESTIONS FOR LECTURE PREPARATION AND ENRICHMENT

Supplemental Readings

Cairns-Smith, A. G. 1985. The first organisms. Scientific American, June.

Peterson, I. 1984. Microsphere excitement. Science News 125: 408.

Vidal, G. 1984. The oldest eukaryotic cells. Sci. Am., February.

Weisburd, Stefi. 1986. The microbes that loved the sun. Science News. 129: 108-110; Feb. 15.

Films

Cell Biology (COR, 1981, 17 min.) Evolution of eukaryotic cells is discussed.

Topics for Discussion and Library Research

1. Origin of multicellularity. See article by: Valentine J. 1978. "The evolution of multicellular plants and animals," Sci. Am. Sept.

2. Origin of cells. See articles by: Vidal, G. 1984. "The oldest eukaryotic cells." Sci. Am., February; Dickerson, R. 1978.

"Chemical evolution and origin of life." Sci. Am. Sept.;
Schopf, J.W. 1978. "The evolution of the earliest cells."
Sci. Am., Sept.

ESSAY QUESTIONS

1. Explain why the earliest organisms were most likely heterotrophic prokaryotes.

2. Discuss at least two lines of evidence supporting the theory that eukaryotic cells originated from a symbiotic union of different types of ancient prokaryotic cells.

3. Explain how small organic molecules, which are thought to have formed in the early oceans, could eventually give rise to a living cell. In other words describe a probable sequence of events, starting from these small organic molecules, which resulted in the origin of living cells.

CHAPTER 21   CLASSIFICATION OF ORGANISMS

Outline

I.   Binomial Nomenclature
II. Taxonomy
III. Systematics and Its Tools
   A. Interpreting the Characteristics of Organisms
   B. Monophyletic or Polyphyletic?
IV. Taxonomic Methods
   A. Phenetics
   B. Phylogenetic Systematics
   C. Evolutionary Systematics
   D. Cladistics
V.   The Five Kingdoms
   A. Kingdom Monera
   B. Kingdom Protista
   C. Kingdom Fungi
   D. Kingdom Plantae (Plants)
   E. Kingdom Animalia (Animals)
   F. Difficulties with the Five Kingdom System
Box: Constructing a Cladogram and Producing a Classification from It.

Summary

Taxonomy is the branch of biology concerned with relationships between organisms and with their classification. The basic unit of classification is the species; each species is given a unique Latin binomial, consisting of the genus name and species epithet.

Species are grouped into progressively more inclusive taxa. The main levels in the taxonomic hierarchy from most to least inclusive, are: kingdom, phylum, class, order, family, genus, and species. A taxon in each higher level contains one or more taxa of the next lower level. Taxa are not units intrinsic in nature, waiting to be discovered by humans, but instead are artificial constructs invented by humans to help us think about living organisms in an orderly manner. Modern biologists have many conflicting viewpoints about how the rules of taxonomy should be applied and where the lines should be drawn to define taxa.

In theory, living things are classified by phylogenetic relationships, but these are often difficult to disentangle, and the sheer number of existing species precludes the drawing up of a phylogenetic tree encompassing all known organisms. In practice, therefore, living things are usually classified by morphology. Other features, such as physiology, biochemistry, behavior, and geographic distribution, are also used.

Pheneticists advocate using phenotypic characters as the criteria for setting up a classification scheme, whereas cladists insist on strict adherence to phylogenetic criteria. Evolutionary systematists consider both phylogeny and the genetic similarities that give rise to similar morphology, and it is this system, imperfect as it is, that has given us many different and somewhat conflicting classification schemes in use today.

This book uses the taxonomic system that divides organisms into five kingdoms: Monera, the prokaryotes; Protista, the unicellular eukaryotes; Plantae, the plants; Fungi, the fungi; and Animalia, the animals. This classification is based largely on the mode of nutrition and cellular organization of organisms. Several evolutionary lines of organisms are almost certainly grouped in each kingdom.

Objectives

1. Give the meaning of the following words and use them correctly: taxonomy, taxon, morphology, type specimen, species, phylogeny, monophyletic, polyphyletic, convergent evolution.

2. Describe Linnaeus's contribution to taxonomy and the basis for his classification.

3. State the theoretical basis for modern biological classification and discuss some of the problems of constructing satisfactory classification schemes.

4. Write the Latin binomial of an organism correctly.

5. List in order seven main hierarchical levels into which organisms are placed.

6. Explain what is meant by saying that characters are ancestral, derived, homologous, analogous, conservative, or convergent.

7. List the five kingdoms used in this book, and state the criteria used to assign species to each kingdom.

What's new or expanded in the third edition

Section 21-C, Systematics and Its Tools, is new and includes material on the type of information systematists use to construct phylogenies. The various types of characters, such as ancestral or derived, homologous or analogous, are discussed as ways of interpreting the characteristics of organisms. The terms monophyletic, polyphyletic clade and grade are defined.

Section 21-D, Taxonomic Methods is also new and contains information on the three main schools of taxonomic thought. The pheneticists classify organisms according to their similarity to one another. One group of phylogeneticists, the evolutionary systematists, hold that classification should reflect genealogical and genetic relationships at the same time. Cladists on the other hand, emphasize the genealogy and believe that taxon should be monophyletic. The problems with and importance of each of these schools of taxonomic thought are discussed.

SUGGESTIONS FOR LECTURE PREPARATION AND ENRICHMENT

Correlative Laboratory Exercises

Topic 14 Classification of Organisms

In Topic 14 students learn about taxonomy and have an opportunity to classify a confier using a taxonomic key. Depending on availability of different taxonomic keys students could be asked to classify other organisms collected on a field trip.

Supplemental Readings

Wexler, Mark. 1986. What's in a name? National Wildlife 24(4):12-13, June/July

Films

Diversity of Life (IU, 1981, 27 min.) Presents distinguishing characteristics of a variety of organisms representing the five kingdoms of classification.

The Infinite Variety ((Life on Earth Series) Fl, 1981, 58 min.) Presents diversity of life and progression of life forms from simple to complex.

Student Activities

Have students identify common organisms using dichotomous (taxonomic) keys.

Ideas for Demonstrations

1. Evolutionary trees reflecting different systems of classification.

2. Classification using dichotomous keys.

Topics for Discussion and Library Research

1. Comparison of various systems of classification.

2. Molecules reflecting evolutionary conservatism: cytochrome C, histones, ribosomal RNA, tubulin, etc. Discuss why they are conserved.

3. Assignment of humans to each taxon-characteristics allowing placement

4. Relationship of shared derived characteristics and degree of ancestry.

5. Biochemical determination of evolutionary relatioship using proteins and nucleic acids.

6. Molecular clocks.

ESSAY QUESTIONS

obj 7   1. Describe the major distinguishing characteristics of each of the five kingdoms.

obj 5   2. For humans identify the kingdom phylum, class, order, and family, and for each taxon describe the characteristic(s) of humans that allow placement in that taxon.

3. Based on your knowledge of proteins and nucleic acids which would probably give a more accurate view of evolutionary relationships? Explain your answer.

obj 1   4. Distinguish between the members of the following paired terms: phenetic/phylogenetic/cladistic; ancestral/derived character; homologous/analogous character; genus/species; taxon/clade

5. How would you classify porpoises if you were a cladistic taxonomist? a phenetic taxonomist? a phylogenetic taxonomist?

obj 1   6. Define a type specimen, and explain its usefulness in taxonomy.

7. Why aren't morphological features the most accurate criterion for classifying organisms?

CHAPTER 22 VIRUSES

Outline

Summary

Viruses resemble cells in that they contain nucleic acid and protein molecules, and some are surrounded by membranous envelopes of
lipid and protein. Unlike cells, viruses lack the metabolic machinery
to synthesize proteins and to generate energy, and many viruses can be
crystallized. Cells reproduce by dividing in two, but hundreds of
viruses may be produced in a host cell after infection by a single
virus particle.

A virus particle's capsid or envelope proteins bind to the surface
of a host cell by means of specific protein-receptor interactions.
The viral genome, consisting of either DNA or RNA, but not both, enters
the cell interior. In a lytic cycle, the virus immediately takes over
the host cell's metabolic machinery, causing it to transcribe and
replicate the viral genome and manufacture virus-specific capsid (and
envelope) proteins. The viral components are then assembled into
numerous new viral particles, which are freed by lysis of the host cell.
In a lysogenic cycle, the viral genome becomes incorporated into the
host's DNA and is replicated and passed along to the cell's progeny at
each division. Eventually the viral genome is excised from that of
the host, possibly taking along some of the host's genetic material,
and the production and release of virus particles takes place as in the
lytic cycle. Another kind of cycle involves the gradual production
and release of viral particles, leaving the host cell intact, at least
for a while.

Viral disruption of host cells is responsible for many diseases
including some tumors, in plants and animals. Some plant diseases are
caused by viroids, which are short, naked strands of RNA that do not
code for protein. Prions, which appear to be glycoproteins without
any associated nucleic acid, cause diseases of the central nervous
system. The mechanisms by which viroids and prions cause disease are
still unknown.

Objectives

1.   Discuss similarities and differences between viruses and living
     organisms.

2.   Describe the structure of a virus.

3.   Describe lytic and lysogenic cycles and the continuous production
     of new virus particles in the Semliki Forest virus.

4.   Explain how the genome of an RNA virus is replicated.

What's new or expanded in the third edition

     Tables 22-1 and 22-2 are new and should be useful for students.
In table 22-1 the differences between viruses and cells are listed.
In Table 22-2 the characteristics of each of the major groups of viruses
that infect animals are listed.

     Section 22-D describes the release of viruses, such as the Semliki
Forest virus, from living host cells. Figure 22-6 illustrates reproduction of the Semliki Forest virus.

     Section 22-G on viroids has been expanded and includes new
information about their structure and that of their RNA. In figure
22-9 (page 453) the RNA of a viroid is depicted. Section 22-H is new
and provides information about prions, glycoprotein particles capable
of causing diseases in animals.

     Section 22-I discusses hypotheses concerning the evolutionary
origin of viruses and the evolution of viruses themselves.

SUGGESTIONS FOR LECTURE PREPARATION AND ENRICHMENT

Ancillaries

     Overhead transparencies (OHT) #99 (page 447) and #90 (page 449)
illustrate the reproductive cycles of a lytic and a lysogenic phage,
respectively. Ask students to compare the two types of reproduction.
OHT #91 (page 450) shows reproduction of a Semliki Forest virus in a
living host cell. Ask students to compare with reproductive cycles
of lytic and lysogenic phage. OHT #92 (page 451) illustrates two
different ways by which the genome of an RNA virus may be replicated.

Supplemental Readings

Baum, Rudy. 1985. AIDS epidemic continues, moving beyond high risk
     groups. Chemical and Engineering News 63:19-26, April 1.

Bennett, D. 1985. Like sheep virus, AIDS virus affects brain. Science
     News 127:22, January 12. A short report about the discovery of
     HTLV-III in human brain cells and about the similarities between
     that AIDS linked virus and a virus that causes a chronic, de-
     generative nueurological disease in sheep.

Chasan, Daniel. 1986. The polio paradox. Science 86 7(3):36-39, April.

Marx, Jean. 1985. More progress on the HTLV family. Science 227:
     156-157, January 11.

Marx, Jean. 1985. More about the HTLV's and how they act. Science 229:
     37-38, July 5.

Morse, G. 1984. Viroids: Nature's littlest killers. Science News 126:
     91-93.

Prusiner, S. 1984. Prions, Sci. Am., October.

Sanders, F. K. 1981. Viruses (2/E) Carolina Biology Reader.

Schiefelbein, S. 1984. The man who found the AIDS virus. Science
     Digest 92 (7): 62-65.

Silberner, Joanne, 1985. Cancer virus redux. Science News 127: 346-347
     June 1. An update on the association of viruses and certain cancer.

Simons, K., Garoff, H., and A. Helenius. 1982. How an animal virus
     gets into and out of its host cell. Sci. Am., February.

Whitaker, J. and D. Kingsbury. 1984. Viruses and the pathogenesis of
     multiple sclerosis. Trends in Nueurosciences 7: 57-61.

<u>Films</u>

Invasion of Virions (Fl, 1981, 50 min.) Discusses selected viruses as well as the latest molecular antiviral techniques such as recombinant DNA, interferon, vaccines, and drugs.

<u>Ideas for Demonstrations</u>

1. Electron micrographs showing different sizes, shapes and external features of viruses.

2. Diagrams showing lytic and lysogenic infections.

<u>Topics for Discussion and Library Research</u>

1. Common viral diseases of animals.

2. Comparison of living cells and viruses--similiarities, differences

3. Origin of viruses

4. Specificity of virus and host cell

5. Comparison of lytic and lysogenic infections

6. Association of viruses, oncogenes, and cancer

7. Use of viruses, particularly retroviruses, in genetic engineering.

8. Viroids. See articles by: Lewin, R. 1983. Viroid origin in jumping genes? Science <u>222</u>:915; and, Morse, G. 1984. Viroids: Nature's littlest killers. Science News <u>126</u>: 91-93.

<u>ESSAY QUESTIONS</u>

obj 3   1. Compare a lytic infection with a lysogenic infection regarding the effect on the host cell and the activity of the virus.

obj 1   2. Describe three characteristics shared by both viruses and all living organisms.

obj 1   3. Would you classify viruses as living or nonliving? Explain your answer.

4. What properties or characteristics of viruses make them especially useful as vectors in gene transfer experiments?

5. Distinguish between the members of the following paired term: lytic/lysogenic phage; virus/viroid/prion; retrovirus/bacteriophage.

obj 1   6. Describe four differences and one similarity between viruses and cells.

7. Compare lytic and lysogenic infections with that exhibited by the Semliki Forest virus.

CHAPTER 23   BACTERIA

Outline

I.   Prokaryotic Cells
    A.   Extracellular Structures
    B.   Structure in the Cytoplasm
II.   Reproduction in Prokaryotes
III.   Bacterial Metabolism and Ways of Life
    A.   Autotrophic Bacteria
    B.   Nitrogen-Fixing Bacteria
    C.   Heterotrophic Bacteria
IV.   Classification of Prokaryotes
    A.   Archaeobacteria
    B.   Eubacteria
    C.   Gram-Positive Bacteria
    D.   Spirochetes
    E.   Rickettsia
    G.   Purple Bacteria
    H.   Green Sulfur Bacteria
    I.   Cyanobacteria
V.   Bacteria and Food
VI.   Bacterial Diseases
    A.   Control of Bacterial Disease
    B.   Drug Resistance
VII.   Symbiotic Bacteria
VIII.   Origin of Mitochondria and Plastids

Summary

The kingdom Monera contains all the prokaryotes. The archaeobacteria and eubacteria probably represent two distinct evolutionary lines of prokaryotes; hence, this kingdom is like the four eukaryotic kingdoms in being polyphyletic.

Prokaryotic cells are smaller and less complex than eukaryotic cells, and they have different cell wall composition: peptidoglycans in eubacteria, and various other compounds in archaeobacteria; Gram-negative eubacteria also have an outer lipopolysaccharide layer, which confers resistance to many antibiotics and also produces disease symptoms in host animals. A prokaryote's genome is in the form of a single, circular DNA molecule with little associated protein. Prokaryotes lack membrane-bound organelles, but some have internal membranes, such as mesosomes or systems of membranes containing the molecules of respiration or photosynthesis. Some bacteria have loco-motory flagella. Under adverse conditions, many bacteria produce spores, which can disperse to new locations and resume growth.

Most bacterial cells reproduce by binary fission. Genetic recom-bination can occur by the transfer of a variable amount of DNA from a donor to a recipient bacterium, but the frequency and evolutionary importance of such events in nature is unknown. Mutation and rapid reproduction, coupledwith small size and metabolic diversity, are believed to account for the evolutionary success of bacteria.

Three billion years ago, bacteria were the earth's only inhabi-tants, living in communities of many different, interdependent species. Some were autotrophs, absorbing raw materials from their environments and making their own food; photoautotrophs used solar energy, whereas chemoautotrophs obtained energy from chemical reactions, mostly of sulfur or nitrogen compounds. Other bacteria evolved ways of living heterotrophically, exploiting their neighbors for food. When a cell died, or eliminated its wastes, it provided raw materials for other bacteria, and so nutrients were recycled in the bacterial community. Today, bacteria are still the most numerous and ubiquitous organisms on earth, and they are still playing all of these roles, although the eukaryotes (which may themselves be the descendants of cooperative prokaryote symbioses) have become the predominant photosynthesizers and the most conspicuous heterotrophs. Nitrogen-fixing bacteria (including many cyanobacteria) support eukaryotes by converting N_2 into a form that can be used by higher plants to make amino acids, and saprobic bacteria play the vital ecological role of decomposers, breaking down organic material and permitting its constituents to be recycled. Although many bacteria are free-living, numerous others form symbiotic relationships--parasitic, commensal, or mutualistic--with other bacteria or with eukaryotes. Some bacteria are pathogens, producing toxins that cause disease, and some are part of the normal flora of animals. The chloroplasts, and possibly mitochondria, of eukaryotes are also thought to have evolved from intracellular symbiotic bacteria. Chloroplasts show many similarities to the cyanobacteria and Prochloron, which differ from other photosynthetic bacteria in possessing chlorophyll a and in using water as a hydrogen donor, releasing molecular oxygen as a photosynthetic by-product.

Bacteria significant to the human economy include cyanobacteria, which are often members of "blooms" produced by an excess of nutrients in bodies of fresh water; actinomycetes, common soil organisms from which many antibiotics were first procured; and nitrogen-fixing symbionts in the root nodules of legumes. We use some bacteria to produce foods such as yogurt, cheeses, and vinegar. Food poisoning is caused by ingesting exotoxins or pathogenic bacteria in food. Bacterial diseases have played major, often devastating roles in human history. Immunization, improved hygiene, and antibiotics have reduced human and animal deaths from bacterial disease. One disadvantage of antibiotics is that their use selects for mutant bacteria, and transferable plasmids, resistant to the antibiotic in question.

Objectives

1. Use the following terms correctly: capsule, glycocalyx, mesosome, spore, plasmid, heterocyst, aerobe, obligate anaerobe, facultative anaerobe, autotroph, heterotroph, saprobe, photoautotrophy (= photosynthesis), chemoautotrophy, nitrogen fixation, decomposer organism, pathogen.

2. List and describe the four sources of genetic change known among prokaryotes, and discuss the contributions of these sources and of reproductive rate to the evolutionary success of prokaryotes.

3. List the three main shapes of bacteria and give their Latin names.

4. Describe the distinguishing characteristics of prokaryotic cells, and of archaeobacteria, eubacteria, and these special groups of eubacteria: actinomycetes, spirochetes, and cyanobacteria.

5. Explain what is meant by a "bloom" of cyanobacteria; list some factors that can cause such blooms, and describe measures to prevent them.

6. State how photosynthesis in cyanobacteria and Prochloron (and eukaryotes) differs from that of other bacteria.

7. Describe the metabolism of a sulfur bacterium and the conditions that encourage or discourage the growth of these bacteria.

8. Summarize the ecological significance of prokaryotes, including their roles in food production, nitrogen fixation, nitrification, and decomposition.

9. Give some examples of the use of bacteria in food production.

10. Describe the difference between bacterial endotoxins and exotoxins, and explain how each causes disease.

11. Explain how drug resistance arises in bacterial populations, including the roles of natural selection and plasmid transfer (Sections 23-B and 23-F).

What's new or expanded in the third edition

Section 23-A has been expanded and includes new material on extracellular layers. Also included in this section are new figures (23-2, 23-3, and 23-4) showing the glycocalyx, and bacterial pili and flagella. Figure 23-5 is an electron micrograph of a cyanobacterial cell dividing by binary fission. Section 23-B contains new information on plasmids and their role in bacterial resistance to antibiotics.

Section 23-C incorporates material on bacterial metabolism which existed as separate sections in the second edition.

Section 23-D has been expanded and includes new material on characteristics of archaeobacteria, Gram-positive bacteria, purple bacteria, and green sulfur bacteria. Table 23-1, which is also new, lists the characteristics of the major groups of bacteria presented in this section.

In section 23-G the different types of symbiotic relationships of bacteria are described, as well as the effects of these relationships on the symbionts. Figures 23-21 to 23-23 illustrate some of these symbiotic relationships.

SUGGESTIONS FOR LECTURE PREPARATION AND ENRICHMENT

Correlative Laboratory Exercise

Topic 15 Kingdom Monera and Protista (parts)

In Topic 15 students study a variety of single-celled organisms from bacteria to diatoms and dinoflagellates using a cyanobacterium Anabaena, a mastigophoran Euglena, and diatoms, and prepared slides of dinoflagellates. Students are introduced to microbiological culture techniques when they perform exercises designed to demonstrate the presence of bacteria in the air and in their own mouths before and after brushing.

Supplemental Readings

Bacteria

Deyrup, M. 1981. Deadwood decomposers. Natural History 90(3): 84-91.

Dixon, B. 1986. Overdosing on wonder drugs. Science 86 7(4):40-43, May.

Friedman, M. 1982. Biochemical ecology of intracellular parasites. TIBS 7: 332-334.

Kosikowski, Frank. 1985. Cheese. Sci. Am., May.

Morgan, Diana and Terence Monmaney. 1985. The bug catalog. Science 85 6(6):37-41. July/August. A description of products made using microoganisms.

Preuss, Paul. 1985. Industry in ferment. Science 85 6: 52-46, July/August. A discussion of techniques used to grow microorganisms and problems of growing them.

Radetsky, Peter. 1985. The Rise and (maybe not the) Fall of Toxic Shock Syndrome. Science 84 6(1): 72-79. Discusses how little is known about the role of tampons and the cause of TSS despite identification of a bacterial strain associated with the disease.

Raloff, Janet. 1985. The bugs of rust. Science News 128: 42-44.
   An account of investigations to determine how microorganisms
   influence the corrosion of metals.

Thomsen, D. 1984. Swimming for the good life. Science News 125:
   298-299.

Wolfe, M. 1984. PeeWee Predator (Bdellovibrio). Science News 125:
   60-61.

Films

A New Look at Leewenhoek's "Wee Beasties" (WNSE, 1975, 12 min.)
   Introduces protists.

Ideas for Demonstrations

1. Electron micrographs of bacteria showing various structures.

2. Slides showing gram-negative and gram-positive bacteria.

3. Slides showing different shapes of bacteria; coccus, bacillus,
    spirillum.

Topics for Discussion and Library Research

1. Ecological importance of monerans

2. Comparison of cyanobacteria and bacteria.

3. Archaebacteria

4. Reasons for success of monerans, particularly bacteria

5. Methods of genetic exchange among bacteria: transformation,
    transduction, conjugation and transfer of plasmids

6. Types of bacterial metabolism

7. Effect of antibiotics on bacteria.

8. Transmission of antibiotic resistant bacteria from animals to
    humans. See articles by: Chinnici, M. 1985. Concern about
    antibiotics. Science Digest 93(2): 16; and Franklin, D. 1984.
    Drug resistance link from animal to man. Science News 126: 119.

ESSAY QUESTIONS

obj 8 1. Describe three characteristics of bacteria which have contributed
           to their biological success and ability to live everywhere.

obj 4 2. How does the survival of all organisms depend on bacteria?

obj 4 3. Compare and contrast cyanobacteria and bacteria regarding pre-
           sence and nature of external and internal structures, and process
           of acquiring energy.

obj 1 4. Discuss differences in photosynthesis between plants and bacteria.

obj 1 5. Distinguish between the members of the following paired terms:
           pili/flagella; conjugation/transduction/transformation; faculta-
           tive anaerobes/obligate anaerobes/aerobes; mesosome/plasmid;
           saprobe/autotroph.

obj 6 6. Compare photoautotrophs, chemoautotrophs and heterotrophs
           regarding source of energy for the synthesis of organic compounds,

and the nature and source of raw materials used for synthesis.

obj 8   7. Contrast nitrogen fixation with nitrification, and describe the types of organisms responsible for each process.

obj 4   8. List and identify one distinguishing feature for each of five different groups of bacteria.

obj 4   9. Describe three differences and two similarities between archaeo-bacteria and eubacteria.

obj 12   10. List the three types of symbiotic relationships involving bacteria, and for each indicate using +, -, or 0 the effect of the symbionts on each other.

CHAPTER 24   PROTISTA AND THE ORIGIN OF MULTICELLULARITY

Outline

Summary

     The origin of eukaryotic cells led to the evolution of a wide
array of unicellular heterotrophic and autotrophic organisms. Those
without close relatives among the multicellular organisms are classified
in the kingdom Protista. Protists may house a complex organization
within a single cell.

     Autotrophic protists live either free in the phytoplankton, or
attached to moist surfaces, or as symbionts inside larger organisms.
The clues to their phylogeny include such conservative characters as
photosynthetic pigments, form of food storage, chemistry and form of
the cell wall or other cell covering, and presence, type, and arrangement of flagella.

     Heterotrophic protists may be free-living predators, eating other
protists, bacteria, and small multicellular organisms, or may be
symbionts or parasites of larger forms of life. Three major phyla are
characterized by their type of locomotion: Zoomastigina move by means
of flagella, Sarcodina by pseudopodia, and Ciliophora by cilia. The
fourth phylum contains at least two lineages of parasitic forms with
complex life histories. Some parasitic protists have an enormous
impact on human health, which in turn may place tremendous burdens on
the economy in the form of health care expenses and lost labor capacity.

     Small organisms, such as protists and bacteria, are well adapted to
exploiting habitats and ways of life that provide only limited food
and space. Tiny organisms can reproduce rapidly and many of them can
form spores or cysts resistant to adverse conditions such as drying or
cold.

     Selective pressure for large size probably favored the evolution
of some ancient protists into multicellular fungi, plants, and animals.
In protists, division of labor occurs within the cytoplasm and organelles
of a single cell. In multicellular plants and animals, division of labor
among cells and tissues is added to the division of labor among the
organelles within each cell.

Objectives

1. Give the definitive characteristics of members of the kingdom
    Protista.

2. Describe the three main types of locomotion found among protists.

3. Explain what phytoplankton are, their ecological importance, and
    what factors control the fluctuation in their numbers.

4. List distinguishing characteristics of members of the following

groups: Chrysophyta, Pyrrophyta, Euglenophyta, Sarcodina, Zoomastigina, Ciliophora.

5. Place each of the following in the correct phylum: dinoflagellate. Gonyaulax, Euglena, diatom, Trypanosome , Amoeba, Paramecium, Plasmodium.

What's new or expanded in the third edition

Many sections have been expanded and include new information concerning the pathogenicity of some of the unicellular organisms. E.g., figure 24-8 (page 494) illustrates the life history of Plasmodium vivax which causes human malaria.

SUGGESTIONS FOR LECTURE PREPARATION AND ENRICHMENT

Ancillaries

Overhead transparency #93 (page 494) illustrates the life history of Plasmodium vivax, the organism causing human malaria. Ask students how to eradicate malaria based on the life history of the pathogen.

Correlative Laboratory Exercises

Topic 15 Kingdom Monera and Kingdom Protista

In Topic 15 students study a variety of single-celled organisms from bacteria to diatoms and dinoflagellates using a variety of techniques. Students observe living specimens of a cyanobacterium Anabaena, a mastagaphoran. Euglena, and diatoms, and prepared slides of dinoflagellates. Students are introduced to microbiological culture techniques when they perform exercises designed to demonstrate the presence of bacteria in the air and in their mouths before and after brushing.

Supplemental Readings

Bonner, J. T. 1983. Chemical signals of social amoebae. Sci. Am., April.

Leedale, G. 1971. The Euglenoids. Carolina Biology Reader.

Films

Protists: Threshold of Life   (NGS, 1974, 12 min.) Examination of drop of pond water to view small organisms.

Ideas for Demonstrations

1. Slides of whole mounts of protists.

2. Living cultures of protists.

Topics for Discussion and Library Research

1. Relationship among protists.

2. Comparison of five phyla of protozoans regarding method of locomotion, manner of acquiring food, lifestyles.

ESSAY QUESTIONS

1. Suggest two factors that might affect and limit the size of unicellular organisms.

obj 4 2. Explain why euglena might be classified as either an animal or plant?

obj 4 3. List and describe one distinguishing characteristic for each of the five phyla of protozoans.

obj 1 4. Compare and contrast a "typical" cell from an animal with one of the animal-like protists. Describe similarities and differences.

CHAPTER 25 FUNGI

Summary

Members of the kingdom Fungi are eukaryotic saprobes and para-
sties that obtain their nutrients by absorption and have a cell wall
in at least some stages of the life history. Spores are involved in
both sexual and asexual reproduction.

On the basis of sexual reproductive structures, the true fungi can
be classified into four main divisions Oomycota Zygomycota Ascomycota,
and Basidiomycota . A fifth, Deuteromycota, consists of all the true
fungi for which no sexual reproduction is known.

The most important ecological role of fungi is as decomposer
organisms, which break down dead plants and animals and absorb the
resulting small food molecules. Inevitably, however, some of these
molecules escape the fungi, and minerals released by fungal breakdown
are important to green plants, which absorb and reuse these vital
nutrients.

Fungi are also important as parasites, causing diseases of both
plants and animals. Most fungal diseases attack plants. Once
established, a fungal disease of a plant is often impossible to
combat, and fungal diseases of animals can be cured only with much
difficulty. Thus prevention of infection is important in combating
fungal diseases.

Lichens are symbiotic associations between fungi and gree algae
or cyanobacteria. Lichens are important food producers in cold or
barren areas; they may also help to form soil from bare rock. Other
fungi form associations known as mycorrhizae with the roots of higher
plants and benefit these plants by increasing their supply of minerals.

Many fungi produce toxic compounds that serve to deter predators.
reduce competition from bacteria or other fungi, or even catch animal
prey as dietary supplements.

Fungi are economically harmful because they destroy seed, standing crops, and harvested food, as well as clothing, homes and other possessions. Fungi also cause disease and death to human beings livestock and pets. On the positive side of the ledger, fungi are useful in the production of many edible fruiting bodies, of fermented foods, and of drugs, antibiotics, and various organic chemicals.

The slime molds live either as coenocytic plasmodia or as unicellular amoebas. They feed by engulfing food particles, and they lack rigid cell walls. These characteristics suggest affinities with the protozoan amoebas; slime molds are classified as fungi because they form fruiting bodies with   walled spores, a habit strongly suggesting fungal alliances.

Objectives

1. Describe why the activity of fungi as decomposers is vital to life on earth.

2. Describe the major characteristics of fungi, and tell how fungi differ from plants and animals.

3. Define the terms saprobe, parasite, hypha, mycelium, dikaryon, haustorium, spore, sporangium, ascus, basidium, fruiting body, symboisis.

4. Describe both sexual and asexual life histories of a fungus such as Rhizopus, the black bread mold.

5. List the divisions of the fungi and the distinguishing characteristics of each.

6. Explain why there are many more fungal diseases of plants than of minerals.

7. List or recognize ways in which fungi are economically beneficial and ways in which they are economically harmful.

8. List at least three ways in which fungi may spread.

9. Discuss methods of controlling fungi.

10. State what lichens and mycorrhizae are, and explain their ecological roles.

What's new or expanded in the third edition

In section 25-B the subsection describing the common aspects of fungal life histories is new, as are figures 25-3 and 25-4 (page 501) which illustrate life histories of fungi, plants and humans.

In section 25-j the mycorrhizae are described in greater detail. The two types of slime molds are presented in separate sections and described in greater detail.

SUGGESTIONS FOR LECTURE PREPARATION AND ENRICHMENT

Ancillaries

Overhead transparencies (OHT) number 94-97 illustrate the life histories of four different divisions of fungi. In OHT #94 (page 503) sexual reproduction is an oomycete is illustrated while in OHT #95 (page 504) sexual reproduction of a zygomycete is shown. In OHTs #96 (page 505) and #97 (506) a generalized scheme of sexual reproduction in ascomycetes and in basidiomycetes is diagrammed. Ask students to compare all four types of sexual reproduction.

Correlative Laboratory Exercise

Topic 16   Fungi and Lower Plants

Parts of Topic 16 covering fungi could be assigned.   Students learn about different classes of fungi through direct observation of preserved and living representative specimens.

Supplemental Readings

Ahmadjian, V. 1982.   The nature of lichens.   Natural History 91(3): 30-37.

Monmaney, Terence, 1985.   Yeast at work.   Science 85 6: 30-36. July/ August.

Kaufman, W. and H. Ellis. 1985.   Mushrooms take mysterious shapes. Natural Wildlife 23 (6):4-9, Oct./Nov. photographic essay.

Ideas for Demonstration

1. Microscopic display of fungi of blue cheese or another cheese.

2. Display of foods, drugs, chemicals produced by fungi and bene- ficial to humans.

3. Specimens of lichens.   These can be collected and exhibited.

4. Specimens of fungi.   These can be collected and exhibited.

Topics for Discussion and Library Research

1. Ecological role of fungi.

2. Comparison of sexual reproductive structures of different classes of Eumycophyta.

3. Fungal diseases of animals and plants.

4. Symbiotic relationships of fungi. See article by Ahmadjian, V. 1982.   The nature of lichens. Natural History 91(3):30-37.

ESSAY QUESTIONS

obj 9   1. What two characteristics of fungi make the control of fungal diseases difficult?

obj 5   2. Compare and contrast the slime molds and true fungi.

obj 10 3. All plants are believed to have arisen from one group of green algae. How might fungi have assisted photosynthetic plants in their transition to land?

obj 2   4. Distinguish between the members of the following paired terms: plasmodium/pseudoplasmodium; lichen/mycorrhiza; yeast/mold; thallus/fruiting body; and, dikaryotic/coenocytic.

obj 5   5. List and describe one distinguishing characteristic for each of the five classes of the true fungi (Eumycophyta).

CHAPTER 26   LOWER PLANTS

Outline

Summary

The three main groups of multicellular algae included in the plant kingdom probably arose independently from different groups of photosynthetic protists. These lower plants have not evolved the adaptation that enable higher plants to live on land; hence the multicellular algae are largely restricted to marine and freshwater habitats. Furthermore, because they require light for photosynthesis they live only in shallow water where sufficient light is available. Holdfasts or gelatinous secretions attach most forms to rocks or other substrates, and air bladders in some forms allow the photosynthetic parts of the plant to float near the surface, where there is adequate light. Plants in the intertidal zone are subject to desiccation when they are exposed to heat and air at low tide. A gelatinous coating helps these plants to retain moisture, and dark pigments screen the cells from the sun's rays.

Basic differences in biochemistry and physiology seem to have favored different groups of algae in different habitats. The red algae tend to live highup the shore or in the deepest layers of water that are penetrated by sunlight. Brown algae dominate shallow waters, particularly in colder seas. Green algae are present in most marine environments but are usually less conspicuous there, whereas many species flourish in freshwater and moist terrestrial habitats.

Multicellular algae provide food for various forms of marine life. Their ability to accumulate essential minerals from seawater has also made them useful as food for livestock and humans. In addition, they produce various economically useful substances.

Alternation of diploid and haploid generations, with similar or different body structure, is characteristic of plants. Sexual reproduction can often be seen as an adaptation that carries the species through hard times via the production of a resistant zygote. Vegetative reproduction can spread favorable genetic combinations in good times.

Objectives

1. List the characteristics that set members of the plant kingdom apart from members of the other kingdoms.

2. List or recognize the distinguishing characteristics of members of the divisions Rhodophyta, Phaeophyta, and Chlorophyta.

3. State how each of the following is of adaptive advantage to the algae that possess it: gelatinous secretion, accessory photosynthetic pigment, holdfast, air bladder, sexual reproduction, zoospores.

4. Define the following terms, and be able to use them: spore, gamete, zygote, fertilization, zoospore, holdfast, stipe, blade, air bladder.

5. Briefly explain alternation of generations, stating which stages in the life history of a plant are diploid and which are haploid.

What's new or expanded in the third edition

Figure 26-3 (page 521) is an electron micrograph of a chloroplast from a red alga. Sections 26-C and 26-F have been expanded and include new information on the method of sexual reproduction for red and green algae.

SUGGESTIONS FOR LECTURE PREPARATION AND ENRICHMENT

Ancillaries

In overhead transparency (OHT) #98 (page 527) the life history of Ulva, a green alga, is shown. Ask students to compare with the life histories of other green algae.

Correlative Laboratory Exercises

Topic 16 Fungi and the Lower Plants

Parts of Topic 16 could be assigned. Through direct observation of living and preserved specimens students study the general features of unicellular and multicellular green algae, brown algae and red algae. The gametophyte and sporophyte generations of the bryophytes are also examined through direct observation of specimens.

Supplemental Readings

Weisburd, S. 1985. The world's deepest-dwelling plant. Science News 127:4, January 5. A report about a coralline, red alga growing at 268 meters below the surface, making it the deepest dwelling plant visible to the unaided eye.

Ideas for Demonstrations

1. Preserved or living specimens representing gametophyte and sporophyte generations of higher green algae, like Ulva, and brown algae. These can be collected or ordered from a biological supply company.

2. Microscope demonstration of unicellular and colonial forms of chlorophytes like Chlamydomonas, Volvox, Pandorina, Ulothrix, Spirogyra and Acetabularia.

Topics for Discussion and Library Research

1. Alternation of generations. Comparison of gametophyte and sporophyte regarding size, complexity, formation, relationship to other generation, genetic makeup.

2. Comparison of lower and higher green algal forms.

3. Types of sexual reproduction: isogamy, anisogamy, oogamy.

4. Evolutionary relationship among algae and between algae and plants.

ESSAY QUESTIONS

obj 5 1. Under what conditions is sexual reproduction likely to occur in lower green algae and how does it occur?

obj 5   2. Discuss the roles of mitosis and meiosis in producing the gametophyte and sporophyte generations of higher green algae.

obj 4   3. Distinguish between the members of the following paired terms:
oogamy/isogamy; phycobilin/laminarin; blade/holdfast/stipe;
sporophyte/gametophyte; zoospores/spores.

CHAPTER 27   HIGHER PLANTS

Summary

     Land offers plants advantages that are not found in water: more
sunlight, more carbon dioxide, and more oxygen. However, land plants
must have adaptations that allow them to cope with the problems of a
terrestrial existence: lack of water, evaporation of the water that
is available, and lack of support. Rhizoids or roots allow land plants
to obtain water from the soil. Tracheophytes have evolved vascular
tissue, which transports water taken in by the roots, supports the stems
and leaves in the air, and transports food from the photosynthetic
parts to the roots. A waxy cuticle retards evaporation from the leaves
and stems, and stomata allow gases to enter the leaves with minimal
water loss. Leaves expose large surface areas for photosynthesis and
hormones coordinate the activities of different parts of the plant with
one another and with cues from the environment. In the most advanced
land plants, pollen grains and pollen tubes permit sexual reproduction
without the need for water in which sperm can swim, and seeds supply
food and protection to young individuals, increasing their chances of
survival.

     The adaptations of plants to life on land show several evolutionary
trends:

     1.   In bryophytes, the gametophyte became dominant and the
          sporophyte became dependent on it. In the vascular plants, the
          sporophyte became the dominant stage in the life history; during
          this shift, the size of the sporophyte progressively increased,
          while that of the gametophyte decreased.

     2.   The increase in size of the tracheophyte sporophyte was accom-
          panied by an increase in strength and efficiency of its vascu-
          lar tissue.

     3.   As tissues of tracheophyte sporophytes became more and more
          specialized, new organs were added progressively; stems, stems
          with roots and microphyll leaves, megaphyll leaves, and woody
          tissues.

4. The male gametophyte evolved into a waterproof pollen grain, which travelled to the female gametophyte before releasing the sperm. Sperm no longer faced a long, dangerous swim to the egg.

5. The female gametophyte of all land plants retains the egg and protects the zygote as it develops into an embryo: in higher land plants, the female gametophyte itself is retained on or in the sporophyte parent, which contributes food and protective coatings to the seed, a new dispersal structure containing the embryo of the next sporophyte generation.

6. In the higher vascular plants, the spore, a single haploid reproductive cell that is the dispersal stage of lower land plants become differentiated into megaspores, which give rise to female gametophytes, and microspores, which give rise to pollen grains (male gametophytes). Instead of being shed, the megaspores, remain in the sporophyte, which protects the female gametophyte and plays a major role in the production of the seed. Seeds replaced spores as the dispersal stage in life history.

7. As plant structure and reproduction became more and more independent of water and moisture in the environment, plants underwent adaptive radiation and spread into more and more different habitats.

Objectives

1. Define the following words briefly, and use them correctly: vascular tissue, cuticle, stomata, gametophyte, gamete, egg, sperm, sporophyte, spore, sporangium, meiosis, fertilization, zygote, embryo, rhizoid, rhizome, stem, root, leaf, microphyll, megaphyll, pollen, pollination seed, stamen, carpel, fruit.

2. Contrast water and land environments as habitats for plant life.

3. List the problems faced by plants living on land that are not faced by plants living in water, and for each problem name the adaptation(s) of land plants that allow them to survive in the face of the problem.

4. List the characteristics of embryophytes and explain why embryophytes are believed to be descended from green algae.

5. List the adaptations of bryophytes that allow them to live on land, and the characteristics that restrict them to very moist land environments.

6. Trace the evolutionary advances shown bryophytes, lycopsids (club mosses) and sphenopsids (horsetails), ferns, gymnosperms, and angiosperms.

7. Compare and contrast any of the groups mentioned in objective #6 with respect to structure, reproduction, and life history.

8. Place plants correctly into one of the groups listed in objective #6.

9. (a) Explain what alternation of generations is (b) trace the increasing dominance of the sporophyte during evolution of vascular plants, giving examples; and (c) discuss the selective value of this shift; (d) correctly identify any embryophyte as a sporophyte or gametophyte, and point out or explain where the opposite generation would be found.

What's new or expanded in the third edition

Table 27-4 (page 533) has been expanded and lists additional classes. Section 27-D has been expanded and provides a more general introduction

to the characteristics of the lower vascular plants. The description
of the conifers in section 27-E contains more details. Table 27-7
(page 548) provides a summary of the general characteristics of seed
plants and of each of the four major classes.

SUGGESTIONS FOR LECTURE PREPARATION AND ENRICHMENT

Ancillaries

In overhead transparencies numbers 99-101 the life histories of
a moss (page 535), a fern (page 542), and a pine (page 547) are illustrated. Ask students to compare the three life histories regarding the
size of the gametophyte, the size of the sporophyte, and the relationship between the gametophyte and sporophyte. Also have them identify
features of the plants and their methods of sexual reproduction which
allow these plants to live on land.

Correlative Laboratory Exercises

Topic 16   Fungi and the Lower Plants

Topic 17   Higher Plants

Parts of Topic 16 could be assigned. Through direct observation
of living and preserved specimens students study the gametophyte and
sporophyte generations of the bryophytes.

In Topic 17 students study the general features of club mosses,
horsetails, ferns and conifers by direct observation of living and
preserved specimens.

Supplemental Readings

Niklas, Karl. 1986. Computer-simulated plant evolution. Sci. Am., March.

Vietmeyer, N. 1985. Plants that eat pollution. National Wildlife 23
    (5):10-11, Aug/Sept.

Student Activities

Have students collect specimens representing the gametophyte and
sporophyte generations of ferns and mosses.

Have them make a collection of different monocots, dicots, and conifers. Using taxonomic keys, have them indicate the class for each
organism.

Ideas for Demonstrations

1. Living or preserved specimens of representative vascular
    plants for each class.

2. Display of flowers, fruits, seeds, cones to show adaptations for
    attaching pollinators or dispersing pollen or seeds.

3. Microscope slides of pollen from different types of angiosperms
    and gymnosperms.

4. 2" x 2" slides of life histories of seed plants. They can be
    purchased from biological supply companies.

Topics for Discussion and Library Research

1. Alternation of generations. Comparison of gametophyte and
    sporophyte regarding size, complexity, formation, relationship
    to other generation, genetic makeup.

2. Problems and adaptations associated with terrestrial living.

3. Reproductive patterns including comparison of gametophyte and sporophyte generations, spore formation, gamete formation.

4. Comparison of gymnosperms

5. Evolutionary origins of seed plants.

ESSAY QUESTIONS

1. Discuss the roles of mitosis and meiosis in producing the gametophyte and sporophyte generations of higher green algae and bryophytes.

obj 3   2. List four adaptations possessed by terrestrial plants and give the significance or importance of each adaptation for the survival of the plant on land.

obj 3   3. Discuss the adaptations possessed by both aquatic and terrestrial plants that are associated with the photosynthetic way of life.

obj 6   4. Describe three problems faced by plants in the transition from an aquatic to terrestrial environment. Describe three adaptations or strategies that solve the problems for plants.

obj 3   5. Discuss three factors which have contributed to the reproductive success for angiosperms.

obj 1   6. For the bryophytes and ferns compare the sporophyte generations regarding size, morphology, method of acquiring food and dominance relative to gametophyte generation.

obj 1   7. Distinguish between the members of the following paired terms: sporophyte/gametophyte; embryophyte/Tracheophyte, evergreen deciduous; archegonia/antheridia; microphyll/megaphyll.

obj 6   8. Compare the life histories of a moss, a pine tree and an apple tree regarding manner of fertilization and nature of early embryonic development.

9. Compare angiosperms and gymnosperms regarding the composition of their vascular tissue, the presence of accessory reproductive structures, the process of pollination, and the events of fertilization.

CHAPTER 28   THE LOWER INVERTEBRATES

Outline

I. Animal and Environment
II. Phylum Porifera: Sponges
III. Phylum Cnidaria (Coelenterates)
   A.   Class Hydrozoa
   B.   Class Scyphozoa (Jellyfish)
   C.   Class Anthozoa (Sea Anemones and Corals)
IV. Body Symmetry
V. Phylum Platyhelminthes: Flatworms
   A. Class turbellaria
   B.   Class Trematoda (Flukes)
   C.   Class Cestoda (Tapeworms)

VI. Parasitism
VII. Phylum Nematoda: Roundworms
VIII. Phylum Rotifera

Summary

The so-called lower invertebrates introduced in this chapter are believed to have evolved in the sea, where most forms still live. These animals are either planktonic, or bottom-dwelling with planktonic larvae. Some have adapted to life in fresh water, in damp terrestrial habitats, or in the watery interior of a host's body.

The sponges, phylum Porifera, exhibit a primitive level of organization, with specialized cells but no tissues or organs. They are sessile filter feeders, using their flagellated choanocytes to draw water into the body and strain out food particles. Their cells show marked independence of one another.

Members of the phylum Cnidaria have two well-developed tissue layers separated by a mesoglea, but they lack most organs. Both sessile polyps and swimming medusas have the same body plan- a ring of tentacles bearing nematocysts surrounds the mouth, which leads into a blind sac, the gastrovascular cavity. Hydra, jellyfish, corals, and sea anemones belong to this group.

The Platyhelminthes, or flatworms, show several more advanced features, including bilateral symmetry, cephalization, and three well-developed tissue layers; there are several organ systems, but not a circulatory system. The digestive system has only one opening, the mouth. Free -living flatworms and parasitic flukes and tapeworms belong to this phylum.

The Nematoda (roundworms) and the Rotifera ("wheel animals") possess complete digestive tracts, with both mouth and anus, and many other organ systems, a fluid-filled body cavity, the pseudocoelom, may serve for transport, but there is no circulatory system as such.

Objectives

1. Use the following terms correctly: invertebrate, primitive, plankton, zooplankton, sessile, motile, larva, filter feeder, hermaphroditic, gonad, gastrovascular cavity, pharynx, parasite, ectoparasite, endoparasite.

2. List the characteristics of the kingdom Animalia and of the phyla Porifera ; Cnidaria, Platyhelminthes, Nematoda, and Rotifera.

3. When presented with any member of the phyla in objective 3, name the phylum to which it belongs.

4. Explain the adaptive advantages of the following characteristics: radial symmetry, bilateral symmetry, cephalization, mobile stage of the life history, sessile stage of the life history.

What's new or expanded in the third edition

This chapter is essentially the same as the one in the second edition. Some sections contain a few more details, such as 28-A. The essay provides information on minor invertebrate phyla, such as Nemertina, Ctenophora, and Acanthocephala.

SUGGESTIONS FOR LECTURE PREPARATION AND ENRICHMENT

Ancillaries

In overhead transparency (OHT) # 102 (page 557) the evolution of animals is diagrammed. The life histories of a colonial member and a solitary member of the Class Hydrozoa are shown in OHTs #103 (page 562) and #104 (page 563). Ask students to compare them.

Correlative Laboratory Exercises

Topic 18   Lower Invertebrates

In Topic 18 students study representative organisms from the phyla Porifera, Cnidaria, Platyhelminthes, Nematoda, and Rotifera by viewing living and preserved specimens. Students dissect Ascaris to examine internal structures.

Ideas for Demonstrations

1. Preserved or living specimens

2. Microscope slides showing stages in the life cycles of parasites

3. Preserved specimens (or plastic mounts) of parasites.

Topics for Discussion and Library Research

1. Relationship of symmetry and cephalization

2. Evolutionary trends evident in lower animal phyla, such as cephalization, development of three tissue layers, increased specialization of cells, and division of labor among cells.

3. Parasitism, relationship between host and parasite

4. Adaptations of parasites to host

5. Comparison of lower invertebrate phyla

6. Advantages of tube-within-a-tube body plan

ESSAY QUESTIONS

obj 4 1. What three evolutionary trends are evident in the progression from sponges to cnidarians to flatworms?

2. Describe two characteristics which are unique to animals, and not associated with organisms in other kingdoms.

3. For each of the organisms listed below describe one characteristic that could be used to distinguish it from the organism
   in parentheses:

      a) sponge (cnidarian)
      b) cnidarian (ctenophore)
      c) ctenophore (free-living flatworm)
      d) free-living-flatworm (nemertean)
      e) nemertean (roundworm)

4. Consider a free living flatworm and a parasitic flatworm.
   What general features are adaptations to a parasitic way of
   life?

5. Distinguish between the members of the following paired terms:
   zooplankton/phytoplankton; sessile/motile; choanocyte/
   nematocyst; medusa/polyp; hermaphroditic/parthenogenetic.

6. Compare ectoparasites and endoparasites regarding method of
   acquiring food and adaptations associated with their way of
   life.

CHAPTER 29 SOME HIGHER INVERTEBRATES

Summary

     A coelom is a fluid-filled body cavity that originates as a space
between layers of mesoderm during embryonic development. The coelom permitted the evolution of more efficient modes of digestion, circulation,
and reproduction and thus led to an enormous burst of adaptive radiation
that resulted in the spectacular variety of coelomate animals.

     The phylum Annelida includes the classes Polychaeta (bristle worms)
which contains mostly marine forms: Oligochaeta (earthworms and the like)
which contains mostly freshwater or terrestrial forms; and Hirudinea
(leeches), which contains mostly freshwater forms. Many polychaetes and
oligochaetes are segmented and move by means of a hydrostatic skeleton
acting together with their setae. Leeches lose their segmentation
during development, and move by means of powerful body muscles.

     The members of the phylum Bryozoa are tiny aquatic animals
living colonially within an exoskeleton attached to the substrate.
The animals feed by means of a lophophore, a crown of tentacles around
the mouth.

     Most members of the phylum Mollusca are unsegmented marine animals.
A mantle covers most of the body and usually secretes a calcareous
shell; gas exchange occurs through gills in the mantle cavity or through
the lining of the mantle cavity itself. Molluscs also have a muscular
foot, which is used for locomotion or burrowing: cephalopods use their
tentacles, derived from the foot, for gripping prey. The main
molluscan classes are the Amphineura, or chitons: the Gastropoda, or
snails and slugs; the Bivalvia, or shellfish; and the Cephalopoda, the
nautiluses, squids, and octopuses. Many of the gastropods are well
adapted to life in terrestrial habitats.

     The phylum Arthropoda contains more known species and a larger
weight and number of individuals than are found in any other animal
phylum. Arthropods are highly successful in marine, freshwater, and
terrestrial habitats. They have segmented bodies and a varied array of
jointed appendages used for feeding, locomotion, fighting, and
sensing stimuli in the environment. The entire body of an arthropod is
covered with an exoskeleton, which is flexible at the joints; the exoskeleton protects the body from injury and desiccation. The crustaceans
are mainly marine, but there are many freshwater forms and a few that

are terrestrial. The classes Arachnida and Insecta contain mainly animals adapted to life in a variety of terrestrial environments.

Objectives

1. State what a coelom is and discuss its evolutionary importance to animals.

2. List the distinguishing characteristics of annelids, bryozoans, molluscs, and arthropods.

3. Discuss reasons for the success of the annelids, molluscs, and arthropods.

4. When presented with an annelid, mollusc, or arthropod, name the phylum to which it belongs.

5. Name, describe, and give an example of each of the three classes of annelids.

6. Name, describe, and give examples of four classes of molluscs.

7. Name, describe, and give examples of each of three major classes of arthropods.

8. Describe the adaptations of insects to a terrestrial way of life.

What's new or expanded in the third edition

In section 29-B the characteristics of protostomes, and deuterostomes are described in general terms. In section 29-D the features of bryozoans or "moss animals" are described, as well as their reproduction and development. Figure 29-8 (page 580) shows diagrammatically a section of a bryozoan colony.

SUGGESTIONS FOR LECTURE PREPARATION AND ENRICHMENT

Ancillaries

Overhead transparency # 105 (page 574) illustrates the three basic body plans of animals. Ask students to identify the body plan found in vertebrates, and the advantages/disadvantages of each body plan.

Correlative Laboratory Exercises

Topic 19 Higher Invertebrates: Annelids and Mollusks

Topic 20 Higher Invertebrates: Arthropods

In Topic 19 students dissect a clam and an earthworm to examine internal features. They also investigage locomotion and behavioral responses of earthworms.

Students examine the external anatomy of a spider, crayfish, and grasshopper, and the internal anatomy of a crayfish and grasshopper in Topic 20.

Supplemental Readings

Carolina Biology REaders
    Pringle, J. W. 1983. Insect Flight (2/E)

    Tata, J. R. 1983. Metamorphosis (2/E)

Fincher, Jack. 1985. The bug wars. Science Digest 93(8): 56-59, August.
     Article about use of insects and biocontrols to battle crop pests.

Jackson, Robert. 1985. A web-building jumping spider. Sci. Am., Sept.

Weisburd, STefi. 1985. Sulfide searchers. Science News 127:108, February
     16. A short report about a worm that can detect sulfide molecules
     and live in sulfide rich waters that would kill most other organisms.

Films

Ants and Aphids (AVED, 1976, 26 min.) Describes life history of aphids
     and relationship of ants and aphids and ecological aspects of
     underground communities of ants.

Insects Helpful to Man (IEB, 1977, 17 min.) Surveys insects beneficial
     to humans.

Living Machines (NOVA) (TLV, 1980, 52 min.)   Covers natural engineering
     found in living organisms

Secrets of Alien World (BCR, 1980, 52 min.) Deals with various features
     of insects including anatomy, behavior, life cycles, mimicry, etc.

Success Story: How Insects Survive (EBEC, 1979, 28 min.) Presents life
     cycles, behavior, reproduction of insects.

Ideas for Demonstrations

1. Preserved or living specimens representing animal phyla.

2. Preserved specimens of parasites

3. Slides (2'x2") showing general features of organisms from each
    phylum and class

Topics for Discussion and Library Research

1. Advantages of having a coelom

2. Comparison of four phyla

3. Adaptations for terrestrial living

4. Success of insects

5. Limits to size--Why can't a grasshopper be as large as a cat?

6. Advantages and disadvantages of aquatic and terrestrial living

ESSAY QUESTIONS

obj 1   1. Describe four advantages of having a coelom.

2. Describe three problems associated with living on land and how
    insects have dealt with each problem.

obj 2   3. For each organism below describe one characteristic that can be
    used to distinguish it from the organism in parentheses:
       a) gastropod (bivalve)
       b) bivalve (cephalopod)
       c) cephalopod (crustacean)
       d) crustacean (insect)
       e) insect (annelid)

obj 2   4. Give two reasons why a grasshopper could not be as big as a cat.

obj 8   5. Discuss two major factors that account for the success of the insects on land and their great diversity as a group.

obj 3,8 6. Compare and contrast the insects' and oligochaetes' solutions to problems of desiccation, reproduction on land, support, gas exchange and waste removal.

CHAPTER 30 THE ORIGIN OF VERTEBRATES

    I.   Phylum Echinodermata
         A. Class Crinoidea: Sea Lilies and Feather Stars
         B. Class Asteroidea: Sea Stars
         C. Class Ophiuroidea: Brittle Stars, Serpent Stars
         D. Class Echinoidea: Sea Urchins and Sand Dollars
         E. Class Holothuroidea: Sea Cucumbers
   II.   Characteristics of Chordates
  III.   Phylum Hemichordata Acorn worms
   IV.   Chordate Subphylum Urochordata: Tunicates
         A. Class Ascidiacea: Sea Squirts
    V.   Chordate Subphylum Cephalochordata
   VI.   Vertebrate Characteristics
  VII.   Class Agnatha: Jawless Fish

Summary

     The echinoderms are close relatives of the chordates. This rela-
tionship is deduced from the embryology of members of the two groups,
and is not evident in the adults. Adult echinoderms are pentaradially
symmetrical; the body is usually covered with a thin epidermis overlying
a calcareous endoskeleton. Tube feet and a water vascular system are
unique features of this group. The echinoderms are all marine, living
as filter feeders, carnivores, grazers, or scavengers.

     The phylum Hemichordata contains animals that resemble echinoderms
in their embryology, lophophorates in the possession of hollow tentacles,
and chordates in the possession of pharyngeal gill slits.

     The phylum Chrodata contains those animals with a notochord, a
hollow dorsal nerve cord, and pharyngeal gill slits. Most chordates
living today are vertebrates--chordates in which the notochord is surrounded or replaced by a vertebral column of bone or cartilage. Uro-
chordates and cephalochordates are the only living invertebrate chordates.

     Among living chordates, the tadpole-like larva of tunicates probably
bears the closest resemblance to the animals from which all chordates e-
volved. The ancestors of chordates were filter feeders. They drew in
water containing plankton through the mouth, extracted the food, and
pushed the surplus water out through the pharyngeal gill slits. Feeding and not gas exchange is almost certainly the primitive function of
gills. With increasing size and larger food, greater speed to catch the
food became selectively advantageous. The notochord is the primitive
vertebrate skeleton. With myotomes attached to it at the sides of the
body, it permitted fast swimming by throwing the body sideways in S-
shaped folds; this was probably the most important factor in the success
of early vertebrates. Such sinusoidal locomotion can be seen today in
animals like the lamprey and sharks. With fast locomotion, development
of the head region with sense organs out in front became more important.

Objectives

1. List characters that would distinguish members of the following taxa:
    Echinodermata, Hemichordata, Chordata, Urochordata, Cephalochordata,
    Vertebrata, Agnatha.

2. Describe the habitat and mode of life of members of the groups listed
    in objective #1.

3. When presented with any echinoderm, name the class to which it belongs.

4. Describe the evolutionary advances of early chordates and vertebrates
    over their ancestors, and explain the adaptive value of these new charac-
    teristics.

What's new or expanded in the third edition

Table 30-1 lists the characteristics and organisms belonging to each of the four deuterostome phyla. Section 30-C is new and describes the characteristics of hemichordates and their relationship to chordates and other invertebrates.

SUGGESTIONS FOR LECTURE PREPARATION AND ENRICHMENT

Ideas for Demonstrations

    1. Microscopic slides of larval forms of echinoderms, tunicates

    2. Whole mounts of amphioxus and ammocoetes, and other deutero-stomes

    3. Trip to museum of natural history.

Topics for Discussion and Library Research

    1. Evolutionary relationships among chordates

    2. Chordate characteristics

    3. Comparison of chordates

    4. Evolutionary trees

ESSAY QUESTIONS

obj 1   1. List the distinguishing characteristics of the chordates and describe the functional significance of each.

        2. Distinguish between members of the following paired terms: radial symmetry/bilateral symmetry; acoelomate/coelomate/pseudocoelomate; deutoerostome/protostome; homologous/analogous; and, proglottid/protonephridia.

obj 1   3. Identify and describe one distinguishing feature for each of the following phyla: Echinodermata, Hemichordata, Chordata.

obj 2   4. For each of the following identify the phylum or subphylum, and its method of acquiring food: sea star; sea squirt, acorn worm, amphioxus, and the lamprey.

158

CHAPTER 31   VERTEBRATE ANATOMY AND EVOLUTION

Summary

     The agnathan fishes, the first vertebrates, probably gave rise to
the bony and cartilaginous fishes, which were the dominant forms of
animal life on earth in the later Paleozoic era. The bony fish gave rise
to the first terrestrial vertebrates, amphibians, which still had largely
aquatic reproduction. With the evolution of the amniotic egg, the
adaptive radiation of land vertebrates began. Reptiles--adapted to
every way of life, from swimming in the sea to flying through the air--
were the dominant animals throughout the Mesozoic era. Early quadrupedal
reptiles evolved into dog-like primitive mammals, and bipedal dinosaurs
gave rise to birds. With the extinction of many reptile groups towards
the end of the Cretaceous, birds and mammals inherited the earth and
have radiated widely ever since. Meanwhile, the bony fish of the
super order Teleostei have been undergoing an adaptive radiation in
aquatic habitats.

     Both cartilaginous and bony fish showed two major advances over
the agnathans: first, the evolution of jaws enabled them to snap and
bite their food; and second, paired pectoral and pelvic fins provided
balance while the body or tail still gave the main impetus for locomotion. Bony fish also evolved an operculum covering the gill openings,
and many have a swimbladder, which provides buoyancy control and allows
for gas exchange with the air. Some fish evolved lungs, also used for
gas exchange in shallow, oxygen-poor water.

     Amphibians evolved from fish with air-breathing lungs and sturdy
paired fins able to support the body on land. With their thin, moist
skin still used as a major gas exchange surface, and eggs that must be
laid in water, amphibians have remained in moist habitats, most in or
near bodies of fresh water.

     The reptiles, birds, and mammals have well-developed air-breathing
lungs, waterproof integuments, and a set of three embryonic membranes
that frees their reproduction from dependence on free water. This suite
of characters makes members of these three classes fully emancipated
from water. Reptiles, birds, and a few mammals lay waterproof amniotic
eggs. Most mammals are viviparous. All three groups show advances
allowing more effective locomotion on land, with the legs stronger and
further under the body, and claws on the toes.

     Birds' feathers provide lightweight insulation as well as strong
flight surfaces. The structure of most birds is highly modified for
flying, with a greatly reduced, lightened, and streamlined skeleton.

Birds and mammals are both endothermic, using rapid metabolism to generate body heat, which is retained by a layer of fat under the skin and an outer layer of feathers or hair. Parental care is well developed in both groups; parents warm their embryos and young by incubation and protect and teach them. Many birds fetch food for their young, and female mammals nurse their young with milk from the mammary glands.

Objectives

1. List characters that would permit you to distinguish members of the following classes: Chondrichthyes, Osteichthyes, Amphibia, Reptilia, Aves, Mammalia.

2. Name the class of any vertebrate presented to you.

3. State the order in which the following groups appeared in the fossil record: invertebrates, agnathans, Chondrichthyes, bony fishes, amphibians, reptiles, birds, mammals.

4. List the classes of the subphylum Vertebrata.

5. List and explain the problems encountered by previously water-dwelling vertebrates in adapting to life on land and explain adaptations that enable modern terrestrial vertebrates to live on land.

What's new or expanded in the third edition

Section 31-H has been expanded and describes the importance of the integument and kidney as factors contributing to the success of mammals.

SUGGESTIONS FOR LECTURE PREPARATION AND ENRICHMENT

Correlative Laboratory Exercises

Topic 21 Introduction to the Vertebrates

Topic 21 covers the vertebrates. Students study representative organisms from each of the classes except agnathans.

Supplemental Readings

Bower, Bruce. 1985. A mosaic ape takes shape. Science News 127: 26-27, January 12. Report about fossil find of bones from Proconsul, an unspecialized, primitive hominoid.

Brownlee, Shannon. 1985. What's in a face. Discover 6(2):38-51. An examination into the evolutionary significance of a face.

Brownlee, Shannon. 1985. On the track of the real shark. Discover 6(7):26-38, July. The shark's anatomy, behavior, and reproduction are discussed.

Diamond, Jared. 1985. In quest of the wild and weird. Discover 6(3). 34-42, March. A story about cryptozoologists and their searches for unusual animals, such as the Lochness monster and the Yeti.

Gould, Stephen Jay. 1985. The most compelling pelvis since Elvis. Discover 6(12): 54-58, December.

Gould, STephen Jay. 1986. Fuzzy wuzzy was a bear. Andy Panda, too. Discover 7(2):40-48, February. Report on reclassification of the panda as a bear.

Films

A New Era (TLV, 1982, 55 min.) Covers the behavior and physical development of hominids from Homo erectus to Cro-magnon man.

Ideas for Demonstrations

1. Slides (2" x 2") of animals in their natural environments.

Topics for Discussion and Library Research

1. Evolutionary relationships among chordates and among vertebrates.

2. Comparison of vertebrates including extinct forms

3. Family tree of chordates and vertebrates

4. Human evolution. See article by: Pilbeam, D. 1984. "The descent of hominoids and hominids." Sci. Am., March; Rukang, W. and L. Shenglong. 1983. "Peking Man." Sci. Am. June; Hay, R. and M. Leakey, 1982. "The fossil footprints of Laetoli." Sci. Am. February.

5. Disappearance of Dinosaurs. See article by: Russell, D. 1982. "The mass extinction of the late mesozoic." Sci. Am., January. Gould, S. 1984. "Sex, drugs, disasters, and the extinction of dinosaurs." Discover 5(3):67-72.

6. Human speech. See article by: Laitman, J. 1984. "The anatomy of human speech." Natural History, August. Discusses techniques used to determine the anatomy of ancestor's vocal tract, how it functioned, and how it compares with the vocal tract of modern humans.

ESSAY QUESTIONS

obj 5. 1. Arthropods and vertebrates may be considered the most highly evolved representatives of their evolutionary lines. Members of these groups have successfully made the transition from aquatic to terrestrial living. They also have independently evolved many similar solutions to problems of survival and reproduction on land. Discuss ways in which the groups are similar and different regarding terrestrial living.

2. Humans are relatively hairless. Explain how this might have occurred from the perspective of the theory of punctuated equilibrium and the theory of evolution by natural selection.

3. What human features originated as adaptations to arboreal life?

4. Describe three trends in the evolution of humans from early australopithecines to Homo sapiens, and the selective value of each.

obj 1 5. What three characteristics of mammals give them a definite advantage over reptiles, comparable in size in a variable environment?

obj 1 6. List and describe one distinguishing characteristic for each of the vertebrate classes.

obj 5 7. Describe three problems faced by vertebrates on land and for each problem describe a mammalian adaptation.

CHAPTER 32   ANIMAL NUTRITION AND DIGESTION

Essay: Diet and Cardiovascular Disease

Essay: Scurvy

Summary

     Because animals are heterotrophs, their diet must contain all of
the organic and inorganic substances they need for metabolism, growth,
and energy. Animals obtain fats, carbohydrates, and proteins, and vitamins and minerals, in their food.

     The function of digestion is to break food down into molecules that
can be absorbed into the body from the gut. In vertebrates,digestive
enzymes are synthesized in the salivary glands, pancreas, and lining of
the stomach and small intestine. Many animals, particularly herbivores,
harbor symbiotic microorganisms, which secrete digestive enzymes, in the
alimentary canal.

     Digested food is absorbed into the blood and extracellular fluid
by diffusion, facilitated diffusion, and active transport across the
enormous surface area of the small intestine.

     The liver plays a major role in controlling the fate of newly
absorbed food molecules. It stores excess glucose as glycogen, syn-
thesizes many blood proteins, and converts nitrogenous and other wastes
into a form that can be excreted by the kidneys. Excess carbohydrates
or protein is converted into acyltriacylglycerols and stored in
the fat cells of adipose tissue.

     Feeding is regulated by long-term and short-term control mechanisms
that are not well understood. These controls ensure that the alimentary
canal is efficiently occupied most of the time and that the animal
maintains its body reserve of fat without spending unnecessary time
feeding. All animals have complicated regulatory systems and control
what, as well as how much, they eat.

Objectives

1.   Name the major classes of macronutrients and micronutrients and list
     the general functions of each class.

2. Explain the selective advantages of the following digestive adaptations found in the animal kingdom: extracellular digestion, discontinuous feeding, digestive tract with mouth and anus, crop, gizzard, and caeca.

3. List the parts of the human digestive tract in order, and state what happens to food in each part of the tract.

4. List the organs that secrete digestive enzymes in mammals, and state the type of substrate digested by the enzymes secreted by each organ.

5. List the parts of the gut in which various substances are absorbed, and which types of substances are absorbed in each part.

6. Describe the digestive adaptations of herbivorous and carnivorous mammals and of birds.

7. Discuss how symbiotic microorganisms contribute to the nutrition of their hosts.

8. List the functions of the mammalian liver, and explain the importance of this organ.

What's new or expanded in the third edition

Section 32-A contains new information on the relationship between diet and health.

Table 32-6 now lists the digestive enzymes produced and released by the small intestine.

SUGGESTIONS FOR LECTURE PREPARATION AND ENRICHMENT

Ancillaries

Overhead transparencies (OHT) #106 (page 645) and #107 (page 646) illustrate the digestive systems found in an earthworm, an insect, and a human. Ask students to compare the parts of each system and relate each to the type of food ingested by the organism.

Correlative Laboratory Exercise

Topic 1   Biological Chemistry

Topic 5   Cell Structure and Function

Topic 22   Digestion

In Topic 1 students perform simple tests to demonstrate the presence of carbohydrates (Benedict's, Iodine), proteins, (Biuret) and fats (Sudan III) in known and unknown substances. Amino acids are separated by paper chromatography.

In topic 5 students use microscopes to study prepared slides showing the four kinds of animal tissues. Cross sections through the small intestine are examined to learn about the organization of cells in tissues and organs.

In Topic 22 the anatomy of the digestive system is studied by dissecting fetal pigs. Students become familiar with the component parts, their function, and relationship to each other.

Supplemental Readings

Allen, A. 1983. Mucus a protective secretion of complexity. TIBS 8: 169-173.

Baldwin, R. L. 1984. Digestion and metabolism of ruminants. Bioscience 34 (4):244-249.

Brown, Michael. 1986. Here's the Beef: Fast Foods are hazardous to your health. Science Digest 94(4): 31-36; April.

Dusheck, Jennie. 1985. Fish, fatty acids, and physiology. Science News 128: 252-254, Oct. 19.

Grady, D. and S. Siwolop. 1984. An anti-cancer diet? Discover 5(6) 23-26.

Kolata, Gina. 1985. Obesity declared a disease. Science 227: 1019-1020.

Kolata, Gina. 1985. Why do people get fat? Science 227:1327-1328.

Raloff, J. 1985. Tracing disease to trace minerals. Science News 127 357-358, June 8.

Raloff, Janet. 1986. Rinsing away decay (tooth decay) Science News 129:251-253, Apr. 19.

Films

Human Body: Digestive System (2/E) (COR, L981, 16 min.) Describes digestion from ingestion to metabolism.

Student Activities

1. Have students determine their caloric intake and output using Table 34-1 on page 715 in Biology by Villee/Solomon/Davis. Have them keep records for a week, then ask them to speculate on how their dietary habits and energy requirements correlate with their weight.

2. Have students try to determine the amounts of fats, carbohydrates, and proteins in their diet.

Ideas for Demonstrations

1. Teeth. Exhibit skulls of vertebrates representing fish, amphibian, reptiles, birds and various mammals to demonstrate relationship between form and function for teeth.

2. Microscope slides of histological preparations of stomach, small intestine, large intestine and esophagus to show similarity in structure.

3. Specimens of ecto-and endoparasites like fleas and tapeworms respectively.

4. Vitamin requirements. Examine labels from bottles of vitamins, and other food products.

Topics for Discussion and Library Research

1. Hormonal control of digestion
2. Role of digestive enzymes
3. Adaptations reflecting life styles and modes of nutrition
4. Symbiotic relationships--advantages, disadvantages
5. Ways of increasing surface area for absorption in a confined space

6. Small intestine. See article by: Moog, F. 1981. "The lining of the small intestine." Sci. Am., Nov.

7. Protective mechanisms. See article by Davenport, H. 1972. "Why the stomach does not digest itself." Sci. Am., Jan.

8. Malnutrition

9. Effects of starvation

10. Anorexia nervosa-causes, treatments; and bulimia

11. Osteoporosis

12. Vitamin deficiencies and effects

13. Metabolic effects of drugs

14. Dieting. See article by: Bennett, W. and J. Gurin. 1982. "Do diets really work?" Science 82 3(2)42-54.

15. Anticancer diets. See articles by: Ames, B. 1983. "Dietary carcinogens and anticarcinogens." Science 221: 1256-1264; Grady, D. and S. Siwolop. 1984. "An anti-cancer diet?" Discover 5(6):23-26.

16. Overpopulation and the unevenly distributed world food supply

17. Megavitamins

ESSAY QUESTIONS

1. Distinguish between the members of the following paired terms: anabolism/catabolism; glycogenesis/glycogenolysis; chylomicron/ cholesterol; and, complete/partially incomplete/totally incomplete proteins.

obj 1 2. State the importance of each of the following for the cell or organism: (a) calcium, (b) iron, (c) vitamin A, (d) vitamin D, (e) sodium.

obj 1 3. Describe the components of an ideal diet and indicate the necessity of each.

4. What is meant by the term basal metabolic rate? Identify three factors that affect it.

obj 1 5. What is a vitamin? List and briefly describe the function in the body of five different vitamins?

obj 8 6. Identify five essential minerals and give the function of each.

7. How is the liver involved in regulating blood sugar level? in the metabolism of amino acids, and fats?

obj 6 8. Compare and contrast the adaptations associated with the digestive system of a terrestrial herbivore and terrestrial carnivore.

9. Distinguish between the members of the following paired terms: commensalism/mutualism; digestion/egestion; herbivore/carnivore/ omnivore; goblet cell/parietal cell; and pepsin/pepsinogen.

10. Describe three mechanisms by which the stomach is protected against self digestion.

obj 2 11. Cite three advantages of a one-way tube-type digestive system.

12. According to an old farmer's tale raccoons wash their food before eating to clean it. Based on what you have learned about the digestive system in aquatic and terrestrial vertebrates, suggest a more scientifically correct explanation for the raccoon's behavior.

obj 5 13. In vertebrates the absorptive area of the small intestine has been increased in a variety of ways without increasing in bulk. Describe three ways.

14. What is the function of (a) bile; (b) the pyloric sphincter, (c) peristaltic contractions; (d) the epiglottis, and (d) gastrin?

obj 3 15. It is possible to live without a stomach, without part of the small and large intestine, but not without the liver. Symptoms of liver disease include jaundice, swelling in legs and the abdominal cavity, and insensitivity to drugs. Explain each symptom in terms of liver function.

obj 4 16. What three properties of enzymes are reflected by their activity or involvement in digestion?

17. Several digestive enzymes are released from the organ of production as inactive molecules which are then activated by other enzymes secreted into the digestive tract. Identify two such enzymes and explain the adaptive value of this two step process.

obj 3 18. List three functions of the large intestine.

obj 2 19. Compare the digestive systems of hydra, a planaria, and an earthworm as to the manner in which ingestion and egestion occur and the location of digestion.

obj 2 20. Distinguish parasitism, mutualism, and commensalism, and give an example of each type of symbiotic relationship.

21. Of the three kinds of symbiotic relationships (parasitism, mutualism, commensalism) which type would you expect to exhibit the greatest specialization as to adaptations?

CHAPTER 33   GAS EXCHANGE IN ANIMALS

Outline

Essay: Human Adaptations to High Altitudes

Summary

All animals whose cells carry out respiration must obtain oxygen from their environment and expel carbon dioxide. Since carbon dioxide is much more soluble in water than is oxygen, obtaining sufficient oxygen is the more difficult of the two. The amount of oxygen an animal needs depends largely upon its metabolic rate, which increases with activity and, in a warm-blooded animal, with increasing surface-to-volume ratio and decreasing size.

Gas exchange with the environment can take place only across a moist surface. Small or inactive animals can obtain all their oxygen by diffusion across the general body surface. A high surface-to-volume ratio is found in animals whose bodies are small, flattened, or covered with projections. Larger or more active animals usually have part of the body specialized as a respiratory surface and transport gases to and from this surface by way of a circulatory system.

The four main types of respiratory organs are the body surface, gills, lungs, and tracheal systems.

In organisms with lungs, the gas content of the blood is regulated by controlling the rate of breathing and, therefore, the gas composition in the alveoli.

Many animals have respiratory pigments in their blood that vastly increase the blood's oxygen-carrying capacity. The oxygen dissociation curve for a pigment shows the oxygen pressures at which the pigment will pick up and release oxygen. A study of these curves shows that the dissociation properties of pigments are adapted to the oxygen pressures under which they must normally operate.

Carbon dioxide is transported mainly in the form of bicarbonate ion, an important buffer that helps to maintain the pH of the body fluids at a constant level.

The lungs of vertebrates are closely related to the swimbladders of bony fishes. The swimbladder is a gas-filled organ that permits the fish to change its buoyancy; it may also be used as an accessory breathing organ.

Objectives

1. Distinguish between the processes of ventilation and respiration.

2. Discuss the advantages and disadvantages of air and water as respiratory media.

3. Describe, in qualitative terms, the relationship between metabolic rate, size (for a homeothermic animal), and environmental temperature.

4. Compare and contrast lungs and gills with respect to structure, function, and their advantages and disadvantages.

5. Explain how the countercurrent exchange mechanism works in the gills of a bony fish: state the importance of this adaptation to the fish.

6. Explain how the positive pressure and negative pressure mechanisms of breathing work, and state the advantages of a negative pressure breathing mechanism.

7. Describe how birds' respiratory systems differ from mammals' in structure and operation. List at least three functions of birds' air sacs.

8. Describe the main differences in structure and function between the tracheal systems of insects and other types of respiratory systems.

9. (a) State the function of respiratory pigments; (b) draw an oxygen loading curve for hemoglobin and label both axes, the loading tension, and the unloading tension, and state their signficance to the organism; (c) state the main factor governing whether hemoglobin loads or unloads oxygen; (d) state how pH influences loading and unloading; and (e) predict the change in shape and position of such a curve with a change in the animal's size or environment.

10. Compare and contrast the transport of oxygen and carbon dioxide in the blood.

11. Describe how hemoglobin, other blood proteins, and carbon dioxide buffer the blood.

12. Explain how ventilation movements are regulated in the human body.

13. List and explain two ways ventilation of the tracheal system is enhanced in an active insect.

14. Describe two functions of the swimbladder of bony fishes.

What's new or expanded in the third edition

Section 33-D contains new material on and a new figure (33-12, page 669) illustrating ventilation in birds.

SUGGESTIONS FOR LECTURE PREPARATION AND ENRICHMENT

Ancillaries

Overhead transparency (OHT) #108 (page 661) illustrates the mechanics of gas exchange between the respiratory medium and body fluids at the respiratory surface and between the body fluids and living cells. OHT #109 (page 667) shows diagrammatically the anatomy of the human respiratory system including the alveoli. Ventilation in a bird is shown in OHT #110 (page 669). Ask students to compare ventilation in a human and in a bird.

Correlative Laboratory Exercise

Topic 23 Gas Exchange

Students examine different types of respiratory structures using preserved specimens. The gills of a fish and necturus, and the tracheal system in a grasshopper are studied. The fetal pig is dissected to reveal the internal parts and features of the mammalian system. Students also perform a series of activities designed to demonstrate some of the conditions affecting respiratory rate.

Supplemental Reading

Feder, Martin, and Warren Burggren. 1985. Skin breathing in vertebrates. Sci. Am., November.

Films

Smoking/Emphysema: A Fight for Breath (MG, 1974, 12 min.) Uses graphics, animation and live action to illustrate gas exchange in lungs, effects of smoke contamination of lungs, and emphysema.

Student Activities

1. Have students determine respiratory rate under various conditions, such as sitting, taking an exam, walking, etc.

2. Have students determine heart rate under the same conditions. Then, have them graphically display the two rates and see if they can make any correlations between the two rates, such as whether or not they increase or decrease to the same degree, at the same rate, or which returns to normal more quickly.

Ideas for Demonstrations

1. Diffusion. Set up demonstration showing diffusion of solid in liquid to show how slow the process is.

2. Tracheal System. Dissect a grasshopper whose tracheal system has been injected.

3. Preserved specimens of lungs, normal and diseased.

4. Microscope slides of histological preparations of normal and diseased lung tissue.

5. Show tracheal cartilage.

Topics for Discussion and Library Research

1. Diseases of respiratory structures, such as emphysema, cancer, pneumonia, bronchitis, Brown Lung, black lung.

2. Comparison of four types of respiratory structures.

3. Control or respiration

4. Evolutionary relationship of swim bladder and lungs

5. Effectiveness of countercurrent exchange systems. See article by: Schmidt-Nielsen, K. 1981. "Countercurrent systems in animals." Sci. Am., May.

6. Structure of bird's respiratory system.

ESSAY QUESTIONS

obj 4 1. The four principal types of respiratory structures share the same characteristics. List the four types of structures and describe the three shared characteristics.

2. Distinguish between the members of the following paired terms: bronchi/parabronchi; organismic respiration/cellular respiration; air sac/swim bladder; bronchioles/alveoli; and, trachea/pharynx/larynx.

obj 2 3. What type of compromise had to be worked out in the evolution of respiratory structures in terrestrial organisms? What two contradictory needs had to be met?

obj 2 4. Describe two problems faced by aquatic animals regarding gas exchange and two adaptations or solutions related to these problems.

obj 1 5. Compare breathing (ventilation) in a human, a reptile, a bird and a fish. Describe similarities and differences.

obj 8 6. What factors might have contributed to the development of two different respiratory systems in terrestrial organisms (vertebrates and insects)?

7. Countercurrent exchange systems are present in the respiratory structures of fish and birds. Describe the characteristics of this type of system and how it operates in either birds or fish. Why is it such an efficient system?

8. Cigarette smoke has been shown to destroy cilia that line the respiratory tract, to cause a thickening of the walls of the bronchioles, and to rupture some of the alveolar walls. Describe the normal function for each structure destroyed by cigarette smoke.

9. Trace the pathway of a molecule of carbon dioxide from the liver where it is produced to outside the body. Indicate all major structures, vessels and the forms in which it may be transported.

obj 10 10. Compare the transport of oxygen in blood with that of carbon dioxide as to physical principles involved in the process, and the role of hemoglobin.

obj 3 11. Which of the following organisms (cat, elephant, mouse) has the highest metabolic rate? The lowest metabolic rate? Explain your answers.

obj 6 12. Compare positive pressure breathing and negative pressure breathing regarding the roles played by the nose, mouth, tongue, diaphram, and muscles surrounding the thoracic cavity.

obj 9 13. Identify and describe three functions of hemoglobin in the human body.

14. Describe two conditions under which oxygen dissociates from hemoglobin and two conditions under hemoglobin picks up oxygen.

170

CHAPTER 34   ANIMAL TRANSPORT SYSTEM

Outline

I.   Transport in Invertebrates
   A.   Cnidaria
   B.   Planaria
   C.   Annelida
   D.   Insects
II. Circulation in vertebrates
   A.   Fish
   B.   Amphibians and Reptiles
   C.   Mammals and Birds
III. The Mammalian Circulation
   A.   Blood Vessels
   B.   The Circuit of Blood in the Body
   C.   The Heart Cycle
   D.   Blood Pressure and Circulation
   E.   The Circulatory System's Adjustment to Exercise
   F.   Diseases of the Circulatory System
IV. Blood
   A.   Inflammation and Clotting
   B.   Control of Blood Composition
   C.   Human Blood Group
V.   The Lymphatic System
VI. Temperature Regulation
   A.   Acclimation
   B.   Endotherms and Ectotherms
   C.   Torpor and Hibernation
   D.   Behavioral Thermoregulation
   E.   Physiological Thermoregulation

Essay: Adaptations of Diving Mammals

Summary

Most animals have transport systems that move molecules and heat
within the body. In many primitive animals, transport of food is
carried out by the gastrovascular cavity. Animals with coeloms have
true circulatory systems. An open circulatory system has few blood
vessels, and blood bathes the cells directly. The closed circulatory
systems of many invertebrates and of all vertebrates have blood vessels
through which blood is pumped by the heart.

The circulatory systems of vertebrates show an evolutionary trend
from single to double circulation. The double circulation of birds and
mammals achieves complete separation of oxygenated and deoxygenated blood
as well as elevation of the blood pressure in the body's capillaries.

The quick and orderly flow of blood is accomplished by a muscular
pump, the heart, and a set of pipes, the blood vessels. Blood flows
through the circuit from the region of high pressure, the contracting
ventricles of the heart, through the vessels at progressively lower
pressure, until it returns to the heart. Valves in the veins and the
heart prevent backflow. Blood pressure and blood supply in various parts
of the body may be regulated by dilation and contraction of arterioles and
capillaries and by changes in heartbeat rate and volume of blood pumped by
the heart at each stroke.

The circulatory system responds to changes in the body's activities
so that the body's new needs are met. During exercise, the amount of
blood flowing and the rate of flow are increased, and more blood is di-
verted to the active muscle tissues.

Blood is a tissue consisting of a watery matrix that carries salt, proteins, and blood cells. White blood cells defend the body. Red blood cells contain hemoglobin, a protein that combines with oxygen in the lungs and releases it in the capillaries of the body tissues. The blood platelets are important components in the clotting mechanism of the blood. Clotting helps to plug the vessel walls after injury, preventing loss of vital fluids or entry of pathogenic organisms.

The lymphatic system consists of vessels that collect extracellular fluid, proteins, and digested fats, and empty them into the venous system.

Living cells can function only at certain temperatrues. Animals cope with adverse temperature changes either by tolerating them or by making behavioral or physiological responses that help to maintain their bodies within a suitable temperature range. Ectotherms have more behavioral than physiological adaptations for thermoregulation. They may move into hotter or colder areas, or they may sunbathe, burrow, or huddle together to maintain a favorable body temperature. Torpor, hibernation, and estivation are temporary reductions in metabolic rate that allow many animals to reduce the energy they would have to expend on thermoregulation under extreme conditions.

Thermoregulation by physiological mechanisms is most apparent in endotherms. They produce large quantities of metabolic heat and regulate its escape into the environment by such means as insulation, alteration of the blood supply to the skin, regulation of the temperature of blood reaching the extremities, and evaporation of water from the surface.

Objectives

1. Describe the basic transport system in a cnidarian, an earthworm, an insect, a fish, and a mammal.

2. Describe how an open circulatory system such as that of an insect differs from the closed circulatory system of an earthworm or a vertebrate.

3. Describe the double circulation of birds and mammals and list its selective advantages over the single circulation of fishes. Describe the circulation of amphibians and reptiles, and explain how their systems meet the needs of these animals.

4. Describe the structure, and state the main functions, of arteries, veins, capillaries, and the heart.

5. Describe the locations of valves in the circulatory system, and briefly explain their structure and function.

6. Trace the flow of blood through the mammalian circulatory system, indicating the sites at which oxygen, carbon dioxide, and food molecules enter and leave the bloodstream, and using the correct names for the chambers of the heart and for the major arteries and veins labeled in Figures 34-10b and 34-11.

7. Describe adjustments made in the circulation as the body's needs increase during exercise.

8. List the principal substances found in blood.

9. State the principal functions of red blood cells, white blood cells, and platelets.

10. List four ways in which the liver helps to maintain the blood contents at a steady level; state why the hepatic portal system is important to the regulation of the blood's composition.

11. Explain why the ABO blood groups of recipient and donor must be matched for a successful blood transfusion.

12. Describe how and why an Rh-negative mother's blood may damage the blood of a baby born to her.

13. List or recognize four functions of the lymphatic system.

14. Describe the mechanism and routes by which fluid moves between the circulatory and lymphatic systems.

15. Define ectothermy and endothermy and explain the differences between them.

16. Describe how endothermic and ectothermic animals regulate the temperatures of their bodies.

What's new or expanded in the third edition

In section 34-B are two new figures (34-7 and 34-8, page 684) which show cross sections through an artery, a vein, and a capillary. Figure 34-9 (page 685) shows a capillary bed while figure 34-13 (page 688) illustrates the major arteries of the human body.

Section 34-C has been expanded and includes a subsection on diseases of the circulatory system.

SUGGESTIONS FOR LECTURE PREPARATION AND ENRICHMENT

Ancillaries

The blood vessels of an earthworm are diagrammed in overhead transparency (OHT) #111 (page 681). OHT #114 (page 687) presents a general outline of mammalian circulation. Ask students to compare the two types of transport systems.

In OHTs #112 (page 682) and #113 (page 686) blood flow through the hearts of various vertebrates including the human heart is diagrammed. Ask students to compare blood flow patterns through the hearts and relate to the organism's metabolic rate and need for oxygen.

Correlative Laboratory Exercises

Topic 21 Introduction to the Vertebrates

Topic 24 The Transport System in Vertebrates

Topic 25 Function of the Transport System

In topic 21 students studied organ systems in preserved specimens representing the vertebrate classes. These organisms can be set up as a demonstration for the circulatory system. Ask students to compare the hearts and organization of the circulatory system.

In topic 24 students study the structure of the heart using preserved organs, and the circulatory system in a fetal pig by dissection. Living capillaries are observed in the webbed foot of a pithed frog.

In topic 25 students perform activities to demonstrate the buffering capacity of plasma, to determine hemoglobin content of blood, to study factors affecting heart rate in themselves and in pithed frogs.

Supplemental Readings

Brown, M. and J. Goldstein. 1984. How LDL receptors influence and artherosclerosis. Sci. Am., November.

Caplan, Arthur. 1982. The artificial heart. The Hastings Center Report 12(1): 22-24.

Christopherson, Lois. 1982. Heart transplants. The Hastings Center Report 12(1): 18-21.

Langone, J. 1984. Cholesterol: the villain revealed. Discover 5(2): 19-29.

Levenson, Thomas. 1985. The Heart of the Matter. Discover 6(2):82-84, January. A discussion of ethical issues raised by organ transplantations and replacement particularly those involving the artificial heart, and the baboon hearts.

O'Neil, Paul, 1985. The Heart that Failed. Discover 6(11):14-21, Jan. An account of the transplantation of a baboon's heart into an infant who was born with a defective heart unable to effectively pump blood through the systemic circuit.

Preston, Thomas. 1985. Who benefits from the artificial heart? The Hastings Center Report 15(11):5-7.

Randal, Judith. 1982. Coronary artery bypass surgery. The Hastings Center Report 12(1):13-14.

Rice-Evans, C. and M. Dunn. 1982. Erythrocyte deformability and disease. TIBS 7:282-286.

Robinson, Thomas, Factor, Stephen, and Edmund Sonnenblick. 1986. The heart as a suction pump. Sci. Am., June.

Sanders, Howard, 1985. Improved drug delivery. Chemical and Engineering News 63(13)L30, April 1.

Silberner, Joanne. 1985. Anatomy of atherosclerosis Science News 127: 170-171, March 16. Atherosclerosis may result from the body's attempt to heal itself.

Silberner, Joanne. 1986. The heart and heredity. Science News. 129: 126-127, Feb. 22.

Films

The Lymphatic System (IFB, 1979, 15 min.) Presents physiology and anatomy of this system and a comparison with circulatory system.

Student Activities

1. Have students measure heart beat under different conditions, such as sitting, standing, after walking around room, etc. Ask why heart rate changed with activity performed.

2. Have students measure blood pressure under different conditions such as sitting, standing, after exercise, before and after taking a test, etc. Ask why pressure changed with activity.

Ideas for Demonstrations

1. Vertebrate hearts. Preserved specimens can be purchased from biological supply companies.

2. Microscope slides of histological preparations of normal and abnormal blood, and blood vessels.

3. Effect of drugs on heartbeat. Expose frog heart or fish tail to various drugs such as acetylcholine, epinephrine, and atropine and observe effect.

Topics for Discussion and Library Research

1. Evolution of heart in vertebrates.

2. Relationship of circulatory system, body size, and body temperature.

3. Cardiovascular diseases. See article by: Johansen, K. 1982. "Aneurysms." Sci. Am., July.

4. Effect of cigarette smoking on heart rate, blood pressure, etc.

5. Artificial blood. See article by Glaser, V. 1984. Stand-ins for blood. Biotechnology, February.

6. Mechanical heart, heart transplantation. See articles by: Jarvik, R., 1981. "The total artificial heart." Sci. Am., Jan.; Caplan A. 1983. "Organ transplants." The Hastings Center Report 13(6):23-32; Rachels, J. 1983. "Barney Clark's key." The Hastings Center Report 13(2):17-19; Annas; G., 1983. "Consent to the artificial heart." The Hastings Center Report 13(2):20-22.

7. Abnormalities of erythrocytes. See articles by: Cohen, C. and D. Branton. 1981. "The normal and abnormal red cell cytoskeleton: a renewed search for molecular defects." TIBS 6(10):266-268; Rice-Evans, C. and M. Dunn. 1982. "Erythrocyte deformability and disease." TIBS 7(8):282-286.

ESSAY QUESTIONS

obj 1, 2   1. What is the function of the circulatory system in insects? Explain why the circulatory system of insects limits the size to which they can grow.

2. If the coronary arteries are incapable of carrying blood to the heart, it stops beating and the organism dies. Explain why this is so considering that the heart pumps the blood throughout the body.

obj 13   3. What are the functions of the lymphatic system and why is it necessary?

obj 4   4. Explain why a four chambered heart is more efficient than a three chambered one.

5. Distinguish between the members of the following terms: fibrinogen/albumin; plasma/serum; erythrocyte/leukocyte; atrium/ventricle; and, atrioventricular node/sinoatrial node.

6. What effect would a hole between the right and left atria in a human heart have on the distribution of oxygenated blood through the systemic circuit?

obj 6   7. Correlate the events of the heart beat with the flow of blood through the heart.

8. What are the metarterioles and what role do they play in regulating blood pressure?

obj 8   9. List five cells found in blood, and describe the function of each.

obj 4   10. Using a microscope you are examining a slide on which are cross sections of three types of blood vessels. Blood vessel #1 has the smallest lumen, a thin wall which appears to be one cell thick. Blood vessel #2 has a much larger, irregular shaped lumen around which are three distinct layers of cells organized

in concentric rings. Blood vessel #3 has a round lumen the same size as that in #2, and is also enclosed by three layers of cells similar to #2.
Identify each type of blood vessel and explain your answer.

obj 7 11. Consider the following equation:
Cardiac output = stroke volume x heart rate

    a) What effect(s) does acetylcholine have on cardiac output and heart rate?
    b) What effect(s) does norepinephrine have on cardiac output and heart rate?

    12. Write an equation relating cardiac output, peripheral resistance and blood pressure.

CHAPTER 35   DEFENSES AGAINST DISEASE

Summary

     All animals have nonspecific defense mechanisms that protect them
from diseases. Examples of nonspecific mechanisms include skin,
interferon, phagocytes, and bactericidal fluids. Vertebrates, and to a
lesser extent invertebrates, are also protected by much more specific
immune responses.

     Immune responses are characterized by specificity, by the recogn-
nition of antigens as either part of the body or as foreign, and by
"memory" that the body has encountered a particular foreign antigen
before. As a result, the second or later reaction to an antigen is
faster and more extensive than the first.

     T lymphocytes are responsible for the cell-mediated rejection of
tissue transplanted from other individuals. The histocompatibility
antigens label cell surfaces and determine whether or not a tissue or
organ transplant will be rejected by the recipient's immune system.
T lymphocytes also play many roles in a variety of other immune responses.
Many cancers are attacked by the immune system, which recognizes tumor
cells as foreign by the presence of different antigens on their surfaces.

     B lymphocytes are responsible for the humoral immune response
triggered by binding of antigens with antibodies in the blood. The
body produces hundreds of thousands of different kinds of antibodies that
bind antigens with greater or lesser specificity.

     Exposure of the immune system to an antigen causes a primary
immune response, in which the lymphocytes that produce the antibody
specific to that antigen are stimulated to divide and to produce and
release more antibody. After the invasion has been defeated, an en-
larged clone of these lymphocytes remains as the body's "memory" of
the antigen, so that a secondary immune response to the antigen is greater
and more rapid than the first. Foreign antigens are destroyed by
phagocytes such as macrophages, which are stimulated to engulf the
antigen only when it is bound by an antibody; in the case of some
bacteria this reaction requires the assistance of the complement reactions.

Vaccination stimulates a primary immune response to an antigenic pathogen so that the body responds with an effective secondary response if it later encounters the pathogen.

The vast diversity of immunoglobulins in the body is produced by recombination of relatively few genes, each of which specifies part of an immunoglobulin molecule. The body does not produce antibodies to its own antigens. In some unknown way, the immune system comes to tolerate the body's own antigens during embryonic development.

Anaphylactic shock and allergic reactions occur when an allergen induces mast cells bound to E group immunoglobulins to release histamine.

Objectives

1. Describe three unspecific defenses of animals against disease.

2. List three characteristics of an immune response and give an example of each.

3. State what each of the following is and describe its role in immune responses: antigen, antibody, histocompatibility antigen, bone marrow, lymph node, thymus gland, bursa of Fabricius, T lymphocyte, B lymphocyte, macrophage, memory cell.

4. Describe what is known of the cell-mediated immune response, and give an example of such a response.

5. Describe the steps by which a bacterium is destroyed during a primary humoral immune response that does not involve the complement reaction.

6. List three roles played by lymphocytes in the immune system.

7. Explain how vaccination protects against a serious case of a disease.

8. Describe how an allergic reaction comes about.

9. Describe the role of the immune system in cancer therapy.

What's new or expanded in the third edition

The introduction has been expanded and includes information about past epidemics and current health problems caused by pathogens.

In section 35-B the subsection on the cells of the immune system includes more information and details. The subsection (35-C) on the major histocompatibility complex has also been expanded. Section 35-1 contains new information on and figures (35-8, page 715) illustrating the immunoglobulins. Defenses against cancer is the subject of section 35-M. The discussion focuses on natural killer cells, immunological surveillance, and development of vaccines against certain types of cancer caused by viruses.

SUGGESTIONS FOR LECTURE PREPARATION AND ENRICHMENT

Ancillaries

Overhead transparency (OHT) #115 (page 706) illustrates a cross section through human skin, a nonspecific defense mechanism. OHT #116 (page 715) shows the molecular structure of immunoglobulins and their interaction with antigens.

Correlative Laboratory Exercise

Topic 25 Function of the Transport System (parts)

In this exercise students study different types of cells found in the blood.

Supplemental Readings

Beauchamp, Gary, Yamazski, Kunio, and Edward Boyse, 1985. The chemo-sensory recognition of genetic individuality. Scientific American, July.

Bolotin, Carol. 1985. Drug as hero. Science 85. 6(5):68-71. Story about cyclosporine.

Buisseret, D. 1982. Allergy. Sci. Am., August.

Collier, R. J. and D. Kaplan. 1984. Immunotoxins. Sci. Am., July.

Dinarello, Charles and Sheldon Wolff. 1982. Molecular Basis of Fever in Humans. The American Journal of Medicine, May.

Donelson, John and Mervyn Turner. 1985. How the trypanosome changes its coat. Scientific American, February.

Godson, G. Nigel. 1985. Molecular approaches to malaria vaccines. Scientific American, May.

Kiester, Edwin, Jr. 1984. A Little Fever is Good For You. Science 84 5(9):168-173. Discusses benefits of fever in fighting infections.

Langone, John. 1985. AIDS: Special report. Discover 6(12):28-53. Dec.

Laurence, Jeffrey. 1985. The immune system in AIDS. Sci. Am., December

Lerner, R. 1983. Synthetic vaccines. Sci. Am., February

Marrack, Philippa and JOhn Kappler. 1986. The T cell and its receptor Sci. Am., February.

Marx, Jean. 1985. The immune system "belongs to the body." Science 227: 1190-1192. A brief report on research into the interactions of the nervous systems and disease susceptibility.

Marx, Jean. 1985. Antibodies made to order. Science 229: 455-456. Brief account of chimeric antibodies and their use as "magic bullets."

Miller, Julie. 1985. A vaccine for all seasons. Science News 127: 379-382, June 15. Genetic engineering is being used to remodel the small pox vaccine to provide immunity against other diseases.

Miller, Julie Ann. 1985. Mouth immunity. Science News 128:221-222, Oct. 5.

Moser, Penny W. 1985. Rocky times for Rocky. Discover 6(15):72-77. May. An account of the spread of the rabies virus among raccoons living along the east coast.

Raeburn, Paul. 1985. Multipurpose vaccines. High Technology, April.

Tonegawa, Susumu. 1985. The molecules of the immune system. Sci. Am., October.

Films

Body Defenses Against Disease (2/E) (EBEC, 1978, 14 min.) Presents the immune system.

Ideas for Demonstrations

1. Ouchterlony plates to show antigen-antibody reaction.

2. Blood typing.

Topics for Discussion and Library Research

1. Antibody diversity. See article by: Leder, P. 1982. "Genetics of antibody diversity." Sci. Am., May.

2. Allergy. See article by: Buisseret, B. 1982. "Allergy." Sci. Am., August.

3. Autoimmune disease. See articles by: Rose, N. 1981. "Auto-immune diseases." Sci. Am., February. Koffler, D. 1980. "Systemic lupus erythematosus." Sci. Am., July; Hopson, J. 1980. "Battle at the isle of self." Science 80, March/April.

4. Vaccines--synthetic and natural. See articles by: Lerner, R. 1983, "Synthetic vaccines." Sci. Am., February; Wilson, T., 1984. "Engineering tomorrow's vaccines." Biotechnology, January; Maranto, G. 1984. "Renaissance for vaccines." Discover 5(9): 61-63.

5. T and B lymphocytes--differences, nature of receptors on membranes, various T-cells.

6. Immunologically privileged sites, particularly the uterus. Discuss embryo transfer using surrogate mother.

7. Comparison of specific and nonspecific defnese mechanisms.

8. Histocompatibility antigens. See article by: Steinmetz, M. and L. Hood. 1983. "Genes of the major histocompatibility complex in mouse and man." Science 222: 727-733.

9. Monoclonal antibodies. See articles by:

   Flannery M. 1984. Monoclonal antibodies, The American Biology Teacher 46(7):403-405.

   Kolata, G. 1983. The "magic" in magic bullets. Science 222: 310-312.

   Marx, J. 1983. Suppressing autoimmunity in mice. Science 221: 843-845.

   Milstein, C. 1980. Monoclonal antibodies. Sci. Am., 254 (4): 66-74, October.

   Nowinski, R.C. et al. 1983. Monoclonal antibodies for diagnosis of infectious diseases in humans. Science 219: 637-644.

   Teillaud, J-L. et al. 1983. Monoclonal antibodies reveal the structural basis of antibody diversity. Science 222. 721-726.

   Vitetta, E. et al. 1983. Immunotoxins: A New approach to cancer therapy. Science 219:644-650.

ESSAY QUESTIONS

1. Distinguish between the members of the following paired terms: antigens/antibody; cell-mediated/antibody-mediated immunity; B lymphocyte/T lymphocyte; plasma cell/phagocyte; and C-region/ V-region.

2. Distinguish between a primary and secondary response. In which type are memory cells important?

obj 7.   3. Distinguish between active and passive immunity. Which provides long term protection? Which type is induced by injection of vaccines?

obj 3   4. Describe three differences between B and T lymphocytes.

obj 4   5. Compare and contrast the mechanisms of antibody-mediated and cell mediated immunity.

        6. If antibodies are structurally and functionally similar, explain how they are able to form complexes with the many thousands of different kinds of antigens.

obj 4   7. Why are organ transplants usually unsuccessful?

obj 1   8. Distinguish between specific and nonspecific defense mechanisms and given an example of each.

        9. Some people born with immunodeficiency diseases can be treated by a bone marrow transplant. However, the bone marrow must be processed before it can be transplanted into the recipient. Explain why the marrow must be processed before transplantation.

      10. Immunosuppressive drugs are given to people receiving organ transplants. The drugs are necessary to increase the chances for a successful transplantation. However, the use of drugs causes other problems for the person. Identify two problems associated with their use.

      11. Children with DiGeorge Syndrome, a congenital abnormality, are lacking both the thymus and parathyroid glands. Speculate on how a child with this disease could be identified.

      12. Explain the immunological basis of allergy and briefly describe the events that occur during a hay fever allergic response.

CHAPTER 36 EXCRETION

Outline

Essay: Adaptations of Mammals to Sodium-Deficient Environments

Summary

     Living cells require a relatively constant chemical environment. Cells
are continuously altering their immediate environment by taking in substances from it and converting them into new substances, some useful, some
wastes which must be removed from the cell and from its immediate environment. Various specialized mechanisms have evolved in the animal kingdom as
a means of maintaining a constant internal chemical environment in the face
of the continuous flow of materials between the external environment, the
extracellular fluid, and the interiors of cells.

     The problem of excretion at first seems to be simply the problem of
removing nitrogenous wastes before they reach toxic levels; however, the
availability of salts and water in the animal's environment imposes restric-
tions on how this removal can be accomplished, and the animal must have
adaptations that allow it to dispose of nitrogenous wastes while at the
same time maintaining the proper salt and water (osmotic) balance in its
body fluids. When all of these factors are taken into consideration, excretion is seen to require not only collection and disposal of excess
substances, but also a means of retaining those that are needed.

     The function of the vertebrate kidney is to maintain the composition
of all of the body's fluids within the narrow limits necessary if the cells
of the body are to function. The basic unit of the kidney is the nephron
a long tube closely associated with a capillary bed of the circulatory
system. Blood plasma is filtered, under hydrostatic pressure, into one end
of this tube. As the filtrate passes through the nephron, substances needed
by the body are resorbed through the cells of the nephron tubule into the
extracellular fluid, and then into the capillaries, either by diffusion or
by active transport. Unwanted substances are secreted from the blood into
the filtrate. After being changed in these ways during its passage through
the tubule, the filtrate is collected as urine. Homeostatic mechanisms
under hormonal control regulate the amount and composition of the urine
produced.

Objectives

   1.   (a) List four substances excreted by the human body; (b) name the
        organ(s) that excrete(s) each substance; (c) state the difference
        between excretion and egestion.

   2.   (a) State the origin of nitrogenous wastes in animal metabolism;
        (b) name three common nitrogenous wastes considered in this chapter;
        (c) state the advantages and disadvantages of each substance as an
        excretory end product, and relate these advantages and the dis-
        advantages to the animal's habitat; (d) name the animal groups

commonly associated with each of these excretory end products; (e) use your knowledge of parts (c) and (d) to predict the main nitrogenous waste excreted by an animal.

3. Explain the relationship between nitrogenous waste formation, osmoregulation, energy expenditure, and habitat as factors in the problem of body fluid regulation. Interpret Figures 36-3 and 36-7 (in Self-Quiz) as they relate to this problem.

4. (a) List two problems encountered by a freshwater animal in maintaining homeostasis, and the adaptations of freshwater bony fish that enable them to cope with these problems; (b) list the problems encountered by animals in maintaining homeostasis in a hypertonic environment, and the adaptations of (a) marine Chondrichthyes, (2) marine bony fish, (3) marine birds; and (4) marine mammals in meeting these problems.

5. List three essential steps common to the action of excretory organs in animals.

6. Name the excretory structures found in the following forms: planarians, earthworms, vertebrates, and insects; briefly explain how each works.

7. Define the terms resorption and secretion, and be able to explain kidney function in terms of these activities.

8. Draw or identify, and give the functions of the following parts of a nephron and its associated structures; nephric (Bowman's) capsule; glomerulus, renal artery, renal vein, proximal convoluted tubule, distal convoluted tubule, loop of Henle, collecting duct (tubule).

9. Explain how the osmotic functions of the loop of Henle, and the collecting ducts concentrate the glomerular filtrate.

10. Describe the effects of vasopressin, aldosterone, renin, angiotensin, blood pressure, sweating, and excessive bleeding on the volume and composition of the urine, as these are outlined in this chapter.

SUGGESTIONS FOR LECTURE PREPARATION AND ENRICHMENT

Ancillaries

In overhead transparency (OHT) #117 (page 726) the urea cycle is diagrammed. OHT #118 (page 734) illustrates the concentration of urine in the nephron. Ask students to comment on the relationship between the length of the loop of Henle and the ability of the kidney to concentrate urine.

Correlative Laboratory Exercise

Topic 19 Higher Invertebrates: Mollusks and Annelids

Topic 20 Higher Invertebrates: Arthropods

Topic 21 Introduction to the Vertebrates

Topic 26 Excretion and Reproduction

In topics 19-21 students study the organ systems in preserved specimens representing mollusks, annelids, crustaceans, insects, and different classes of vertebrates. The excretory systems of the organisms listed above could be set up as a demonstration to accompany the laboratory on Topic 26. Ask students to generate a table listing the different types of excretory structures, their roles in osmoregulation and metabolic waste removal, their association with a capillary network, the degree to which filtration, reabsorption and secretion occur, and the nature of the final product.

In Topic 26 students continue their dissection of the fetal pig to study the anatomy of the excretory system.

Supplemental Readings

Carolina Biology Reader

Moffat, D.B. 1978. The Control of Water Balance by the Kidney.

Dantzler, W. H. 1982. Renal adaptations of desert vertebrates. Bioscience 32 (2): 108-114, February.

Student Activities

1. Have students measure the amount of fluid taken in, and excreted, over a 24 hour period. Repeat for a week. Graph the results to see if there is a correlation between amount of fluids taken in and excreted.

2. Vary conditions under which urine is collected. Have them eat salty/sugary foods or refrain from drinking for a day. Graph results and compare with graph from activity above.

Ideas for Demonstrations

1. Osmosis. Fill dialysis bags with the same solution and place in beakers containing solutions which are hypertonic, hypotonic and isotonic to the solution in the bag. Weigh bag before placing in beaker and after designated time interval.

2. Amount of filtrate produced per hour by kidney. Fill flasks with 7.5 liters of water to demonstrate amount of filtrate produced per hour.

Topics for Discussion and Library Research

1. Comparison of excretory systems

2. Problems in terrestrial living reflected in adaptations seen in excretory system.

3. Correlation of type of excretory system and type of environment

4. Function of the nephron

5. Diseases of excretory system

ESSAY QUESTIONS

obj 2   1. Explain the relationship between the type of nitrogenous waste produced, and the kind of environment in which the organism lives.

obj 8   2. Which part of the nephron would be modified in an animal living in the desert? in a marine environment? Explain your answers.

obj 2,   3. Compare the osmoregulatory adaptations of freshwater and marine
4   bony fish?

obj 4,   4. Describe briefly how excretion is accomplished in a (a) grass-
6   hopper; (b) crayfish; (c) earthworm, (d) shark, and (e)
         marine fish.

obj 5   5. Compare the three processes involved in urine formation regarding location, importance and mechanism of each process.

6. Distinguish between the members of the following paired terms: urea/urine; excretion/elimination; metanephridium/nephron; ureter/urethra; and, renal corpuscle/renal tubule.

7. How might the urine of a vegetarian differ from that of a heavy meat eater?

obj 3   8. Insects and terrestrial vertebrates are faced with the same problem, conservation of water. However, their excretory systems are quite different. Why are their systems different?

obj 1   9. List the three principal metabolic waste products in mammals, and describe how each is excreted or removed from the body.

obj 7 10. Draw a diagram of the human excretory system. Identify and give the function of the component parts.

obj 8 11. Describe the function in urine formation of each of the following: glomerulus, Bowman's capsule, proximal convoluted tubule, distal convoluted tubule, collecting duct, peritubular capillary network, afferent arteriole.

12. Urinalysis, the physical, chemical, and microscopic examination of urine is not only an important diagnostic tool, but can also be used to monitor certain diseases, such as diabetes mellitus. Of the three processes involved in the production of urine, which one is responsible for a positive test for sugar in the urine? Explain.

obj 10 13. You have just consumed four ounces of salted peanuts and a candy bar. Now, you are very thirsty. Outline the sequence of events occurring within your body in response to ingesting the food. Then, outline the sequence of events operating to restore homeostasis for your body fluids.

CHAPTER 37   SEXUAL REPRODUCTION

Outline

  I. Reproductive Patterns
 II. Human Reproductive Organs
     A. Female Reproductive Organs
     B. Male Reproductive Organs
III. Physiology of Sexual Intercourse
 IV. Hormones and Reproduction
     A. Male Hormones
     B. Female Hormones
     C. The Menstrual Cycle
     D. Hormones of Pregnancy
  V. Fertilization and Implantation
     A. Birth
 VI. Birth Control
     A. Vasectomy and Tubal Ligation
     B. Abortion

Essay: Sexually Transmitted Diseases

Summary

Almost all animals can reproduce sexually, as a large, motile egg is fertilized by a small, motile sperm. This usually involves the coordination of the anatomy, physiology, and behavior of two parents. Many aquatic species shed their gametes into the water, and both fertilization and development occur externally. Internal fertilization combined with external development permits fertilization to occur before the egg is surrounded with the impenetrable layers that will protect it as it develops outside the mother's body. Internal fertilization and development provide maximum protection of the developing embryo.

In humans, the male and female parents produce sperm and eggs in the testes and ovaries, respectively. Sexual maturation during puberty, maturation of gametes, and the female menstrual cycle are controlled by hormones. Hormones secreted by the placenta control pregnancy, and hormones also control birth and lactation.

The male's testes, which produce sperm, lie in the scrotum. Semen forms as glandular secretions join the sperm in the tubes leaving the testes. The penis is composed of spongy tissue which becomes engorged with blood during sexual stimulation; it can then be introduced into the vagina. Sexual stimulation may eventually result in orgasm by both sexes and in ejaculation of semen by the male.

When a mature egg is released from the ovary, it travels through an oviduct, where it may be fertilized by a sperm. The fertilized, developing egg then descends into the uterus, where it implants in the uterine wall. Part of the embryo develops into the new individual, and part forms the embryonic part of the placenta and the membranes surrounding the embryo.

The fetus cannot survive outside the uterus until about six months after fertilization. Birth occurs at about nine months and involves powerful uterine contractions that expel the fetus and placenta from the uterus through the vagina.

Humans commonly control their reproduction by techniques that either prevent fertilization or prevent a developing embryo from completing its growth in the uterus.

Objectives

1. Explain the advantages and disadvantages of these three reproductive

patterns: external fertilization and development; internal fertilization and external development; internal fertilization and development.

2. List the organs in the human female and male reproductive tracts, give their functions, and explain how conception occurs.

3. Name the most important androgen and the organ in the male primarily responsible for its secretion.

4. Name the four hormones that interact in producing the female menstrual cycle, and explain what hormonal events lead to the release of an egg from the ovary.

5. Give the role s of human chorionic gonadotropin and oxytocin in pregnancy, and the source of each.

6. Describe how implantation occurs. Give the function of the placenta, amnion, chorion, allantois, and umbilicus.

7. State how "the pill", IUD, diaphragm and jelly, condom rhythm, induced abortion and sterilization of males or females operate as birth control methods. State the part of the reproductive process with which each method interferes.

What's new or expanded in the third edition

The material in the sections in the second edition dealing with embryonic development can be found in chapters 11 and 12 in the third edition.

In section 37-A different types of reproductive patterns are described and compared to one another. Table 37-1 lists examples of animals showing the three main types of reproduction patterns: external fertilization and development, internal fertilization and external development, and internal fertilization and development.

In Section 37-D male hormones are described in greater detail and a new subsection on female hormones has been added. Figure 37-9 (page 748) relates the changes occurring in the levels of the hormones involved in the menstrual cycle with the developmental changes occurring in the ovary in the production of a mature ovum, and in the uterine endometrium in preparation for pregnancy.

Section 37-E presents new information on fertilization both internal and external in a "test tube," and on implantation of the embryo into the endometrium. The development of the placenta and the four extraembryonic membranes (amnion, allantois, chorion, yolk sac) are also described in the text and in the accompanying figures (37-12, page 752, 37-14, page 753).

The essay presents a discussion of sexually transmitted diseases, such as Herpes, AIDS, Chlamydial infections, and gonorrhea.

SUGGESTIONS FOR LECTURE PREPARATION AND ENRICHMENT

Ancillaries

Overhead transparencies (OHT) #119 (page 744) and #120 (page 746) show the reproductive tracts of a female and male. Ask students to compare the two tracts. The events of the menstrual cycle are shown in OHT #121 (page 748). The hormonal cycle is correlated with the ovarian and uterine phases of the cycle.

Correlative Laboratory Exercises

Topic 21   Introduction to the Vertebrates

Topic 26   Excretion and Reproduction

For Topic 21 a demonstration could be set up in which the reproductive systems of representative vertebrates are displayed.

In Topic 26 students study the anatomy of the reproductive system through dissection of their fetal pigs. Students observe a display of various contraceptives.

Supplemental Readings (Also see Chapter 13)

Austad, Steven. 1986. Changing sex nature's way. International Wildlife 16(3):29, May/June.

Carolina Biology Reader

Hart, G. 1984. Sexually Transmitted Diseases

Castleman, Michael. 1985. Toxics and male infertility. Sierra 70(2): 49-52, March/April. A report on the effects of environmental toxins on fertility.

Diamond, Jared. 1985. Everything else you always wanted to know about sex. Discover 6(4)70-82, April. The sexual behavior, anatomy, and reproductive strategies of various animals are discussed from an evolutionary perspective.

Djerassi, C. 1984. The making of the pill. Science 84 5(9):127-129. November. The story of the development of the birth control pill.

Gold, Michael. 1985. The babymakers. Science 85 6(3): 26-38, April. A discussion of infertility and in vitro fertilization (where, when, how, why it's done).

Grobstein, C., et. al. 1983. External human fertilization: An evaluation of policy. Science, October 14.

Lagercrantz, Hugo and Theodore Slotken. 1986.   The "stress" of being born. Sci. Am., April.

Mapletoft, R. 1984. Embryo transfer technology for the enhancement of animal reproduction. Biotechnology 2(2):149-160.

Maranto, G. 1984. Clones on the Range. Discover. 5(8):34-38.

Maranto, G. 1984. Choosing your baby's sex. Discover 5(10):24-27.

Roberts, Leslie. 1986. Sex and cancer. Science 86 7(6):30-33, July/Aug.

Silberner, Joanne. 1985. Babymaking: Expanding horizons. Science News 128:378-379, Dec. 14.

Films (Also see chapter 12)

The Beginnings of Life (PF, 1975, 26 min.) Deals with oogenesis, spermatogenesis, fertilization, and implantation.

Birth Control: The Choices (CF, 1976, 25 min.) Presents different methods of birth control, their limitations, side effects, uses.

Human Reproduction (CRM/Mc, 1981, 20 min.) Presents reproductive systems of male and female, fertilization, development, and birth.

Ideas for Demonstration

1. Birth control devices. These are available from family planning clinics.

2. Microscope slides of histological preparations of human gonads

3. Living sperm

4. Models or preserved specimens of reproductive systems

5. Preserved specimens of pregnant uteri, placentas

Topics for Discussion and Library Research

1. Sexually transmitted diseases such as nongonococcal urethritis (NGU), and chlamydia infections

2. Comparison of birth control methods

3. Ethical aspects of reproductive technologies

4. Reproductive technologies, such as embryo transfer, in vitro fertilization, surrogate mothers, etc. See articles by: Seidel, G. et al. 1981. Superovulation and embryo transfer in cattle. Science 211:351-358, and Cherfas, J. 1984. Test tube babies in the zoo. New Scientist, December 6.

5. The placenta. See article by: Beaconsfield, P., Birdwood, G., and R. Beaconsfield, 1980. The placenta. Sci. Am., August.

6. Effect of teratogens on human development.

ESSAY QUESTIONS

obj 2 1. Compare the reproductive systems of human males and females regarding basic components, organization and events of gametogenesis.

2. Describe one similarity and two differences in the sexual response of human males and females.

obj 1 3. Identify two evolutionary trends in animal reproduction that are associated with terrestrial living and greater reproductive efficiency.

obj 7 4. List five different methods of birth control, and for each, identify one advantage and one disadvantage.

obj 1 5. Describe the advantages and disadvantages associated with both sexual and asexual reproduction.

obj 2, 3 6. Distinguish between the members of the following paired terms: seminal vesicle/prostate gland; seminiferous tubules/epididymis; penis/clitoris; FSH/LH; and, testosterone/progesterone.

obj 4 7. If the portal system between the hypothalamus and the anterior lobe of the pituitary was severed, what effect would this have on a woman's ability to become pregnant?

obj 3, 4 8. Describe the role of hormones in the production of sperm and the egg in humans.

9. A woman has a 28 day menstrual cycle. She wants to avoid pregnancy, but doesn't want to use any birth control device. What information would you give her about the events of her cycle, and what advice would you give her about her choice of birth control method?

10. Identify a sexually transmitted disease caused by each of the following pathogenic agents: a bacterium, a virus, a protozoan, and a fungus. Of the above which can be cured by a medical treatment?

obj 5 11. Identify two hormones involved in lactation, and explain their roles.

obj 4, 12. Discuss the effect of continuous presence of estrogen and pro-
   7   gesterone on a woman's menstrual cycle.

obj 7 13. Why has it been more difficult to develop a "pill" for males comparable to that for females? In your answer discuss differences and similarities between male and female systems.

obj 1 14. Identify and discuss three consequences of fertilization.

obj 6 15. Describe the function of the placenta, the amnion, the yolk sac, and the allantois in human embryonic development.

CHAPTER 38 NEURONS

Outline

Summary

Information passes along a neuron in the form of electrical changes across the neuron plasma membrane. When it reaches a synapse, the information is usually transmitted as a chemical that can cross a synaptic cleft to the membrane of the next cell and disturb its electrical balance in turn.

The resting neuron has two sources of stored energy; a high external concentration of Na^+ and a high internal concentration of K^+. This asymmetrical ion distribution is maintained, in the long run, by the sodium-potassium pump. The differential permeability of the membrane to different ions results in a resting potential across the membrane. Changes in this membrane potential occur when a stimulus opens the gates of ion channels through the membrane, allowing certain ions to cross the membrane and depolarize or hyperpolarize that part of the membrane. Small local changes in the membrane potential in the dendrites or soma may sum temporally and spatially until they exceed the threshold needed for the axon to produce an action potential. An action potential travels down an axon faster if the axon has a large diameter or if it is electrically insulated by a myelin sheath.

The intensity of a stimulus is coded largely in terms of the frequency of action potentials, the total length of a burst of action potentials, and the thresholds of neurons that are firing. The type of stimulus received is coded by the specific wiring of the nervous system.

Some nerves have neurosecretory functions in addition to, or instead of, their better-known role as conveyors of electrical impulses.

Objectives

1. Describe the basic structure and function of neurons.

2. Define the sodium-potassium ionic pump, and explain its role in maintaining the membrane potential.

3. Contrast the properties of local responses (generator potentials and postsynaptic potentials) with those of action potentials.

4. Draw a graph of the potential changes that occur during an action potential, and relate them to the flow of sodium and potassium ions across the axonal membrane.

5. Describe the myelin sheath, and explain its effect on impulse conduction.

6. Draw a model synapse with its principal components, explain the function of each component, and explain how information is transmitted to the postsynaptic cell.

7. Explain the difference between an excitatory and an inhibitory synapse in terms of effect on the postsynaptic membrane.

8. Explain how information about the intensity and type of a stimulus is transmitted in the nervous system.

What's new or expanded in the third edition

In figure 38-2 (page 761) a monopolar sensory neuron has been added.

Section 38-G has been expanded and includes new material on neuro-transmitters, particularly the neuropeptides.

SUGGESTIONS FOR LECTURE PREPARATION AND ENRICHMENT

Ancillaries

The spread of an action potential along an axon is shown in overhead transparency (OHT) #122 (page 767). Ask students to relate to events occurring during generation of an action potential. In OHT #123 (page 769) transmission of a neurotransmitter across a synapse is shown. Ask students why mitochondria are present in the knob and what happens to the neurostranmitter after its release.

Correlative Laboratory Exercise

Topic 27 The Nervous System

The part on neurons could be assigned with this chapter but it would be better to have students do the entire exercise concurrent with or after Chapter 39.

Supplemental Readings

Carolina Biology Readers:

Adrian, R. 1980. The Nerve Impulse (2/E)

Dunant, Yves and Muarice Israel. 1985. The release of acetylcholine. Scientific American, April.

Forman, D. 1984. New approaches to the study of the mechanism of fast axonal transport. TIBS 7: 112-116.

Knudtson, Peter. 1985. Painter of neurons. Science 85 6(7): 66-72. Story about Santiago Ramon y Cajal, a neuroanatomist who received a Nobel prize in 1906 for his work which provided evidence for the neuron doctrine.

Kolata, Gina. 1985. Birds, brains, and the biology of song. Science 85 6(10): 58-63, December.

Llinas, R. 1982. Calcium in snyaptic transmission. Sci. Am., October.

Rowland, L. 1984. Motor neuron diseases and amyotrophic lateral sclero-sis. TIBS 7: 110-112.

Films

The Nerve Impulse (EBEC, 1970, 22 min.) Presents physiology of impulse and synaptic function.

Ideas for Demonstrations

    1. Microscope slides of histological preparations of neurons.

Topics for Discussion and Library Research

    1. Action potential
    2. Comparison of action potentials in neurons and muscle fibers
    3. Reflex arcs--significance from evolutionary perspective
    4. Neurotransmitters--types
    5. Effects of drugs on neurotransmitters

ESSAY QUESTIONS

obj 2 1. What effect does the lack of oxygen have on neural transmission?

        2. Compare neural transmission and muscle fiber contraction regarding the events involving the membrane.

        3. Describe the events that occur after the action potential reaches the synaptic knobs.

obj 3 4. Under what condition(s) is an action potential generated and how is it propagated along the neuron?

        5. Describe two ways by which the speed of conduction can be increased.

        6. Distinguish between the members of the following paired terms: efferent/afferent/association neurons; axon/dendrite; neuron/neurilemma; resting potential/action potential; and, glial cell/cell body.

obj 8 7. How does the nervous system distinguish between an injury to the finger caused by a thumbtack and one caused by a knife?

obj 4 8. A neuron is placed in an isotonic solution and stimulated electrically. What do you expect to happen?

CHAPTER 39   THE VERTEBRATE NERVOUS SYSTEM

Essay: Alzheimer's Disease

Summary

     During the evolution of the nervous system, progressive cephaliza-
tion has resulted in the formation of a brain and major sense organs at
the anterior end of the body. A vast increase in the number of neurons
permitted better control of the many muscles in a large body and more
flexibility of response to stimuli in a complex and changing environment.
     The nervous system of a vertebrate consists of the brain and
spinal cord, which together compose its central nervous system, and
the peripheral nervous system in the rest of the body.

     The vertebrate brain has three major pairs: the forebrain, midbrain,
and hindbrain, whose functions are summarized in Table 39-1. During
evolution, the vertebrate brain has increased in size and complexity.
Some parts of the brain have retained their primitive functions, while
others have taken on new functions as body structure and behavior have
become more complex, and as intelligence has increased. The function of
the brain is to "make decisions". Using information coded as patterns
of action potentials coming from the external or internal environment
via the sense organs, the brain produces a set of directions coded as
another set of action potentials that cause the effector organs to respond.
Information passes through various levels of organization in both sensory
and motor areas as the brain analyzes and integrates sensory input and
determines and executes appropriate responses.

     The spinal cord is primarily a relay station connecting the
brain with the peripheral nervous system, although there are spinal
reflexes in which sensory and motor components interact through the
spinal cord without input from the brain. These reflexes make quick,
local responses to potentially harmful stimuli without waiting for
analysis by higher levels in the brain.

     The peripheral nervous system is divided into the somatic nervous
system which largely serves the muscles under conscious control, and
the autonomic nervous system, which carries motor impulses to the
muscles and glands of the internal organs, under little conscious
control.

     Learning, memory and sleep are complex functions of the nervous
system about which very little is known.

Objectives

1. Define the terms cephalization, ganglion, nucleus, brain, spinal cord, central nervous system, peripheral nervous system, autonomic nervous system, nerve, spinal nerve, cranial nerve.

2. Give the derivation (from forebrain, midbrain, or hindbrain) and known functions of the cerebral hemispheres, cerebellum, medulla, thalamus, hypothalamus, and tectum (colliculi in mammals).

3. Discuss the differences in relative size and function of the structures listed in Objective 2 between the brain of a fish and the brain of a human being.

4. Describe the reticular formation in vertebrates, and explain the relationship of the reticular activating system to arousal.

5. Briefly outline how visual information is processed and projected in the vertebrate brain.

6. Draw a labeled diagram of a simple reflex arc, and describe how it works.

7. Discuss how plasticity in a nervous system is related to learning and behavior.

8. Outline the major structural and functional differences between the parasympathetic and sympathetic nervous systems.

What's new or expanded in the third edition

The introduction contains more details on the nervous systems of invertebrates. In section 38-C the subsection of the forebrain contains new information on the methods used to determine the functions of the different regions in the cerebral hemispheres, and on the functions associated with each hemisphere.

Section 39-H has been expanded and now includes material on learning and memory. The three kinds of memory are described in addition to experiments performed on invertebrates to study learning at the level of neurons.

The symptoms, and hypotheses as to the underlying causes of the changes in the brains of victims of Alzheimer's Disease are discussed in the essay.

SUGGESTIONS FOR LECTURE PREPARATION AND ENRICHMENT

Ancillaries

In overhead transparency (OHT) # 124 (page 779) the nervous systems of representative invertebrates are shown. Ask students to compare them. OHT #125 (page 782) and #126 (page 783) illustrate diagrammatically representative vertebrate brains including a human brain (OHT #126). Ask students to compare the various brains and to relate the size of a part of the brain to how the organism uses that part of the brain in its daily activities and for its survival.

In OHT # 127 (page 788) a simple reflex arc is diagrammed. Ask students to compare with a more complex reflex arc.

Correlative Laboratory Exercise

Topic 27   The Nervous System

In this exercise students identify the parts of the vertebrate brain using preserved specimens of sheep brains. Prepared slides of cross sections of the spinal cord are also viewed. Students learn about sense organs through dissection, and by performing a series of activities designed to demonstrate the sensitivity of the receptors to different stimuli. Various receptors are examined, such as mechanoreceptors, thermoreceptors, chemoreceptors, proprioceptors, and photoreceptors.

Supplemental Readings

Bioscience: May 1984 issue devoted to Developmental Neurobiology.

Edwards, Diane. 1986. A common medical denominator (Down's Syndrome and Alzheimer's Disease). Science NUws 129:60-62, Jan. 25.

Edwards, Diane D. 1986. Nicotine: A drug of choice? Science News 129:44-45, Jan. 18.

Hall, Stephen. 1985. Aplysia and Hermissenda. Science 85 6(4): 30-39. A description of the use of snails to provide insights into the molecular basis of learning.

Kiester, Edwin, Jr. 1986.' Spare parts for Damaged Brains. Science 86 7(2): 32-38, March.

Maranto, Gina. 1985. Coke: The random killer. Discover 6(3):16-21, March. An examination of the effects, hazards, and destructiveness of this drug on the human body.

Shafer, Jack. 1985. Designer Drugs. Science 85 6(2):60-67 Examines effects and consequences of production of synthetic heroin and other drugs.

Snyder, Solomon. 1984. Medicated Minds. Science 84 5(9):141-142, November. Chronicles the discovery and use of drugs for treating mental disease.

Steinhart, Peter. 1985. Do birds have a memory? National Wildlife 23(4): 42-45, June-July.

Winter, Peter and John Miller, 1985. Anesthesiology. Scientific American, April.

Wurtman, R. 1982. Nutrients that modify brain function. Sci. Am. April.

Wurtman, Richard. 1985. Alzheimer's Disease. Scientific American, January.

Films

The Hidden Universe: The Brain (CRM, 1977, 45 min. 2 parts) Covers the functions of the brain and some of the latest diagnostic methods and treatments for brain malfunctions.

The Mind's Eye (Fl, 1981, 50 min.) Explores processing of visual information in the retina and visual cortex.

The Peripheral Nervous System (IFB, 1977, 19 min.) Examines components
   of reflex arc, nerve impulse, and an infant's reflex action.

Student Activities

1. Have students observe newborn babies to identify early reflex
   reactions.

2. Have students diagram and list the sequence of events for
   the patellar reflex, or the reflex exhibited after touching a
   hot stove. Have them indicate muscles involved.

3. Have them make a list of reflexes exhibited by their own bodies
   and then speculate on the adaptive, survival value of each.

Ideas for Demonstrations

1. Reflex arcs. Tapping patellar ligament, or Achilles tendon,
   or shining a light in a person's eye will elicit a reflex
   action.

2. Preserved specimens of brains from representative vertebrates
   to show differences in size and complexity of various parts.

3. Biofeedback.

Topics for Discussion and Library Research

1. Action potential

2. Comparison of action potentials in neurons and muscle fibers

3. Reflex arcs--significance from evolutionary perspective

4. Neurotransmitters--types

5. Effects of drugs on neurotransmitters

6. Effects of drugs on the nervous system. See article by:
   Hazleton, L. 1984. Cocaine and the chemical brain.
   Science Digest 92(10):58.

7. Evolutionary trends associated wtih bilateral nervous system.

8. Comparison of vertebrate brains

9. Biofeedback

10. The September 21, 1984 (Vol. 225) issue of Science contains
    many review articles on the subject of neuroscience.

11. Coverings of the CNS -meninges

ESSAY QUESTIONS

1. Contrast nerve nets and radial nervous systems with bilateral
   nervous systems.

obj 6 2. Your Achilles tendon is tapped and your foot extends. Draw a
   diagram of this reflex arc. Indicate and label neurons and types
   of muscles and use arrows to indicate directions of impulses.

3. Describe how the brain knows (a) the color of your sweater,
   (b) that you are sitting down, (c) the loudness of a musical
   tone, and (d) that a 1% sugar solution is less sweet than a
   10% sugar solution.

4. Does a receptor potential always generate an action potential? Explain, and describe how a receptor potential is produced.

5. Distinguish between the members of the following paired terms: diencephalon/metencephalon/myelencephalon; cerebrum/cerebellum; thalamus/hypothalamus; reticular activating system/limbic system; medulla/pons.

obj 8   6. Describe four differences between the sympathetic and parasympathetic nervous systems.

7. Identify the major function(s) of the (a) cerebrum, (b) cerebellum, (c) hypothalamus, (d) medulla, and (e) thalamus.

obj 2   8. How would a human be affected by damage to the (a) cerebellum, (b) medulla, (c) occipital lobes, (d) temporal lobes, and (e) primary motor areas?

9. In a rat the dorsal root of a neuron leading to the foreleg is severed. In a second rat the ventral root of a neuron leading to the foreleg is severed. Explain the effects of these cuts on the rats.

obj 8   10. Homeostasis for many body functions involves the autonomic nervous system. Explain how this system regulates bodily functions and give specific examples.

11. List and briefly describe the protective coverings over the central nervous system and the origin and function of cerebrospinal fluid.

CHAPTER 40   SENSE ORGANS

Summary

     An animal must be able to detect changes inside its body and in the
world around it in order to produce appropirate physiological and behavioral
responses. Sense organs are collections of cells specialized to react to
particular forms of energy by producing electrical impulses in the nervous
system. Sense organs may detect mechanical stimuli, light, heat, chemical
changes, electric current, or the earth's magnetic field.

     The actual receptors in sense organs may be the dendrites of sensory
neurons or specialized non-nervous cells. Accessory structures may modify
the external stimulus before it reaches the receptor. Adaptation at the
level of the receptor, sensory neuron, or central nervous system changes
the signal transmitted or received in the presence of a constant stimulus.
The central nervous system usually has feedback control of the sensitivity
of sense organs.

     Mechanoreceptors detect mechanical distortions such as pressure,
touch, sound, muscle stretch, movement of joints, and blood pressure.
Hair cells are mechanoreceptors found in lateral line organs, and the
labyrinth and cochlea of the inner ear. Movement of the hair bundle or
depolarizes or hyperpolarizes the hair cell membrane, and this potential
change is transmitted to dendrites of a sensory neuron that synapses with
the receptor.

     Photoreceptors in eyespots, eyes and ommatidia detect light by means
of pigments whose structure is changed by electromagnetic radiation of
appropriate wavelength. This photochemical reaction depolarizes the
receptor cell membrane and causes a generator potential in an adjacent
sensory neuron. Thermoreceptors are sensory neurons that respond directly
to electromagnetic radiation in the infrared region.

     Chemoreceptors are usually dendrites of sensory neurons, although
the taste buds and possibly some internal chemoreceptors of vertebrates
contain non-nervous receptor cells.

     Electroreceptors are found in some bony and cartilaginous fishes;
they detect electric currents generated by organisms.

     The particular collection of sense organs in each animal species
gives its members a unique perception of their bodies and of their
environments.

Objectives

1. Write a short paragraph discussing the general importance of sense organs to an animal.

2. Name the five general types of receptor cells, and name some sense organs in which each is found.

3. Define transduction and generator potential, and explain the importance of each.

4. Define sensory adaptation; state the difference between rapidly adapting and slowly adapting receptors, and explain the relative advantages of each.

5. State what a proprioceptor is, and briefly describe the importance of the muscle spindle to the body.

6. Describe the roles of mechanoreceptors in the inner ear, explain how the ear recognizes differences in pitch, tone, and volume of sounds.

7. Sketch and label the eye of a vertebrate and that of an anthropod.

8. Name the two types of vertebrate photoreceptors, state their function, and describe the role of rhodopsin in vision.

SUGGESTIONS FOR LECTURE PREPARATION AND ENRICHMENT

Correlative Laboratory Exercise

Topic 27 The Nervous System

In this exercise students identify the parts of the vertebrate brain using preserved specimens of sheep brains. Prepared slides of cross sections of the spinal cord are also viewed. Students learn about sense organs through dissection, and by performing a series of activities designed to demonstrate the sensitivity of the receptors to different stimuli. Various receptors are examined, such as mechanoreceptors, thermoreceptors, chemoreceptors, proprioceptors, and photoreceptors.

Supplemental Readings

Hudspeth, A. 1983. Hair cells of the inner ear. Sci. Am., January.

Loeb, Gerald. 1985. The functional replacement of the ear. Scientific American, February.

Films

How Much Do You Smell? (FI, 1981, 50 min.) Presents olfaction and chemical communication in animals.

Inner Ear (FL, 1972, 11 min.)

The Mind's Eye (Fl, 1981, 50 min.) Explores processing of visual information in the retina and visual cortex.

Senses and Perception: Links to the Outside World (EBEC, 1975, 18 min.)

Student Activities

The following activities could be performed in class, and would contribute to the students' understanding of sensory receptors. See Topic 27 in the Laboratory Manual for instructions.

1. Mapping the blind spot.

2. Demonstrating afterimages

3. Locating chemoreceptors on tongue

4. Testing effectiveness of proprioceptors for maintaining balance

5. Mapping thermoreceptors, mechanoreceptors on the skin

Ideas for Demonstrations

1. Preserved specimens of eyes that can be dissected, the shark's vestibular apparatus, and the bones of the middle ear of mammals.

2. Blind spot in humans, night vision.

3. Localization of specific taste receptors on tongue.

4. Localization of receptors in skin for touch, pressure, pain, temperature.

Topics for Discussion and Library Research

1. Comparison of structures of various receptors in skin.

2. Structure of eye and ear

3. Size limitations on eye and ear

4. The hair cell. See articles by: Franklin, D. 1984. Crafting sound from silence. Science NEws 126: 252-254; Hudspeth, A. 1983. Hair cells of the inner ear. Sci. Am., January.

ESSAY QUESTIONS

Obj 7   1. Describe or diagram the human eye and explain how light energy is captured and transduced by the eye into nerve impulses.

obj 6   2. Describe or diagram the human ear and explain how sound energy is captured and transduced by the ear into nerve impulses.

obj 2   3. List and describe three vertebrate mechanoreceptors which utilize the hair cell, and explain how the hair cell functions.

        4. Describe how the brain knows (a) the color of your sweater; (b) that you are sitting down, (c) the loudness of a musical tone; and (d) that a 1% sugar solution is less sweet than a 10% sugar solution.

obj 3   5. Does a generator potential always generate an action potential? Explain, and describe how a receptor potential is produced.

        6. Distinguish between the members of the following paired terms: rod/cone; middle ear/inner ear; receptor potential/ action potential; exteroceptor/interoceptor; and, vestibular apparatus/organ of Corti.

        7. Compare the means by which lower invertebrates and vertebrates sense and respond to environmental stimuli.

8. Describe the stimulus and provide one example for each of the following receptors: mechanoreceptor, photoreceptor, thermo-receptor, chemoreceptor, and electroreceptors.

9. Describe the sequence of events leading to the depolarization of sensory neurons whose axons make up the optic nerve.

CHAPTER 41 MUSCLES AND SKELETONS

Outline

I. Properties of Muscle Tissue
II. Types of Muscle
    A. Smooth Muscle
    B. Cardiac Muscle
    C. Skeletal Muscle
III. Muscle Contraction
    A. Sliding Filament Mechanism
    B. Control of Contraction
    C. Graded Response of an Intact Muscle
    D. Tetanus and Fatigue
IV. How Muscles and Skeletons Interact
    A. Antagonistic Muscles
    B. Reciprocal Inhibition
V. The Vertebrate Skeleton
    A. Joints in the Vertebrate Skeleton
VI. Connective Tissue
    A. Cartilage
    B. Bone
    C. Nonskeletal Functions of Bone

Essay: Electric Fish

Summary

Most of the movement in an animal's body is due to the action of its muscles. A muscle works by shortening so that it pulls against the skeleton or against adjacent tissues.

The contractile mechanism of muscle has been most extensively studied in vertebrate skeletal muscle, although it appears to be similar in all muscle. In the presence of ATP and calcium ions, filaments of the protein myosin form crossbridges to filaments of the protein actin; the swiveling of the cross-bridges moves the filaments past each other shortening the distance between the Z lines of the sarcomere. ATP supplies the energy needed for contraction.

Contraction of a muscle is stimulated by depolarization of the muscle membrane, usually induced by a neurotransmitter released from the axon of a motor neuron or, in the case of smooth or cardiac muscle, by hormones in the body fluids. The arrangement of the neurons that innervate a muscle allows for graded muscle contractions. Smooth, sustained contractions are brought about by trains of closely spaced stimuli from the motor neuron.

The vertebrate skeleton supports the body, protects internal organs, and permits the locomotory muscles to move the animal. Pairs of antagonistic muscles move bones back and forth at joints. Reciprocal inhibition prevents simultaneous strong contraction by both members of a pair of antagonistic muscles.

The vertebrate skeleton is made up of relatively flexible cartilage and harder bone. Cavities in the bone are filled with marrow, which stores fat or forms cells. Tiny spaces in the bony material itself house single cells that deposit calcium. Bones store or release calcium to maintain equilibrium with the body fluids. Hormones maintain a fine tuning of the blood/bone calcium balance.

Objectives

1. Name the three types of muscles found in the vertebrate body, and give the location, innervation, and cellular organization of each type.

2. Describe how electrical impulses are conducted through the heart.

3. Draw a sarcomere from a skeletal myofibril and describe the interaction of its thick and thin filaments during muscular contraction.

4. List the four proteins involved in contraction of skeletal muscle, explain the role of each, and state how calcium and ATP interact with these proteins in the process of contraction.

5. Describe the sequence of events that takes place (on a chemical and cellular level) from the time a nerve impulse arrives at the neuromuscular junction in a skeletal muscle, through contraction of the muscle fiber, to subsequent relaxation of the fiber.

6. Explain why rigor mortis occurs in muscles after death.

7. Explain how the strength and duration of contraction of a skeletal muscle are controlled.

8. Define tetanus and fatigue in skeletal muscle.

9. List three functions of the skeleton as a whole and two non-skeletal functions of the bones.

10. Describe the structure of the bone.

11. Describe the role of bone in maintaining the body's circulating calcium supply and the two ways in which bone releases calcium into the bloodstream.

12. Define cartilage, ligament, tendon, joint, flexor, extensor, antagonistic muscles, and reciprocal inhibition.

What's new or expanded in the third edition

The introduction has been expanded and includes information on the relation between contraction and work, and between the muscle and skeletal systems.

Figures 41-7 and 41-8 (page 819) show the anatomy of a vertebrate skeletal muscle, and an electron micrograph of a resting skeletal muscle respectively. Figure 41-9 (page 820) now includes an electron micrograph of three sarcomeres for comparison with the diagram illustrating the sliding filament model of muscle contraction. Figure 41-11 (page 822) diagrammatically shows a model of how the energy of ATP hydrolysis is involved in sliding the filaments in muscle contraction. Figure 41-19 (page 829) is a series of x-ray photographs showing the growth of a human hand from age 2 to adult.

In section 41-F, the subsection on bone includes new material on bone formation and growth, and the factors affecting these processes. Osteoporosis is also discussed.

SUGGESTIONS FOR LECTURE PREPARATION AND ENRICHMENT

Ancillaries

The anatomy of a vertebrate skeletal muscle is shown in overhead transparency (OHT) #128 (page 819). The human skeleton is illustrated in OHT #129 (page 827).

<u>Correlative Laboratory Exercise</u>

Topic 28 Muscles and Skeletons

In this exercise students examine prepared slides of compact bone, cartilage, striated muscle, smooth muscle, and cardiac muscle. To study muscle physiology the gastrocnemius muscle and sciatic nerve are removed from a pithed frog. The muscle is hooked up to a kymograph which records the responses of muscle when it is stimulated under different conditions.

<u>Supplemental Readings</u>

Bodanis, DAvid. 1985. Muscles from the inside out. Science Digest 93(4): 40, April. An account of the molecules providing energy for muscle contraction.

Caplan, A. 1984. Cartilage. Sci. Am., October.

Carofoli, Ernesto and John Penniston. 1985. The calcium signal. Sci. Am., November.

<u>Carolina Biology Reader</u>

Harrington, W. F. 1981. <u>Muscle Contraction</u>.

Curtin, M. E. 1984. Biological replacement parts. Biotechnology 2(2): 131-137.

Edelson, Richard and Joseph Fink. 1985. The immunologic function of the skin. Scientific American, June.

Frances, M. and D. Duksin. 1983. Heritable disorders of collagen metabolism. TIBS 8:231-234.

Hellerstein, DAvid. 1985. The promise of artificial skin. Science Digest 93(9): 62-65, September.

McNeill, A.R. 1984. Walking and running. American Scientist 72(4) 348-354.

Miller, A. 1982. Molecular packing in collagen fibrils. TIBS 7:13-18.

Roses, A. 1984. Molecular genetics of myotonic and Duchenne muscular dystrophies. TIBS 7: 190-194.

Schommer, N. 1984. Standing straight (scoliosis). Discover 5 (12): 62-68.

Silberner, Joanne. 1985. "Touch-me-nots." Science News 127:58-59, January 26. An examination of the causes of epidermolysis bullosa, a disease characterized by a lack of cohesion between or within the layers of the skin.

Witkowski, J. and G. E. Jones, 1981. Duchenne muscular dystrophy--a membrane abnormality? TIBS 6:IX-XII.

<u>Films</u>

<u>Muscle</u> (Biology Today Series) (CRM, L972, 30 min.) Describes structure and function of three types of muscles, mechanics, and biochemistry of muscle contraction.

<u>The Skin as a Sense Organ</u> (IFB, 1976, 12 min.) Examines, microscopically, the sensory receptors of the skin, such as those for touch, pain, pressure, heat and cold.

Student Activities

1. Using their own bodies have them demonstrate the action of flexors, extensors, abductors, adductors, sphinctors, dilators, pronators, supinators, levators, and depressors.

2. Have them identify bones in their body.

3. As a homework assignment have them list and describe the action of muscles involved in using the hand for writing.

Ideas for Demonstrations

1. Muscle twitch. Isolate the gastrocnemius muscle and sciatic nerve from a frog leg and attach to a kymograph apparatus. Effects on the muscle of various stimuli applied to the nerve can be demonstrated.

2. Vertebrate skeletons. These are available from biological supply companies.

3. Exoskeletons of insects. These can sometimes be found attached to trees at the end of the summer.

4. Skin and derivatives. Slides of histological preparations of skin from various parts of the body can be set up. Skin derivatives such as hair, feathers, nails, claws, fish scales, hooves, antlers, can be shown.

5. Electron micrographs of muscle fibers, myofibrils and myofilaments.

Topics for Discussion and Library Research

1. Factors affecting strength of muscle contraction

2. Biochemistry of muscle contraction

3. Sliding filament theory of muscle contraction

4. Depolarization of muscle cell membrane

5. Organization and histology of bone

6. Scoliosis. See articles by: Schommer, N. 1984. "Standing straight." Discover 5(12):63-68; Trotter, R. 1979. "Preventing the curve." Science News 115: 298.

7. Artificial skin. See articles by/in: Curtin, M. 1984. "Biological replacement parts." Biotechnology, February; Science News. 1981. "Skin for the wounds of burns." Vol. 119:4.

8. Derivatives of skin-hair, feathers, nails, claws, hoofs

9. Structure and function relationship in bone

10. Relationship of form and function for bones. Why does a leg bone have the shape of an I? For more information see book by: Williams, C. 1981. Origins of Form. Architectural Book Publishing Co., New York, Chapter 2 "Struts and Ties," the section on forces that determine form and Chapter 4 "The Forms of Function". See also McMahon, T. and J. T. Bonner, 1983. On Size and Life. Scientific American Books, Inc., New York Chapters 1 "The Natural History of Size," 2 "Proportions and Size," and 4 "The Biology of Dimensions."

ESSAY QUESTIONS

1. List the three types of muscles found in vertebrates and describe three characteristics of each.

2. Discuss the roles of the cellular membrane, the endoplasmic reticulum and mitochondria in muscular contraction.

3. What four events in the contraction process would not occur if ATP were unavailable?

4. Distinguish between the members of the following paired terms: exoskeleton/endoskeleton/hydrostatic skeleton; epidermis/dermis; chitin/keratin; axial/appendicular; and, skeletal/cardiac/smooth muscles.

5. Describe two similarities and two differences between the exoskeleton and endoskeleton.

6. If muscle cells are functionally organized into a motor unit, then how is it possible to make graded movements (i.e. lift five, ten, 15 pounds with one hand)and to thread a needle? Explain.

7. Why does a person pant and sweat after a session of aerobic dancing?

8. Describe one function of the skin. Discuss how the structure of the skin is correlated with this function.

9. Give an example of a cartilage bone and a membrane bone and discuss one similarity and one basic difference regarding these two types of bones.

10. Compare the three types of muscle regarding organization of contractile fibrils, the number of nuclei per cell, location in the body, and function.

CHAPTER 42   ANIMAL HORMONES AND CHEMICAL REGULATION

Outline:

    I.   Hormones
          A. Feedback Control of Secretion
          B. Chemistry of Hormones
          C. Action of Hormones and other Messengers
          D. Receptors and Second Messengers
   II.   Hormonal and Nervous Control
          A. Fight or Flight
          B. The Hypothalmus-Pituitary Connection
  III.   Local Chemical Messengers
          A. Prostaglandins
          B. Neurotransmitters as Local Messengers
          C. Growth factors
   IV.   Hormones and Animal Life
          A. Environmental Control of Reproduction
    V.   Biological Rhythms
          A. Circadian Rhythms
          B. Annual Rhythms
          C. Biological Clocks
   VI.   Pheromones

       Essay: Our Daily Spread

Summary

     The nervous and hormonal systems carry messages that travel be-
tween an animal's cells and coordinate their activities. Hormones may
act on a wide range of cells over a long time; neurons affect specific
cells briefly.

     Animals have three types of chemical messengers: proteinaceous and
lipid hormones, produced by endocrine glands or secretory neurons, and
carried all over the body by the blood; local hormones such as histamine,
growth factors, neuroregulators, and prostaglandins, which usually act
near the cells that produce them; and pheromones, which carry information between different individuals of the same species.

     Each hormone or chemical messenger has only limited effects because
receptors for a hormone are restricted to specific target cells.
Many hormones activate production of cyclic AMP, which acts as a second
messenger inside the cell, triggering the cell's preset response to the
hormone.   The receptor system and secondary messenger for calcium-
linked messengers have also been identified.

     Hormone secretion is usually controlled by negative feedback in
response to some disturbance in the body or to the level of another
hormone in the blood. Hormones and the nervous system often interact
with one another to control both long and short term aspects of an
animal's response to a stimulus. The interaction between the two
systems occurs mainly in the hypothalamus. The hypothalamus receives
nervous signals from the sense organs via the rest of the brain, and
also detects changes in the blood chemistry. It initiates appropriate
responses by way of the nervous system and by way of the pituitary gland,
which releases hormones responsible for the maintenance and activity
of many of the body's other endocrine glands.

     Hormones are involved both in homeostatic mechanisms within the
body and in many of an animal's responses to its environment. Reproductive cycles and color changes may be mediated by hormones.

Animals have endogenous biological clocks that tell them the time
of day; the clocks may be driven to some extent by environmental
stimuli. Although it is clear that an animal's clock interacts with
its nervous and endocrine mechanisms, how the clock works is still not
understood.

Objectives

1. State what a hormone is, and explain how hormones may be identified
   and their action determined.

2. Describe the process of feedback control of hormone production, and
   diagram it using a specific example.

3. Describe what is known about how hormones affect their target organs.

4. Explain the differences in the control exerted by the nervous
   system and by the endocrine system.

5. Describe the role of cyclic AMP in a cell's response to a hormone.

6. Describe the "fight or flight" response, listing six physiological
   changes that occur, and explaining the role of the nervous and
   endocrine systems in the response; discuss the roles played by
   epinephrine and nor-epinephrine and the response.

7. Describe the relationship between the hypothalamus and both the
   anterior and the posterior pituitary gland.

8. Explain the role of the pituitary gland in the body's endocrine
   system.

9. Give two examples each of hormonal responses that maintain homeostasis and of hormonal responses to conditions in the animal's
   environment.

10. Define circadian rhythm, give an example of a biological clock and
    tell what is known about their properties.

11. Define pheromone, and explain the biological roles of pheromones.

What's new or expanded in the third edition

The subsection on receptors and second messengers in section 42-A
has been expanded and includes information on the calcium ion messenger
system and the effects of the binding of calcium ions to phospholipid
membrane receptors.

In section 42-C local chemical messengers, such as prostaglandins,
neurotransmitters, and growth factors are discussed. The actions and
target tissues of these local messengers are described.

The focus of the essay, Our Daily Spread is human circadian
rhythms. The effects and consequences of these rhythms of the body's
physiological functioning, and on a person's daily activities are
discussed.

SUGGESTIONS FOR LECTURE PREPARATION AND ENRICHMENT

Ancillaries

The interrelation of the hypothalamus and pituitary gland is
illustrated in overhead transparency #130 (page 845). Ask students
to compare the interrelation between the hypothalamus and both the

anterior and posterior parts of the pituitary. Ask them to describe the effect on hormone production and/or release by the pituitary if the hypophyseal portal vein were severed.

Supplemental Readings

Benjamin, M., Muyskens, J., and P. Saenger, 1984. Short children anxious parents: Is growth hormone the answer? The Hastings Center Report 14(2):5-9, April.

Berridge, Michael. 1985. The molecular basis of communication within the cell. Sci. Am., October.

Cantin, Marc and Jacques Genest. 1986. The heart as an endocrine gland. Sci. Am., February.

Carmichael, Stephen and Hans Winkler. 1985. The adrenal chromaffin cell. Scientific American, August. An examination of the cells which manufacture, store and secrete a complex mixture of hormones, the most important being adrenalin.

Carolina Biology Readers

Blake, C. 1984. The Pituitary Gland

Palmer, J.D. 1983. Human Biological Rhythms

Palmer, J. D. 1984. Biological Rhythms and Living Clocks

Randle, P. and R. Denton. 1982. Hormones and Cell Metabolism

Wigglesworth, V.B. 1983. Insect Hormones

Fellman, Bruce. 1985. A clockwork gland. Science 85 6(4): 76-81. A discussion of the pineal gland, the hormones it produces and their effects on biorhythms and reproduction.

Franklin, D. 1984. Growing up short. Science News 125:92-81.

Kasol, C. and J. Perez-Polo. 1982. Circadian rhythms in vitro. TIBS 7:59-61.

Miller, Julie Ann. 1985. Eye to (third) Eye. (The Pineal Gland) Science News 128:298-299, Nov. 9.

Restak, R. 1984. Master clock of the brain and body. Science Digest 92(11):54-61.

Snyder, Solomon. 1985. The molecular basis of communication between cells. Sci. Am., October.

Films

Biological Rhythms: Studies in Chronobiology (EBEC, 1977, 22 min.) Examines biological rhythms in various organisms including crabs, humans and mice.

The Endocrine System (EBEC, 1981, 20 min.) Using animation introduces endocrine system including survey of major organs, interactions between hormones and receptors, and regulation.

What Time is Your Body? (TLV, 1975, 23 min.) Examines biological rhythms and how they are studied.

Ideas for Demonstrations

1. Effects of hormones. Using an excised frog heart demonstrate the effects of adrenalin, and acetylcholine on its activity.

Topics for Discussion and Library Research

1. Endocrine disorders

2. Prostaglandins

3. Invertebrate hormones

4. Pheromones

5. Relationship of hypothalamus, anterior lobe of the pituitary, and endocrine gland.

6. Receptors on target calls

7. Hypothalamus. See article by: Restak, R. 1984. Master clock of the brain and body. Science Digest 92 (11):54-61.

8. Circadian rhythms. See July/August, 1983 issue of Bioscience which contains several articles on biological clocks; Kasol, C. and J.R. Perez-Polo. 1982. "Circadian rhythms in vitro." TIBS 7(2):59-61. Hilts, P. 1980. "The clock within." Science 80, December.

ESSAY QUESTIONS

obj 7   1. If the portal system between the hypothalamus and the anterior lobe of the pituitary were severed, what effect would this have on the production of (a) thyroxine, (b) epinephrine, (c) cortisol, (d) oxytocin, (e) prolactin?

obj 7   2. If the connection between the hypothalamus and the posterior lobe of the pituitary were severed, what effect would this have on the body's ability to regulate (a) the concentration of glucose, (b) the production of thyroxine, (c) fluid balance, (d) the production of growth hormone?

3. Distinguish between the members of the following paired terms: TSH/TSH_releasing hormone; adrenal medulla/adrenal cortex;, insulin/glucagon; calcitonin/parathyroid hormone; prostaglandin/pheromone.

4. The nervous and endocrine systems are the principal regulatory systems in the body. Describe four differences between the two systems and explain the advantages of having two systems rather than one.

obj 7   5. Describe the relationship between the hypothalamus, and both the anterior and posterior lobes of the pituitary.

6. In what way is the action of a protein hormone different from that of a steroid hormone? In what way are the two types of hormones similar?

7. Describe or diagram the mechanism involved in regulating the production of glucocorticoid hormones.

obj 6   8. Describe the interaction between the adrenal medulla and adrenal cortex in a stressful situation.

obj 1   9. How could you experimentally distinguish an exocrine gland and an endocrine gland?

obj 1 10. Describe three general characteristics of hormones.

11. A diabetic woman is chased by an angry dog. She becomes very
upset and lapses into a coma. Explain the physiological
events leading to the coma.

12. A person with myxedema, a disease stemming from a thyroid
disorder, can be cured by ingesting extracts of thyroid glands,
while a person with diabetes mellitus must receive intramuscular
injections of insulin. Explain the difference in method of
treatment.

13. Discuss the role of hormones in insect development.

CHAPTER 43   BEHAVIOR

Outline

I. Proximate and Ultimate Causes
II. Genes and Environment
III. Instinct Versus Learning
    A. Adaptive Value of Learned and Innate Behaviors
IV. The Neurophysiological Basis of Behavior
    A. Vertebrate Reflexes and Behavior
    B. Stereotypical Behavior
    C. Sign Stimuli
    D. Drive and Motivation
V. Learning
VI. Development of Behavior
VII. Territorial Behavior
VIII. Conflict and Courtship
IX. Migration and Homing
X. Social Behavior (Sociobiology)
    A Communication
    B. Honeybee Societies
    C. Vertebrate Societies

Summary

The genes that an animal inherits determine the range of behavior patterns it can develop. In addition, most behavior patterns, innate or learned, will not develop normally if an animal is not exposed to the appropriate environmental conditions.

The proximate reason that an animal behaves in a particular way is that it has been exposed to environmental stimuli that induce the behavior pattern while it was in the appropriate physiological state. Ultimately, behavior patterns that must be produced perfectly at the first exposure to the stimulus are usually innate. Learning requires time and energy and is reserved for behavior that must be flexible in meeting local or changing conditions. Many behavior patterns, both innate and learned, become programmed into the nervous system. These stereotyped behaviors may be triggered by sign stimuli and controlled by a small number of neurons with minimal sensory feedback.

Animals are always exposed to a variety of stimuli, which may or may not evoke a response. Action or inaction is determined by factors such as the animal's physiological state and its conscious or unconscious hierarchical ranking of stimuli. Conflict behavior, frequently visible in courtship and territorial displays, is one possible outcome of mutually exclusive behavioral tendencies.

Most animals seldom or never cooperate with other members of their own species, but true societies have evolved in some species of insects and of vertebrates. A society usually consists of genetically related individuals. Communication between individuals is most highly developed in social animals. Vertebrate societies are characterized by hierarchies that determine an individual's access to limited resources. The society provides an individual with protection, and its members cooperate in various aspects of their lives.

Objectives

1. Explain the theoretical difference between innate and learned behavior, and give two examples of each.

2. Explain what is meant by stereotyped behavior, and give two examples. Describe the neurophysiological characteristics of stereotyped behavior.

3. List the selective advantages of innate and learned behavior and stereotyped behavior.

4. Describe what is meant by the filtering and summation of stimuli.

5. Give examples of motivation or drive, sign stimuli, and supernormal stimuli.

6. Explain and give examples of how the reticular formation and hypothalamus of the brain influence motivation for behavior patterns.

7. Describe the characteristics of territorial behavior, and give an example of such behavior.

8. Describe conflict behavior, and explain why it is thought to have played a role in the evolution of threat displays and courtship behavior.

9. Distinguish between habituation conditioning, trial and error learning, insight learning, and imprinting.

10. Summarize what is known about migration and homing in animals.

11. Compare and contrast the societies of honeybees and vertebrates.

12. Describe the functions of threat and appeasement behavior in the maintenance of a dominance hierarchy.

SUGGESTIONS FOR LECTURE PREPARATION AND ENRICHMENT

Correlative Laboratory Exercise

Topic 29 Behavior

In this exercise students observe various types of behaviors including kinesis in sow bugs, different kinds of taxes in fruit flies, schooling in fish and agonistic behavior in Siamese fighting fish.

Supplemental Readings

Alper, Joseph. 1985. The roots of morality. Science 85 6(2):70-76, March. Examines development of moral behavior in children, and speculates on role of empathy.

Batra, S. 1984. Solitary Bees. Sci. Am., February.

Bennett, Dawn. 1985. Making sense of animal sounds. Science News 127: 314-317, May 18.

Bioscience: October, 1983 issue devoted to Behavioral Endocrinology

Blaustein, Andrew and Richard O'Hara. 1986. Kin recognition in tadpoles. Sci. Am., January.

Bower, Bruce. 1986. Skinner Boxing. Science News 129: 92-94, Feb. 8.

Carolina Biology Readers

Goodenough, J. 1984. Animal Communication

Ferrara, Jerry, 1985. Prairie home companions. National Wildlife 23(3) 48-53, April/May. Story about prairie dogs and their society and effects on other animals.

Ghiglieri, Michael. 1985. The social ecology of chimpanzees. Scientific American, June.

Gwinner, Eberhard. 1986. Internal rhythms in bird migration. Sci. Am., April.

Huber, Franz and John Thorsen. 1985. Cricket auditory behavior. Sci. Am., December.

Miller, J. 1984. The mating game. Science NEws 126: 232-235.

Scheller, R. and R. Axel. 1984. How genes control an innate behavior. Sci. Am., March.

Stacey, P. and W. Koenig. 1984. Cooperative breeding in the acorn woodpecker. Sci. Am., August.

Tangley, L. 1984. Sea turtle migration: Smelling their way back home? Bioscience 34(6):353-356, June.

Veit, P. 1982. Gorilla society. Natural History 91(3):48-59.

Wilson, E. O. 1985. Altruism and ants. Discover 6(8):46-49.

Films

Animal Communication (TLV, 1971, 30 min.) Explores variety of signals, such as sound, color and scent used in animal communication.

Animal Migration (BFA, 1977, 12 min.) Covers animal migration of several species of birds, insects, fish and mammals and includes discussion of theories of motivation, orientation, and navigation techniques.

Bird Brain: The Mystery of Bird Migration (TLV, 1976, 27 min.)

Cry Wolf! (TLV, 1976, 15 min.) Covers various aspects of the timber wolf's lifestyle including social relationships, feeding habits, reproduction and growth.

Ideas for Demonstrations

1. Audiovisual material illustrating animal societies and animal communication.

2. Fish schooling

3. Taxes in animals

4. Tropisms in plants

5. Behavior exhibited by male Siamese fighting fish.

Topics for Discussion and Library Research

1. Innate and learned behavior.

2. Bird migration

3. Imprinting

4. Sociobiology

5. Comparison of insect and vertebrate societies

6. Courtship behavior

7. Vertebrate societies. See articles by: Veit, P. 1982, "Gorilla Society." Natural History 91(3):48-59; Luft, J. and J. Altman. 1982. "Mother baboon." Natural History 91(9):30-39; Sunquist, M. and F. 1983. "The tiger singles scene." Natural History 92(1): 44-51; Partridge, B. 1982. "Structure and function of fish schools." Sci. Am., June.

8. Territoriality

ESSAY QUESTIONS

obj 1, 9   1. A man feeds his dog canned dog food at the same time each day. As the man opens the can with an electric opener, he calls the dog. The dog is then fed. Eventually the dog comes whenever it hears the opener. Why?

obj 9   2. In the nursery rhyme "Mary had a little lamb," the lamb follows Mary everywhere. Suggest a biological explanation for the lamb's behavior.

obj 5   3. What is a sign stimulus? What two conditions must be met for the sign stimulus to have an effect?

4. Distinguish between the members of the following paired terms: innate behavior/learned behavior; habituation/imprinting; appeasement/dominance; imprinting/insight; latency/summation.

5. Discuss why behavior is considered an adaptation. Give examples to support your statements.

obj 1   6. How could you distinguish between an innate behavior and a learned behavior?

7. Distinguish between the members of the following paired terms: society/aggregation; pheromone/hormone; home range/territory.

obj 12   8. What is a dominance hierarchy? Describe two advantages of one.

obj 11   9. Societal living could be described as a compromise situation. Describe two advantages and two disadvantages of being a member of a society.

10. Discuss how pheromones are used as a mode of chemical communication.

11. Give three reasons why courtship is necessary for reproduction.

12. Distinguish between reflexes and instinct, and give an example of each.

obj 5   13. Explain why sign stimuli are biologically functional and adaptive.

obj 11   14. Cite three ways in which vertebrate societies differ from insect societies.

CHAPTER 44   STRUCTURE AND GROWTH OF VASCULAR PLANTS

Outline

Summary

A vascular plant grows in one place, making its own food and competing with other plants for the basic resources of sunlight, water, and
minerals. The plant body consists of roots, stems, and leaves, all containing vascular tissue which conducts water, minerals, and food rapidly
from one part of the body to another. This body plan is adapted to
obtaining water and sunlight efficiently. The plant's indeterminate
growth pattern enables it to produce new organs throughout its life; if
it is successful in exploiting its environment, it can continue to grow
and obtain more and more of the resources it needs.

A seed consists of a protective covering, food supply, and plant
embryo with a rudimentary root, stem, and leaves.

Early in life, all cells of the plant can divide. Later most cells
mature, specialize, and lose their capacity to divide. Cells that retain the ability to divide are found in meristems at specific-locations
in the plant body.

Primary growth is principally growth in length and production of
new root and shoot branches. The tips of stems and roots grow longer
through the activity of apical meristems. Stem branches arise from
axillary buds, located at leaf nodes. An axillary meristem thus
becomes the apical meristem of a new branch. Lateral roots arise
from the pericycle tissue inside the mature primary root. This produces
a new apical meristem of a branch root.

Secondary growth is growth in girth by production of secondary
tissues. Vascular cambium, a lateral meristem, produces secondary
vascular tissues. Secondary xylem adds strength and increases the
capacity for conducting water to the leaves; secondary phloem replaces
primary phloem, or older secondary phloem, destroyed as interior tissues grow. The cork cambium, another later meristem produces secondary
protective tissue (cork) which replaces the epidermis that has been
destroyed by expansion of the tissues interior to it.

Monocotyledons and dicotyledons differ in the number of cotyledons
found in the embryo (one versus two, respectively) in the arrangement
of vascular tissue often especially in the stems and leaves, and in the
arrangement of leaf stomata. In addition, very few monocots have

secondary growth, whereas secondary growth is found even in some annual dicots.

Objectives

1. Explain how the basic structure (roots, stems, and leaves) and growth patterns of vascular plants are adapted to their functions.

2. List four functions of the root system and compare the advantages and disadvantages of fibrous roots versus taproots in accomplishing these functions.

3. List the functions of the stem and leaves of a vascular plant.

4. List or point out the parts of a bean seed and of a kernel of corn; state the function or future fate of each part.

5. State what is meant by primary and secondary growth in vascular plants, and describe the sequence of events in primary growth of a root or stem and in secondary growth of a stem.

6. Define the term meristem, and state the role of each of the following in the growth of a plant; apical meristem, zone of elongation, zone of maturation; root cap, terminal or apical bud, axillary bud, intercalary meristem, pericycle, vascular cambium, cork cambium.

7. Sketch a cross section of a leaf and of a mature primary root and stem, and label the following structures if present: epidermis, root hairs, cuticle, stomata, guard cells, endodermis, pericycle, vascular tissue, pith, cortex, collenchyma, palisade and spongy mesophyll, air spaces; give the function of each part.

8. Distinguish between simple and compound leaves, and between alternate opposite, and whorled arrangements of leaves; define node and internode.

9. Briefly contrast the way branches are formed in roots versus stems.

10. Explain how to tell the age of a twig, and identify the external features of a twig, including; bud scales, lateral or axillary bud, terminal bud, leaf scars, bud scale scars, lenticels.

11. List or recognize differences in structure and growth between monocotyledons and dicotyledons.

What's new or expanded in the third edition

Figure 44-16 (page 888) shows scanning electron micrographs of structural defenses on the leaves of certain plants. A longitudinal section of a wheat embryo as seen through the light microscope is shown in Figure 44-25.

SUGGESTIONS FOR LECTURE PREPARATION AND ENRICHMENT

Ancillaries

A diagram of a growing root tip is shown in overhead transparency (OHT) #131 (page 881). Ask students to list areas of actively dividing cells. Tissues of a mature primary root are shown in OHT #132 (page 882). Have students identify tissues in root. In OHT #133 (page 885) the tissues of a mature primary stem of a dicot are shown. Ask students to compare the stem with a root.

The tissues in a leaf can be seen in OHT #134 (page 889). Ask students to compare with tissues found in stems and roots and to relate the structure of the leaf to its functions.

The external features of a twig are shown in OHT #135 (page 892). The structure of a monocot seed is illustrated in OHT #136 (page 894). Ask students to identify the fate of each part of the seed and/or embryo.

Correlative Laboratory Exercises

Topic 30   Plant Structure and Function

Through direct observation of living and prepared specimens using microscopes and through experimentation students learn about the structures and functions of leaves, stems, and roots. E.g., transpiration is demonstrated using a branch from a living plant. Cross sections of monocot and dicot leaves, and roots are viewed using the microscope.

Supplemental Readings

Carolina Biology Readers:

Heath, O.V.S. 1981. Stomata (2/E)

Wooding, F. 1978. Phloem (2/E)

Shigo, Alex. 1985. Compartmentalization of decay in trees. Scientific American, April. An examination of how trees cope with infection or injury.

Student Activities

Have students collect specimens of monocot and dicot leaves, stems and roots. On the basis of their observations have them generate a table summarizing information about leaf vein pattern, type of root, presence of secondary growth, size, etc.

Ideas for Demonstrations

1. Cross sections through trunks of trees to illustrate heartwood, sapwood, growth rings, bark, etc.

2. Microscope slides with stained cross sections through leaves, stems, roots from monocots, dicots and gymnosperms.

3. Microscope slides of cross sections through leaves of hydrophytes, mesophytes and xerophytes, C_4 plants, CAM plants to illustrate differences in placement of stomata organization of vascular tissue, thickness of cuticle, arrangement of cells of mesophyll, etc.

4. Specimens of leaves to show patterns of veins

5. Germinating radish seeds to show root hairs

6. Slides (2" x 2") illustrating parts of plants

7. Zones of growing root. Use soybean sprouts with roots about one and a half inches long. On the root use a thread dipped in ink to mark ten one millimeter intervals from the tip. Carefully secure the sprout to a glass plate which is placed upright in a glass beaker containing a wet paper towel. Cover and leave undisturbed. Check growth at one day intervals.

8. Microscope slides of longitudinal sections through root tips and terminal buds.

Topics for Discussion and Library Research

      1.   Comparison of structures of leaves from different plants

      2.   Comparison of roots and stems from monocots and dicots

ESSAY QUESTIONS

obj 3   1.   Describe the structure of a typical leaf, and how it reflects a compromise between the plant's need for CO_2 and its need to conserve water.

obj 7   2.   Draw diagram representing a cross section through a leaf root, or stem, and on your figure label the surface tissues, fundamental tissues and vascular tissues, in addition to the component parts.

obj 5   3.   In what ways is the upward growth of the tree or outward growth of a branch different from the tree's lateral growth? Describe the specialized tissues and growth processes accounting for the differences.

obj 5   4.   Where are living cells located in a mature tree?

obj 6   5.   Distinguish between the members of the following paired terms: endosperm/cotyledon; plumule/radicle; zone of elongation/maturation/division; apical dominance/apical meristem; and, protoderm/provascular cylinder.

obj 7   6.   What two cell layers are present in roots but not in stems? What are their functions and why are they necessary for the plant's survival?

obj 3   7.   You are looking at cross sections through leaves from plants living in three different environments: temperate, watery, and desert-like. Unfortunately, the labels are missing so you don't know the names of the leaves, but based on your observations you are confident about identifying each. Leaf #1 has stomata on the upper surface and very large intercellular air spaces throughout the mesophyll. Leaf #2 has a very thick cuticle over the epidermis and the stomata are sunk into crypts lined by hair on the undersurface on the leaf. Leaf #3 has a columnar palisade mesophyll layer and a spongy mesophyll with an average amount of intercellular air spaces. The stomata are on the undersurface of the leaf. Identify which leaf is associated with which environment and explain your answer.

obj 11   8.   Describe three differences between monocot and dicot stems.

obj 6   9.   Distinguish between the members of the following paired terms: meristematic/permanent tissue; primary meristem/secondary meristem; surface tissue/fundamental tissue; xylem/phloem; and parenchyma/pith.

220

CHAPTER 45   TRANSPORT IN VASCULAR PLANTS

Outline

Summary

     The conducting cells of xylem and phloem show structural adapta-
tions for their rapid transport of substances. Tracheids, found in
the xylem of both gymnosperms and angiosperms, have pits in their
walls, while vessel cells, found only in angiosperms, may have their
end walls perforated or absent. Conducting cells in the phloem have
sieve areas in their cell walls; the sieve tube members of angiosperms
have well-developed sieve plates in their end walls.

     In xylem, a series of dead, tubular cells conducts water and dis-
solved minerals upward from the roots to the leaves, flowers, and
fruits. Pressure pushes sap up a short distance in the stems of some
plants. In most cases, however, much more upward movement results from
the transpiration of water vapor from the leaves, which in turn creates
a pull from the top of the water column; water follows a water potential
gradient from the soil, through the roots and stem, and out through
the leaves. The cohesion of water and its adhesion to the walls of the
xylem conducting cells is crucial to the transport of water to the top
of tall trees.   Transpiration is controlled to some extent by the
opening and closing of the stomata.

     Phloem transport is still poorly understood. The conducting cells
of phloem form continuous tubes filled with living cytoplasm. The mass
flow theory of phloem transport suggests that a high concentration of
sugar in the phloem cells of leaves creates a low osmotic potential;
water moves into the phloem from the xylem. This uptake of water creates
hydrostatic pressure, which pushes the phloem contents along from one
cell to the next. Phloem distributes sugars, amino acids, hormones, and
some minerals to the roots, fruits, and growing buds.

     An understanding of transport mechanisms in plants, as well as a
knowledge of the pathways followed by various substances within the plant
body, is important in the planning of fertilization, pest control, and
hormone treatment programs in modern agriculture.

Objectives

1. Name the two conducting tissues in plants, give their functions,
    and list substances transported by each.

2. Describe a girdling experiment, and explain what it shows about the
    functions of conducting tissues in trees.

3. Sketch or describe the adaptations of tracheids, vessel elements sieve cells, and sieve tube elements that suit these cells for their roles in transport.

4. Outline the path by which water moves from the soil through a plant to the atmosphere, referring, as appropriate, to the molecular mechanisms and plant structures that make this movement possible.

5. Explain how (1) the root pressure mechanism and (2) the transpiration pull mechanism of xylem transport are believed to work; describe experiments that support each of these theories, and discuss the relative importance of each mechanism in the total conduction that takes place in the xylem of plants; predict how changes in the environment would affect each process.

6. Explain how the structure of the leaf represents a compromise between the plant's need for water and its need to obtain sunlight and carbon dioxide.

7. Sketch two guard cells and the stoma between them and describe in a few sentences the mechanism by which guard cells open the stomatal pore; state the advantage to the plant of the ability to open and close the stomata.

8. Sketch or identify the following features of a woody stem; annual ring, spring wood, summer wood, heartwood, sapwood, secondary xylem, bark, rays, and the approximate position in which you would find vascular cambium and secondary phloem. State the functions of each of these features.

9. Explain how transport in phloem may occur by mass flow in the living plant, and predict how changing relevant conditions will modify the transport occurring in the phloem.

What's new or expanded in the third edition

Figure 45-15 (page 907) illustrates the movement of the "transpiration stream" through a plant. Figures 45-17 (page 910) shows the cell types found in the phloem of angiosperms.

SUGGESTIONS FOR LECTURE PREPARATION AND ENRICHMENT (Also see chapters 44-48)

Ancillaries

Overhead transparency #137 (page 899) shows the arrangement of xylem and phloem in various plant parts. Ask students to point out similarities. OHT #138 (page 901) shows the structure of secondary xylem, and OHT #139 (page 907) illustrates the movement of the "transpiration stream" through the plant's body. Ask students to discuss how xylem is adapted to its functioning as a transport system.

Correlative Laboratory Exercise (see Chapter 44)

Supplemental Readings (also see other chapters in this unit)

Uribe, E. and U. Lutge. 1984. Solute transport and life functions of plants. American Scientist 72(6): 567-574.

Ideas for Demonstrations

1. Cross sections through trunks of trees to show heartwood, sapwood, growth rings, bark, etc.

2. Specimens of leaves to show patterns of venation.

Topics for Discussion and Library Research

1. Mechanism of guard cell control over stomatal opening and closing

2. Mechanisms of transporting materials through phloem and xylem

3. Compromises in plant to meet requirements for photosynthesis yet prevent water loss.

ESSAY QUESTIONS

1. What special adaptations for maximizing photosynthesis while minimizing water loss are present in desert plants?

obj 7 2. What is the function of the guard cells and how do they perform this function?

obj 9 3. Explain how the products of photosynthesis get from the leaves to the root and other parts of the plant.

obj 4 4. What properties of water are important for the uptake and movement of water and solute through the roots and the plant's body?

obj 2 5. Why is girdling eventually lethal for a tree?

obj 5, 9 6. Describe two similarities in the transport of water and of solutes (products of photosynthesis) throughout the plant's body.

7. Distinguish between the members of the following paired terms: tracheid/vessel element; sieve cell/companion cell; sapwood/heartwood; root pressure/guttation; sclereid/plasmodesmata.

CHAPTER 46   SOIL, ROOTS, AND PLANT NUTRITION

Outline

I.   Nutritional Requirements of Plants
II.   Soil
      A. The Soil Solution
      B. Soil Treatments
III. Absorption by the Roots
IV.   Nutritional Adaptations
      A. Mycorrhizae
      B. Carnivorous Plants
      C. Some Other Nutritional Adaptations
V.   Food Storage

ESSAY: Soil Erosion

Summary

     The minerals required by plants are divided into two groups, macro-
nutrients and micronutrients, depending on the quantities needed. Some
nutrients are needed only by plants with special adaptations. The nu-
trional requirements of plants are difficult to assess because different
concentrations or proportions of nutrients, and the ability of plants
to use one nutrient in place of another, may change the outcome of experiments.

     Nutrient deficiencies of plants may result from lack of nutrients
in the soil, a soil pH which makes nutrients unavailable to plants or
unfavorable proportions of one nutrient to another.

     Plants take up most of the water, and minerals they need from the
soil. The nature of the soil is determined mostly by the type of
rock from which it is derived; rainfall, organic matter, soil organisms,
and oxygen are also important in determining the soil quality. All of
these components of soil interact and affect the availability of water
and minerals in the soil solution. Agricultural practices such as
tilling, fertilizing, or liming can improve the soil to meet the needs
of crop plants.

     The soil solution moves freely into the outer region of the apoplast,
between the cells of the root cortex. The endodermis forms a living
selective barrier between the soil solution and the rest of the plant.
The symplast of the root absorbs minerals and moves them through the
endodermis to the xylem, which transports them to the rest of the plant.
Water enters the symplast by osmosis, following the minerals accumulated
mostly by active transport.

     Plants growing in nutrient-poor conditions may show a variety of
adaptations that enable them to acquire a better supply of nutrients.
Many trees form mycorrhizal associations with soil fungi, enabling them
to take advantage of the fungus's superior ability to absorb nutrients
and convert them into usable form; carnivorous plants are adapted to capturing the nutrients in the bodies of insects; epiphytes capture rain
or dust from the air with their leaves; mistletopes tap the vascular
systems of their host plants for water and nutrients.

     Plants can store both organic and inorganic nutrients for future
use in growth or reproduction.

Objectives

1. List or recognize the macronutrient and micronutrient elements needed
    by plants.

2. List and explain several reasons why a plant might show symptoms of nutrient deficiency.

3. List the main components of soil, and explain their role in plant nutrition.

4. Discuss several ways in which minerals become available to plants and ways in which they become unavailable.

5. Define the terms apoplast, symplast, epidermis, root hair, cortex, endodermis, and Casparian strip, and explain the role of each in the uptake of water and minerals by the plant.

6. Define the terms mycorrhiza and epiphyte; explain the nutritional adaptations found in each.

7. Explain how carnivorous plants are adapted to capturing animals and why these adaptations are advantageous to such plants.

SUGGESTIONS FOR LECTURE PREPARATIONS AND ENRICHMENT (Also see chapters 44-48)

Ancillaries

In overhead transparency #140 (page 926) the uptake of substances from the soil by the roots is illustrated. Ask students to compare the symplast and aopolast routes, and to discuss regulation of water flow into the plant's body.

Correlative Laboratory Exercise

Project B Plant Nutrition

This probject requires students to perform experiments, to make observations over a period of time, to record data, and then write a laboratory report according to directions presented in Appendix A of the laboratory manual.

Supplemental Readings

Abelson, Philip. 1985. Plant-fungal symbiosis. Science 229: 617, 16 August.

Films

Carnivorous Plants (NGS, 1974, 12 min.) Covers relationship between form and function and physiological aspects of capturing food.

Student Activities

Have students bring in soil samples. Have them examine the soil chemically to determine the pH and the presence of mineral ions. Also have them look for small organisms using a hand lens or microscope. Ask them to make generalizations about the soil, its composition, chemical features, and the organisms living in it.

Ideas for Demonstrations

1. Effect of nutrient deficiency. Grow plants hydroponically in specially prepared medium deficient in one or more nutrients.

2. Samples of different types of soils

3. Fertilizer. Labels showing composition of fertilizer.

4. Soil sample to show microorganisms and other animals involved
    in ecochemical cycling of nutrients. Place some soil on
    sterile agar plate to reveal microorganisms.

Topics for Discussion and Library Research

1. Application of fertilizers and soil enhancers--benefits and
    problems.

2. Soil formation resulting from action of microorganisms

3. Macro-and micronutrients and effects of deficiencies

4. Growing plants hydroponically

5. Genetic engineering to improve plants.

6. Carnivorous plants

7. Plant-fungal symbiosis

ESSAY QUESTIONS

1. The tissues of the root cortex sometimes contain air spaces, some
    mangroves possess pneumatophores on their roots and cypress trees
    have protruding "knees." Overwatering can kill a house plant just
    as underwatering can. What do these features indicate about roots
    and their metabolism?

2. List the components of an ideal soil and briefly describe the
    necessity for each component.

3. Suppose it were possible to create a soil that had all the
    necessary macro and micronutrients but in which no organisms could
    live, except plants. What effect would this sterile soil have on
    plant's growth and development over a long period of time?

CHAPTER 47 REPRODUCTION IN FLOWERING PLANTS

Summary

     Plants flower in response to specific cues that differ greatly
among the various species, and each of the quarter-million species of
angiosperms has its own distinctive flower structure. In all this
diversity, however, we can find a basic unity in the structure and
function of flowers.

     A flower is an abbreviated shoot, in which all of the cells dif-
ferentiate into parts of the flower stalk or its modified leaves,
the flower parts. Certain cells divide by meiosis, and the resulting
haploid cells develop into the haploid male gametophytes, the pollen
grains, and female gametophytes, embryo sacs. Double fertilization
forms a zygote and an endosperm mother cell. The endosperm mother
call divides and develops into the endosperm, which absorbs food from
the parent plant, and the zygote soon develops into the embryo of a new
plant. The parent plant, besides contributing food to the new embryo
also protects it and its food supply in a seed coat derived from the
wall of the ovule, which in turn is surrounded by the fruit, derived
from the wall of the ovary, another parental structure.

     Much of the evolutionary success of flowering plants is undoubtedly
due to the fact that they have coevolved with animals, and many species
rely on animals, rather than on wind and water, to pollinate their flowers
and disperse their seeds. They devote considerable energy to attracting
animals that will perform these services appropriately, and they
are rewarded by pollination that is efficient and specific and by seed
dispersal that distributes even large seeds over a relatively wide
range.

     Many seeds enter a period of dormancy following their release
from the parent plant. Eventually the seed germinates in response to
environmental cues and establishes itself as a new plant.

     Sexual reproduction results in individuals with new combinations
of genetic characters. In many cases these combinations are less
desirable than those of the parents, from either the point of view of
the human or the plant. Many plants have some means of asexual reproduction, which perpetuates a particularly favorable combination of
genes unchanged, in addition to, or instead of, sexual reproduction.
Humans propagate many plants vegetatively by artificial means such as
rooting and grafting.

Objectives

1. Define the following terms, and use them properly: sepal, petal,

stamen, anther, carpel, pistil, style, stigma, ovary, ovule, pollen, pollen tube, embryo sac, endosperm, seed coat, cotyledon, fruit, pollination, fertilization, germination.

2. Name the parts of a flower, and state the role of each in reproduction of the plant.

3. Explain what is meant by the terms megaspore, microspore, and male and female gametophytes, and tell where each is found in flowering plants.

4. Explain how pollination and fertilization take place in flowering plants.

5. Name the three main parts of a seed, and explain how each develops.

6. List four factors that may be required for germination of a seed.

7. Explain the advantage of asexual, or vegetative, reproduction to a plant, and list some ways in which plants may propagate asexually explain why humans use vegetative propagation of plants, and name some ways in which plants can be propagated by human manipulation.

What's new or expanded in the third edition

Figures 47-12 (page 942) shows the early development of an embryo in a series of illustrations and photographs done at different stages. Figures 47-13 and 47-14 (page 943) show two different kinds of flowers and the fruits which develop from the ovaries. Figure 47-16 (page 944) illustrate two examples of wind dispersal of seeds and fruits. Figure 47-18 (page 945) is a scanning election micrograph of a goosegrass flower on which two fruits are developing. The fruits have hooks which assist in their dispersal. Figure 47-19 (page 846) shows shell formation from the female part of the flower of the peanut plant.

SUGGESTIONS FOR LECTURE PREPARATION AND ENRICHMENT (Also see chapters 44-48)

Ancillaries

The events from pollination to fertilization are shown in overhead transparency (OHT) # 141 (page 940). The early development of an embryo is illustrated in OHT #142 (page 942). Ask students to identify the fate of each part of the embryo and the ovary.

Correlative Laboratory Exercises

Topic 17 Higher Plants (parts)

Topic 31 Plant Reproduction

The section of gymnosperms in Topic 17 could be assigned. In this exercise students examine staminate and ovulate pine cones and pollen from a conifer.

In Topic 31 students examine the reproductive structures of different kinds of flowers for purposes of comparison. They also dissect fruits and seeds and observe each using a microscope. Seedlings growing under different conditions are examined to see the effects of light and hormones on their development.

Supplemental Readings

Albersheim, Peter and Alan Darvill. 1985. Oligosaccharins. Scientific American, September. An examination of oligosaccharins found in plant cell wall and their involvement as regulatory molecules in development, growth, reproduction and defense against disease.

Bennett, D. 1985. Scarlet gilia: Flowering chameleon. Science News 127:69, February 2. A short report about a plant that undergoes color shifting in its flowers to cater to the color preferences of a changing population of pollinators.

Block, Eric. 1985. The chemistry of garlic and onions. Scientific American, March. Discussion of sulfur compounds found in garlic and onions, and their medicinal properties.

Carolina Biology REaders:

Hendricks, S.B. 1980. Phytochrome and Plant Growth

Hillman, W. S. 1979. Photoperiodism in Plants and Animals

Meeuse, B.J.D. 1984. Pollination

Northcote, D. 1980. Differentiation in Higher Plants (2/E)

Miller, Julie, 1985. Somaclonal variation. Science News 128 120-121. August 24. A discussion of the benefits and practical uses of somaclonal variation, spontaneous genetic changes occurring in plant cells grown in vitro.

Student Activities

1. Have students make a collection of various kinds of seeds, and for each seed describe the method of dispersal.

2. Have students make a collection of different types of fruits or bring them to class. Ask students whether or not a tomato is a fruit or a vegetable.

3. Have students observe the germination of radish, mung bean or soybean seeds and then write a short essay describing the process.

Ideas for Demonstrations

1. Slides (2"x2") showing development of embryo in gymnosperms and angiosperm seeds. Available from biological supply companies.

2. Fruits, cones and seeds. Set up a display.

3. Flowers. Set up a display of flowers.

4. Germination of pollen. Sprinkle some pollen from a flower onto a drop of 18% sucrose on a microscope slide. Add a coverslip and examine after one hour. The growth of the pollen tube can be seen.

5. Artificial and naturally occurring asexual reproduction. Show cuttings of stems growing roots and a strawberry geranium or spider plant.

6. Seed germination. Place radish seeds on wet filter paper in a covered petri dish, or soak bean seeds overnight then place on wet filter paper in covered petri dish, or soak bean seeds and place around the edge in a covered glass beaker containing wet vermiculite.

7. Embryo in the seed. Soak bean, pea and corn seeds overnight. Split seeds to reveal embryo.

Topics for Discussion and Library Research

1. Comparison of embryos and seeds from monocots and dicots

2. Strategies of pollination. Coevolution of flowers and animal pollinators; relation of floral structure and method of pollination.

3. Artificial propagation

4. Fruits as means of seed dispersal. See articles by Stiles, E. 1984. "Fruit for all seasons." Natural History. 94(8): 42-53; Martin, W. K. 1973. "Seeds; the carriers of life." Natural History 82 (6):38-59.

5. Form/structure of fruit or seed correlated with method of dispersal.

6. Coevolution of plants and animals-hazards and benfits. See article in Science News, Vol. 112: 138, 1977, entitled "Don't coevolve with a Dodo."

ESSAY QUESTIONS

obj 5 1. Describe three differences between monocot and dicot seeds.

obj 6 2. The seeds of Lodge Pole pines germinate only after charring by fire. Suggest why this might be advantageous for this type of tree.

obj 7 3. Describe one advantage and one disadvantage for both asexual and sexual reproduction.

obj 4 4. Discuss three ways in which animals aid in the propagation of plants.

5. Distinguish between the members of the following paired terms: true fruit/accessory fruit; germinative nuclei/polar nuclei; perfect flower/imperfect flower; staminate/ovulate; and, megagametophyte/microgametophyte.

6. Compare the structure of the seed in both angiosperms and gymnosperms regarding origin and nature of nutritive tissue, appearance of the embryo, and derivation of coverings, if any.

obj 4 7. Describe two differences between angiosperms and gymnosperms concerning the events of pollination and fertilization.

obj 2 8. What three floral features might reflect adaptations to a particular method of pollination?

obj 7 9. Discuss the adaptive advantages and disadvantages of both sexual and asexual reproduction.

obj 7 10. Describe two methods of asexual reproduction in plants.

obj 2 11. Describe a typical flower and identify its parts, using appropriate scientific terminology.

obj 4 12. Describe the production of pollen and preparation of ovules in angiosperms, and summarize the process of fertilization as it occurs in such plants.

13. Outline the adaptive significance of fruits and summarize the processes by which they are formed.

CHAPTER 48   REGULATION AND RESPONSE IN PLANTS

Outline

I.   Plant Hormones
II. Auxin
   A. Apical Dominance
III. Gibberellins
IV. Cytokinins
V.   Abscisic Acid
VI. Ethylene
   A. Senescence
VII. Oligosaccharins
VIII. Response to the Environment
   A. Photoperiodic Control of Flowering
   B. Phytochrome
   C. Phytochrome and the Growth of Seeds
IX. Electrical Response of Plants

Summary

Five groups of plant hormones are known. Auxin, gibberellins, and cytokinins are generally growth-promoting, abscisic acid is often growth inhibiting, and ethylene promotes ripening of fruits and senescence of leaves. Probably no single effect can be attributed to any one of these hormones alone; rather, the interactions of these hormones govern a plant's growth, so that different parts, such as the leaves and roots remain in anatomical and physiological balance with each other. Hormones are also involved in a plant's response to its environment. They enable the plant to respond appropriately to the direction of light, gravity, or prevailing winds, and to changes in daylength and temperature that signal changes in the seasons.

How a plant responds to a particular hormone depends on the tissue that receives the hormone, the concentration of the hormones, the presence and concentration of other hormones, the age and physiological state of the tissue and environmental factors such as temperature. light or photoperiod.   Since plant hormones can change a cell's synthesis of RNA or proteins, a plant's response to a particular hormone is greatly influenced by its genetic makeup, and different species, varieties, or even individual plants will respond to the same treatment in different ways. This has given rise to a large body of conflicting experimental information that defies neat generalizations. However, we are learning that these five kinds of plant hormones play a rich repertoire of roles in the diverse genetic and environmental settings of plants.

Although hormones mediate most plant responses to environmental stimuli, some plants respond to some stimuli by means of electrical action potentials.

Objectives

1. Name or recognize the five kinds of plant hormones (auxins, gibberellins, cytokinins, abscisic acid, and ethylene); list parts of the plant where each is synthesized; and discuss the general biochemical roles of plant hormones.

2. Explain the role of auxin in phototropism and apical dominance, and list or recognize at least two other roles of auxin.

3. List or recognize two main effects each for gibberellins, cytokinins, abscisic acid, ethylene, and phytochrome.

4. List five or more factors that may influence how a plant responds to application of a particular hormone.

5. Explain what is meant by the terms short-day, long-day and day-neutral plants; give the evidence that photoperiodic flowering responses are controlled by changes in phytochrome.

What's new or expanded in the third edition

The effect of light on the coleoptile of oat seedlings is shown in figure 48-2 (page 954). Section 48-H contains new material on factors in the environment affecting the production and distribution of hormones and on tropisms. Also included is a discussion of the effect of phytochrome on seed germination and growth of the young embryo. In section 48-I electrical responses of plants and the mechanisms responsible for these responses are described.

Figures 48-16 (page 964) and 48-21 (page 968) illustrates respectively geotropism and phototropism in plants, and an electrical response in the Mimosa plant in the closing of the leaves.

SUGGESTIONS FOR LECTURE PREPARATION AND ENRICHMENT (also see chapters 44-47)

Correlative Laboratory Exercise

Project A Plant Hormones

This project requires students to perform experiments, to make observations over a period of time, to record data, and then write a laboratory report according to directions presented in Appendix A of the laboratory manual.

In Project A students study the effect of auxin on the growth of lateral buds by excission and substitution method of experimentation. The project requires a minimum of two weeks for completion.

Supplemental Readings

Adams, D. O. and S. FaYang. 1981. Ethylene the gaseous hormone: mechanism and regulation of biosynthesis. TIBS 6(6):161-164.

Albersheim, Peter and Alan Danville. 1985. Oligosaccharins. Sci. Am., September.

Films

Green Machine, Parts I, II (TLV, 1978, 49 min.) Examines photosynthesis flowering, tropisms, hormones, and early embryonic development in plants.

Ideas for Demonstrations

1. Effects of hormones in plants--Reproduce Darwin's and Went's experiments with auxin.

2. Tropisms. Suspend a bean seedling in horizontal position in the dark. Mark the hypocotyl and radicle at one millimeter intervals. Examine after one-two days. Rotate seedling 90° and examine after one to two days. This experiment is designed to demonstrate geotropism in root and shoot.

3. Phototropism. Cover a jar with dark paper or paint except for a narrow vertical slit down one side. Invert the jar over a bean seedling attached to a cork with a large insect pin. Have moist cotton on top of the cork. Shine light through the slit and examine the shoot. (These tropism demonstrations are adapted from: Beckett, B.S. 1976. Biology: A Modern Introduction. Oxford Univ. Press, Oxford, England, Chapter 11.

4. Rapid plant responses. Use Venus fly traps which can be purchased from local garden centers or ordered from biological supply companies.

Topics for Discussion and Library Research

1. Plant tropisms--ecological, physiological, evolutionary perspective.

2. Comparison of plant hormones--chemical derivation and effects on growth and developmental processes.

3. Photoperiodism--evolutionary perspective.

4. Phytochrome--role in leaf abscission, photoperiodism, seed germination, pigment formation in ripening fruit.

ESSAY QUESTIONS

1. Auxins affect indirectly the plasticity of the cell wall along the longitudinal axis. When light is shined on one side of a stem tip, auxins accumulate on the opposite (shaded) side of the tip. Water entry into cells is eventually restricted by the cell wall. Using these three facts, explain
   a) the fact that elongation ceases when the stem tip of a coleoptile is removed;
   b) the fact that once a stem is curved, it remains so permanently, and,
   c) the fact that shading the tip does not prevent elongation

2. Placing a ripe apple near a bunch of bananas hastens the ripening process. Explain why and what you could do to delay the ripening of the bananas.

3. Describe the roles of phytochrome and florigen in the control of flowering.

4. The label on a bottle of plant hormone was accidentally destroyed. You perform a series of controlled experiments to determine its identity. You obtain the following results:
   a) the hormone does not cause elongation or bolting;
   b) it is not an amino acid derivative
   c) it slows down the process of aging and leaf sensecence and abscission
   d) when applied along with a proportionately higher concentration of auxin, to a callus, roots form.
   Based on your observation, you conclude that the unknown hormone is _____. Explain your answer.

6. Plant hormones are neither very large nor very small molecules. Explain the significance of this.

CHAPTER 49   THE BIOSPHERE

Summary

     Two main patterns can be seen in a worldwide survey of the distri-
btuion of organisms:

     1.   Different areas of the world are inhabited by different species
          of plants and animals.

     2.   Terrestrial communities in different parts of the world can be
          divided into a fairly small number of categories, or biomes,
          on the basis of vegetational structure. These biomes are world-
          wide and are not restricted to single continents.

     While the actual species found in an area depend on the area's
evolutionary history, the biome depends mainly upon rainfall, temperature, and soil type. Similar changes in biomes occur with increasing
altitude and increasing latitude.

     The richest biome is tropical rain forest, where high temperatures
and rainfall permit plants to grow throughout the year. Most of the
plant and animal life is found in the canopy among the broad evergreen
leaves of trees. Decomposition is rapid and the soil is poor; at any
one time most of the nutrients are locked in the bodies of living
organisms.

     In temperate deciduous forest the soil is much richer in nutrients
because the trees lose their leaves in the fall, creating a litter layer
that decomposes only slowly. Deciduous forest is an important biome of
North America and Eurasia in areas with warm, moist summers and cold
winters.

     Where the soil is poor or fire is frequent, temperate evergreen
forest replaces temperate deciduous forest. Further north,both are
replaced by taiga, a biome dominated by gymnosperms adapted to growing
in sparse soil and to resisting extreme cold and water loss in winter.

The taiga stretches around the world in the subarctic region.

North of the taiga and above the timberline lie the tundra and alpine grasslands, dominated by cold-resistant woody shrubs or by sedges and grasses, depending on the soil type and the amount of moisture in the soil.

Grasslands receive more rainfall than deserts and less than deciduous forests. Grasslands occur in the drier interiors of continents in the Americas, Asia and Australia. Shrubs and trees may be scattered among the tall grasses. Grasslands are replaced by semi-desert scrub or by small woody shrubs in areas where there is too little water for grasses to grow.

Deserts have hot days, cold nights, and very little rainfall. Their plant life is mainly annuals with very short growing seasons and succulent perennials adapted to the low rainfall.

The distribution of marine organisms is determined by water temperature and by the availability of light and minerals. The littoral and sublittoral zones are well supplied with both light and minerals and support dense communities of life. Coral reefs are specialized sublittoral communities found only in tropical waters. In the open ocean, the availability of light for photosynthesis restricts plankton to the upper layers of the water, but scarcity of nutrients in these layers may limit the numbers of organisms. Larger nektonic organisms are found primarily where their planktonic food is abundant. Dead organisms from the surface layers of the ocean supply food for a community of bacteria and other organisms that live on the deep sea floor.

Although the climate of an area determines the composition of its climax community, patches of the area are always in various stages of ecological succession as a result of disturbances of the climax community. Organisms adapted to living in the unstable communities of early successional stages have effective dispersal mechanisms and perpetuate themselves by continuously colonizing new habitats as they arise in the surrounding climax community.

The limits of their dispersal ability prevent most organisms from colonizing all possible habitats, and so in different parts of the world we find similar communities inhabited by similar species, which have arisen by the convergent evolution of similar adaptations to similar environments.

Objectives

1. Describe the major patterns of air movement in the lower atmosphere, and explain how they affect precipitation at different latitudes.

2. List the three main factors that determine the distribution of biomes.

3. Describe why gradients of vegetation are similar with increasing altitude and increasing latitude.

4. State the conditions under which you would expect to find each of the following biomes, and list the type(s) of plants characteristic of each; tropical rain forest, tropical seasonal forest, tropical savanna, tropical thornwood, desert, temperate forest, temperate woodland, temperate shrubland, temperate grassland, taiga, tundra.

5. List three different types of littoral habitat and the types of organisms found in each.

6. Describe the conditions under which a coral reef may be formed.

235

7. List the main factors that determine the distribution of life in the oceans; describe the ocean surface and ocean bottom communities, and tell how organisms in these communities acquire food.

8. Define the following: community, climax community, fugitive species.

9. Distinguish between primary and secondary succession, outline an example of each, and explain why succession occurs; comment on the extent to which succession leads to a single type of climax community in a given biome.

10. List three examples of major community types that are maintained by fire. Account for the survival of plants in communities where fires occur frequently.

11. Explain why widely separated areas with similar climate usually contain similar species.

12. Define the term "convergent evolution" and give examples.

What's new or expanded in the third edition

In section 49-A soil is discussed as a factor influencing the distribution of animals. Section 49-C has been expanded and includes new material on the process of desertification which is occurring in many parts of the world. The wetlands of the Gulf of Mexico are shown in Figure 49-20 (page 990). In figure 49-28 (page 998) two photographs illustrate the growth pattern of the longleaf pine.

SUGGESTIONS FOR LECTURE PREPARATION AND ENRICHMENT (Also see chapter 52)

Ancillaries

A simplified scheme of the major terrestrial biomes is illustrated in overhead transparency (OHT) #143 (page 974). The biomes are arranged along ecoclines of increasing aridity at different latitudes, illustrating the effects of moisture and temperature on the distribution of plants. In OHT #144 (page 976) the pattern of distribution of the major terrestrial biomes on the Earth's surface is shown. Ask students to point out similarities in distribution of biomes at latitudes above and below the equator.

Supplemental Readings

Billings, William. 1981. Plants in high places. Natural History 90 (10):82-88. October. Discussion of adaptations of plants living on the arctic tundra and high equatorial mountains.

Brownlee, S. 1984. Bizarre beasts of the abyss. Discover 5(7): 71-74.

Brownlee, Shannon. 1985. Death by degrees. Discover 6(1):44-45, January. An account of investigations to determine if death of coral reefs in the Pacific can be attributed to the warm waters of El Nino.

Cloud, P. 1983. Biosphere. Sci. Am., September.

Knutson, Roger. 1981. Flowers that make heat while the sun shines. Natural History 90(10):75-81, October. An examination of plants that act as solar collectors thereby providing warming ovens to accelerate development of pollen and seeds.

Lewin, Roger. 1985. Plant communities resist climatic change. Science 228:165-166, April 12.

Macmahon, J.A. 1982. Mount St. Helens revisited. Natural History 91 (5):14-26.

Morse, Douglass, 1985. Milkweeds and their visitors. Scientific American, July.

Wilson, Edward O. 1985. Outcry from a world of wounds. Discover 6 (6):64-66, June. The author raises concerns about the relentless destruction of tropical rain forests.

Ideas for Demonstrations

1. Slides (2"x2") showing features of major biomes

Topics for Discussion and Library Research

1. Comparison of aquatic ecosystems and biomes

2. Terrestrial biomes

3. Effects of humans on the biome's stability, fragility, ability to withstand stress.

4. CAM plants and adaptations of plants to desert environment

ESSAY QUESTIONS

1. Distinguish between the members of the following paired terms: chapparal/savanna; sublittoral/littoral; tundra/taiga; and nekton/plankton; primary/secondary succession.

obj 4   2. List and describe the major features of four biomes.

3. Describe two similarities and two differences for aquatic and terrestrial habitats.

4. For each biome describe an adaptation of a plant or animal that increases the organism's chances for survival in the particular biome.

obj 9   5. Explain why gradients of vegetation are similar with increasing latitude and increasing altitude.

obj 2   6. Identify three factors that affect the distribution of plants.

CHAPTER 50 ECOSYSTEMS AND COMMUNITIES

<u>Outline</u>

<u>Summary</u>

An ecosystem consists of a community of organisms that are dependent on one another in various ways, plus their physical environment. Two of the most important factors determining the biomass and makeup of an ecosystem are its productivity and nutrient cycles. The productivity of an ecosystem is determined by the availability of light, water, and minerals for photosynthesis. Energy passes from one tropic level to another, with approximately 90% being lost at each step. In consequence, the biomass that an ecosystem can support at each successive trophic level declines rapidly, and energy flow is, for all intents and purposes, one-way.

Nutrients cycle through an ecosystem. They are taken in by organisms as inorganic substances and may remain as minerals or be incorporated into organic molecules. Nutrients may pass through the food web for a time, but eventually they are once again released into the environment as inorganic substances. An ecosystem may be very efficient at conserving and recycling its nutrients. The availability of nutrients often limits the productivity of an ecosystem.

Lakes are convenient ecosystems to study because their boundaries are clearly defined. The distribution of organisms in a lake is determined by the depth of the water and by the distribution of light and nutrients. The seasonal mixing of different layers of water is vital to the lake's nutrient cycling. Nutrient pollution may promote the growth of some organisms at the expense of others, leading to an imbalance that may destroy the character of the ecosystem. Thermal pollution may increase the metabolic rates of some organisms while making oxygen less available for respiration. It may also change the pattern of mixing in the lake so that oxygen and nutrients are not replenished on schedule.

Each community has a structure, determined by the distribution of organisms and by the height and shape of the plants. Community structure may change in response to seasonal, diurnal and tidal cycles. Species diversity is maintained by the ability of potentially competing species to subdivide limited resources (such as food) within habitats, and to specialize in using different habitats. Species diversity may also be maintained by predation, which can prevent one prey species from eliminating others by competition.

The study of islands shows that there is species turnover in communities, with new species moving in and resident species becoming locally extinct. The balance between immigration and extinction establishes an equilibrium number of species which varies from one community to another depending on the community's size, diversity of habitats, and distance from the source of colonists.

Objectives

1. Define the following words and use them in context; ecosystem, community, producer, (primary and secondary) consumer, herbivore, carnivore, decomposer, autotroph, heterotroph, food chain, food web, trophic level, biomass, productivity, eutrophication, oligotrophic.

2. Outline energy flow through an ecosystem and give rough estimates of the energy loss between adjacent trophic levels.

3. Define gross and net primary productivity, and discuss factors that affect them.

4. Describe simplified nutrient cycles for carbon, nitrogen, and a non-atmospheric element such as phosphorus, and point out the important differences between them.

5. Describe the structure of a lake ecosystem, and explain how thermal and nutrient pollution hasten eutrophication.

6. Describe what is meant by community structure, and give some examples of changes in community structure in space and time.

7. Explain how the species diversity of a community is affected by interspecific competition, predation, and the number and types of habitats it contains.

8. Define species turnover, and explain how species diversity may be affected by a community's area (size) and degree of isolation from similar communities.

What's new or expanded in the third edition

Section 50-D has been created and includes material on primary and secondary productivity. Figure 50-13 (page 1012) illustrates food and energy budgets for black swallowtail butterfly caterpillars, and deer.

Section 50-E has been expanded and includes new information on acid rain and its effects on ecosystems.

SUGGESTIONS FOR LECTURE PREPARATION AND ENRICHMENT (Also see chapters 48, 51, 52)

Ancillaries

In overhead transparency (OHT) #145 (page 1009) the general pattern of energy flow and nutrient cycling in an ecosystem is shown diagrammatically. Ask students to relate energy flow and nutrient cycling to food webs—and to comment on their roles in each of these processes. OHTs #146 (page 1015), #147 (1016) and # 148 (1017) show the carbon, nitrogen, and phosphorus cycles, respectively. Ask students to compare the three cycles regarding the reservoir for the element, the roles of producers, consumers and decomposers in cycling the element and the vulnerability of the cycle to human intervention.

Correlative Laboratory Exercise

Project C "The Pond Ecosystem"

In this exercise which requires at least three weeks, students study a microecosystem representing a pond. Microcosms are set up under various conditions using materials and water from a natural pond. Students follow the scientific method in performing their experiments on the microcosms.

Supplemental Readings

Carolina Biology Reader

Foin, T. 1984. Ecological Energetics

Eckholm, E. 1982. Human wants and misused lands. Natural History 91(6): 33-48.

Jungck, J. and R. Bybee. 1984. Rachel Carson. Human ecologist. American Biology Teacher 46(6):302-303.

Maranto, Gina. 1985. The creeping poison underground. Discover 6(2): 74-78 February. A disturbing account of the problems of pollution of aquifers as a result of the seepage of hazardous chemicals and metals located in land fills.

Maranto, Gina. 1985. A once and future desert. Discover 6(6):32-39, June. An explanation of the benefits and problems of irrigation such as salinization of the soil, in California's Central and Imperial Valleys.

Miller, Julie A. 1985. Diet for a blue planet. Science News 127: 220-222, April 6. A report about a new method of farming the sea.

Parker, Tom. 1985. In one day. National Wildlife 23(4):29, June/ July. Astonishing statistics about life in America.

Pimentel, D. and C. Edwards. 1982. Pesticides and ecosystems. Bioscience 32(7): 595-601, July/August.

Powledge, T. 1984. Biotechnology touches the forest. Biotechnology 2(9):763-772.

Raloff, J. 1984. Salt of the earth. Science News 126:298-301.

Raloff, J. 1984. Surviving salt. Science NEws 126:314-317.

Raloff, Janet. 1985. Dioxin: Is everyone contaminated? Science News 128:26-29, July 13.

Sitwell, N. 1984. Our trees are dying. Science Digest 92(9): 39-48.

Waggoner, P. 1984. Agriculture and carbon dioxide. American Scientist 72(2):179-184.

Woodwell, George, 1984. Broken eggshells. Science 84 5(9) 115-117. Examines rise and fall of DDT, the effects of DDT and toxins on the environment, and efforts being made to limit and control the use of broadly toxic substances.

Yulsman, Tom. 1985. The new threat from PCBs. Science Digest. 93(2): 66, February.

Films

Natural Selection: Evolution at Work (MG, 1981, 24 min.) Examines
  evolution at work using as examples the development of resistance
  to toxic substances by animals and plants.

Pond Life Food Web (NGS, 1976, 10 min.) Presents several food chains
  from plankton to carnivores in a freshwater ecosystem.

The Salt Marsh: A Question of Values (EBEC, 1975, 22 min.) Presents
  various ecological aspects of the salt marsh including nutrient
  cycling, food chains, balance between producers, consumers and
  decomposers, primary productivity and human impact on the marsh.

Tomorrow's Children (PE, 1971, 17 min.) Discusses the responsibility
  of humans for the use of the world's resources and the threats of
  continued population growth.

Student Activities

1. Have students collect articles about environmental problems
   from newspapers, news magazines, etc. These articles could
   provide material for class discussions.

2. Have students assay samples of water and/or air for the presence
   of pollutants, microorganisms, etc. Kits can be purchased from
   biological supply companies.

3. Have students either set up an ecosystem or draw a picture
   representing one. Have them identify the biotic and abiotic
   components, and draw a food chain/web characteristic of the
   ecosystem.

4. Comparison of ecosystems. Divide the class into groups of three
   to four students. Assign to each group a particular type
   of ecosystem or habitat that the group can visit at various
   times during the semester. a) Have each group mark off 4
   square meters of the habitat/ecosystem. Then have each group
   identify and record the abiotic characteristics and biotic
   components that are obvious. The identifications need not be
   specific. General names like shrub 1, shrub 2, tree 1, bush,
   etc. will suffice but the experience might contribute more to an
   understanding of ecosystems if specimens are correctly named.
   Approximate numbers of each type of organisms are also recorded.
   b) Have each group collect samples at different sites in the
   ecosystem/habitat and record the abiotic features and biotic
   components in each sample. The designated area should be
   observed and samples taken at least four different times during
   the semester.
   c) After all data is collected, have students record findings
   on a master chart. For each ecosystem/habitat have students
   make diagrams showing food chains/webs, mineral cycles, etc.
   d) For homework have students compare the different ecosystems
   as to amount of species diversity, type of food chain, kinds and
   numbers of organisms at each trophic level, stability over
   period of time, ability to withstand stress, etc.

Ideas for Demonstrations

1. Ecosystems. Set up various ecosytems representing a bog,
   desert, woodland, tropical forest. Fish tanks or covered glass
   jars can be used as containers. Plants can be purchased locally at
   garden centers or from biological supply companies.

3. Sample of polluted air, water.

<u>Topics for Discussion and Library Research</u>

1. Acid rain. See articles by: Maugh, T. 1984. "Acid rain's effects on people assessed." Science <u>226</u>:1408-1410; Sitwell, N. 1984. "Our trees are dying." Science Digest <u>92</u>(9):39-48; Hendry, G. 1981. "Acid rain and grey snow." Natural History <u>90</u>(2):58-65.

2. Pesticides and biocides. See article by: Pimental, D. and C. Edwards. 1982. "Pesticides and ecosystems." Bioscience <u>32</u>(7):595-601.

3. Air pollution. See article by: Kerr, R. 1984. "Carbon dioxide and the control of ice ages." Science <u>223</u>:1053-1054; Allen, R. 1970. "The impact of CO_2 on world climate." Environment, December.

4. Waste management. See articles by: Gould, S. and B. McTigne. 1983. "Radioactive waste." National Wildlife, April/May; Melosi, M. 1981. "The cleaning of America." Environment, October; White, P. 1983. "The fascinating world of trash." National Geographic <u>163</u>(4):425-457.

5. Comparison of aquatic ecosystems and biomes

6. Terrestrial biomes

7. Effects of humans on the biome's stability, fragility, ability to withstand stress.

8. Indoor pollutants

9. Pollutants. See article by: Grady, D. 1983. "The dioxin dilemma." Discover, May.

10. Ecosystem concept.

11. Food chains, webs, trophic levels, productivity

12. Factors affecting distribution of organisms

13. Community succession. See article by: MacMahon, J. 1982. "Mount St. Helens revisited. Natural History <u>91</u>(5)14-26.

14. Application of fertilizers and soil enhancers, effect on ecochemical cycles.

15. Human intervention in ecochemical cycles

16. Soil formation resulting from action of organisms

17. Macro-and micronutrients and effects of deficiency

18. Ecochemical cycles. Assign article by Leopold, A. 1970. "Odyssey of X." In <u>A Sand County Almanac.</u> Ballantine Books, New York. In this beautifully written article Leopold describes the cycling of X and Y from the time these minerals were released from the parent rock to the time they enter the sea and are no longer available. He also describes the effects of humans on the cycling of minerals.

<u>ESSAY QUESTIONS</u>

1. Distinguish between the members of the following paired terms: population/community/ecosystem; producers/consumers; gross productivity/net

productivity; detritus feeder/decomposer; and, food chain/food pyramid.

2. Why are there usually no more than four or five trophic levels in a food chain?

3. Compare energy flow and cycling of matter in an ecosystem. How are they similar? different?

4. In a terrestrial ecosystem, what is the function of (a) a maple tree or grass plant, (b) a deer or grasshopper, (c) an earthworm, (d) nitrogen fixing microorganism, (e) fungus, and (f) a mountain lion?

5. Compare the littoral zone and the intertidal zone regarding nature and diversity of organisms, productivity, and availability of nutrients.

6. In what two ways is succession occurring in aquatic communities different from that taking place on land?

7. From biome to biome the amount of decomposition of organic matter derived from animal wastes, dead organisms and plant litter varies. What factors may be responsible for these differences in the rate of decomposition? What are the consequences of these differing decomposition rates on mineral recycling, soil composition, and on types and numbers of plants and animals living in the biome?

8. Discuss the interrelationship of species diversity, complexity, and community stability in a biome or aquatic habitat of your choice.

9. Discuss the significance/importance of thermal stratification, a thermocline, nutrient stratification, and fall/spring turnovers for biotic components living in a large lake.

10. What property of water is associated with upwelling and turnover in aquatic habitats?

11. How does cultural eutrophication interfere with ecogeochemical cycling of minerals/nutrients?

12. Using a diagram outline the carbon cycle. Identify each type of organism, the role played by each, how carbon enters and leaves the cycle, and the reservoir for carbon.

13. Describe how atmospheric nitrogen becomes available to plants.

14. Describe the nitrogen cycle regarding origin of mineral, role of microorganisms, and uptake by plants.

15. Distinguish between the members of the following paired terms: macronutrient/micronutrient; fertilizer/lime; nitrate reductase/ nitrogenase; nitrifying bacteria/denitrifying bacteria; and symplast/ apoplast.

16. Discuss the statement "in nature, you can never do just one thing" from an ecological perspective.

17. Explain the effects of air pollution on climate and on the health of organisms.

18. Compare an agricultural community with a natural community regarding species diversity, stability, cycling of minerals, energy flow, and factors operating to control population growth.

19. You have been assigned the task of developing an ecologically ideal pesticide/insecticide. Describe at least three criteria that this pesticide must meet.

20. Distinguish between organic and industrial wastes. Describe three ways that water pollution affects ecosystems.

21. You are a member of a committee which was formed to establish criteria for selecting an ecologically suitable site for a landfill. Describe three criteria that this landfill has to meet.

22. Many people believe that the human population's food problems can be solved by harvesting the oceans. Explain why this is not a valid statement from an ecological perspective.

23. Comment on each of the following quotes which were taken from Miller, G. Tyler, Jr. 1985. Living in the Environment (4/E). Wadsworth Publ. Co. Inc., Belmont, CA, page 21.

    a) "Everything must go somewhere, or we can never really throw anything away."
    b) "Everything is connected to everything else, but how?"
    c) "Natural systems can take a lot of stress and abuse, but there are limits."
    d) "In nature, you can never do just one thing..."

24. The earth's resources are finite and self contained. The earth could be considered a spaceship, and compared with manned space labs such as Discovery, Challenger, etc. Develop five "earthmanship" rules designed to maintain the earth's vital life support systems and all organisms great and small.

CHAPTER 51   POPULATIONS

Outline

I.   Habitat and Niche
II. Population Growth
     A.   Factors Affecting Biotic Potential
     B.   Reproductive Strategies and Survivorship
III. Population Forecasts
IV. Carrying Capacity
V.   Regulation of Population Size
     A.   Dispersal and Habitat Patches
     B.   Intraspecific Competition
     C.   Interspecific Competition
     D.   Predation
VI. Winter Moth Caterpillars on English Oak Trees: A Case History
VII. Human Population
     A.   Declining Death Rates
     B.   The Demographic Transition
     C.   The Population Explosion
     D.   Starvation
     E.   The Efficiency of Agriculture
     F.   The Green Revolution
     G.   The Fossil Fuel Shortage
     H.   Pollution

Essay: Private Interest and Public Welfare

Summary

Populations of various species of organisms are the basic biological units of ecosystems. Given ideal environmental conditions, the number of individuals in a population increases goemetrically at its innate capacity for natural increase (r_m). This biotic potential is determined mainly by the age of the (female) parent at first reproduction, but is also influenced by the number of individuals produced at each reproductive event and by the parent's reproductive lifespan. A population seldom if ever, reproduces at its r_m ; environmental resistance slows population increase to r, the actual rate of increase (or decrease), even when the population is growing exponentially. Factors that limit population growth may be density-dependent, for example, predation or competition for resources, or density-independent, for example, bad weather. When growth of a population ceases, under the influence of one or more of these factors, the size of the population may fluctuate at approximately the carrying capacity of the environment for that species.

Survivorship curves for members of a population reflect the population's reproductive strategy. At the two extremes, the members of a population may produce many small offspring and give them no parental assistance in subsequent survival or may produce a few large offspring that are noursihed and trained by the parents. Survivorship curves are the basis for constructing life tables, useful in predicting future changes of population size.

Competition may play an important part in regulating the size of a population. In scramble competition, all members of a species have equal opportunity to share a resource: in times of abundance, the population may increase dramatically, but all may suffer when there is not enough of the resource to go around. In contest competition, the strongest or most aggressive members of a species acquire enough of the resource they need, ˈleaving the weaker members to survive if they can on what is left. If **two** species compete strongly for the same resource, the competitive exclusion principle states that one species will become extinct in the face of the superior competitive ability of the other. However, in both intraspecific and interspecific competition, specialization may partition a resource and allow it to be shared.

Predation is another factor that may cause high mortality in a population. Many specialized predators and parasites are known to keep their prey species at low density. Generalized predators tend to prey on the most abundant prey available until its level is considerably reduced (by predation or by other factors). Generalized predators have been shown to limit the population sizes of prey species in a few cases.

It is clear that many factors influence the size of a population, and that the main factor actually controlling population size may vary from population to population and from time to time for the same population.

The invention of agriculture permitted people to live in denser populations than were possible with a hunter-gatherer economy. The number of people in the world has grown even more rapidly in the last few hundred years as our understanding of nutrition and hygiene has increased. During the industrial revolution, human beings began to switch from wood to fossil fuels as the main source of energy, and this change has accelerated the population explosion. Today the population of many countries is growing faster than is their food production. Food production can be increased dramatically by the techniques of the "green revolution." Among the disadvantages of switching from traditional to modern agricultural techniques are that modern techniques widen the economic gap between small and large farmers, increase a nation's dependence on dwindling supplies of fossil fuel, and involve the use of pesticides and herbicides that may become dangerous pollutants.

The widespread use of fossil fuel and the population explosion are the main factors responsible for the pollution of air and water that threatens human health, especially in industrialized countries.

Objectives

1. Define population, habitat, niche, exponential growth, innate capacity for increase (biotic potential, r_m), actual rate of increase (r), logistic growth, carrying capacity (K), competition, and predation.

2. Draw and interpret any or all of the three main kinds of survivorship curves; relate the survivorship curve for a species to its reproductive strategy.

3. Explain what a life table is and why it is useful.

4. Distinguish between a stable population and a stationary population.

5. Distinguish between density-dependent and density-independent mortality factors; give an example of each.

6. Explain how a species that occupies short-lived patches of habitat could have a relatively constant overall population size over a wide area.

7. Describe the competitive exclusion principle, and discuss its validity.

8. Describe an example of successful biological control of a pest species.

9. Contrast the effects of specialized predation and generalized predation on population sizes of prey species, citing evidence to support your argument.

10. Write a paragraph summarizing your understanding of the factors that limit the sizes of populations and your assessment of their relative importance.

11. Explain why the agricultural revolution is believed to have been responsible for a dramatic increase in the human population.

12. Explain what is meant by the demographic transition, and give some reasons why it occurs, explain why the human population is still growing even though its birth rate is declining.

13. Contrast the efficiencies of subsistence and modern farms, and of vegetarianism and carnivory.

14. Describe the biological basis of the green revolution, and explain its impact on human society, economics, and ecology. Explain why the green revolution has fallen short of original expectations.

15. Explain how agriculture, use of fossil fuels, and the manufacture and use of artificial polymers contribute to pollution.

What's new or expanded in the third edition

Figure 51-4 (page 1035) shows the relationship between generation time and reproductive potential.

SUGGESTIONS FOR LECTURE PREPARATION AND ENRICHMENT (Also see chapters 49, 50, 52)

Ancillaries

Overhead transparency (OHT) #149 (page 1035) illustrates graphically the relationship between generation time and reproductive potential. In OHT #150 (page 1038) graphs of changes in the age structures of the populations of the United States and India over a 100 year period are shown. Ask students to identify factors affecting each population's age structure.

Supplemental Readings

Baker, A. 1983. Prey switching in a simple ecosystem. Sci. Am., December.

Bergerud, A. 1983. Virgin forests under fire. National Wildlife 24 (2):4-11, Feb./Mar.

Bower, Bruce. 1986. Population overload: Mice advice. Science News 129:346-347, May 31.

Carey, John. 1986. The changing face of America. National Wildlife 24(3):18-27. The Environmental Quality Index. 1986. National Wildlife 24(2):29-36, Feb./Mar.

Maranto, Gina. 1986. Are we close to the road's end? Discover 7(1): 28-50, Jan. Report on the effects of atmosphere CO_2 on the environment.

Stranahan, Susan. 1986. The nation tries to unfoul its nest. National Wildlife 24(3):28-35. Apr./May.

Tschirley, Fred. 1986. Dioxin. Sci. Am., February

Udall, James 1986. Losing our liquid assets. National Wildlife 24 (1):50-55, Dec./Jan.

Films

Ecological Realities: Natural Laws at Work (UC, 1976, 13 min.) Introduces basic ecological principles.

Life in Lost Creek: Freshwater Ecology (COR, 1978, 15 min.) Covers several aspects of ecology such as the ecological niche, food chain energetics.

Student Activities

1. Have students draw a typical population growth curve, representing the following situations: (a) no environmental resistance; (b) expansion of carrying capacity by technological means; (c) a population exceeding carrying capacity; (d) decreased biotic potential; (e) introduction of a competitor.

Topics for Discussion and Library Research

1. Characteristics of populations
2. Comparison of survival curves
3. Population cycles. See articles by: Bergerud, A. 1983. "Prey switching in a simple ecosystem." Sci. Am., December; Haber, G. 1980. "The balancing act of moose and wolves." Natural History 89(10): 39-51.

4. Interactions among organisms.

5. Biotic potential vs environmental resistance

ESSAY QUESTIONS

obj 11 1. Discuss the ecological effects of moving from a hunter-gatherer society to agricultural society.

obj 12 2. Why is the human population increasing in spite of a decreasing birth rate in many countries?

3. In 1840 Liebig stated what is known as the "law of the minimum." Describe the meaning of this law and how it has been expanded or modified as more information is accumulated about organisms and ecosystems.

obj 5 4. List four limiting factors and describe how each affects the organisms and ecosystems.

obj 1 5. Distinguish between a habitat and an ecological niche. Why can organisms live in the same habitat but not in the same niche?

obj 9 6. List and describe two types of positive interspecific interactions and explain why each is considered positive.

obj 9 7. List and describe two types of negative interspecific interactions and explain why each is considered negative.

obj 1 8. Why must the growth of populations be controlled and what factors are important in controlling growth?

9. Define population, community, ecosystem, and ecosphere, and indicate how each is related to the others.

10. Draw and label the phases of a typical population growth curve. On it indicate, using arrows, the point at which environmental resistance begins to have an effect, and the part reflecting the biotic potential of the population.

obj 9 10. Explain how destroying the balance between predator and prey can have a negative effect on the ecosystem.

CHAPTER 52   EVOLUTIONARY ECOLOGY

Summary

     Every organism has adaptations that permit it to survive in its
physical environment, to obtain nourishment, to avoid predation, and to
reproduce. Selective forces often exert their effects in conflicting
directions, and the adaptations seen in organisms represent compromises
of the amount of time, nutrients, and energy that can be allotted to
counteracting various pressures. In general, more energy will be
channeled into adaptations that meet stronger selective pressures.

     On the other hand, some adaptations may meet more than one selective
pressure: for example, territoriality may permit an animal to construct
or defend a suitable nest or burrow where it is protected from the
elements, to reserve a food supply free from competition from other
members of its species, to become familiar with good spots to hide or
to stand and fight off predators, and to raise a family in comparative
peace.

     Plants defend themselves from being consumed by herbivores in a num-
ber of different ways: by physical defenses such as spines, tough
cuticles, or silica; by nutrient exclusion; or by toxic chemicals. Plants
expend considerable energy in producing these defenses.

     Some adaptations preclude others; a cryptically colored animal
cannot become an active daytime predator; an animal cannot become a
Batesian mimic unless it can exploit a food source in the vicinity of
its model; and a species that obtains food by lurking and pouncing
cannot defend a large territory against others of its species without
becoming obvious to its prey.

     Some animals avoid being eaten by defending themselves, either
with weapons that allow them to fight or with chemicals that make them
unpleasant or poisonous. Other animals escape from predators; means of
escape include hiding, camouflage, fleeing, unpredictability, or congre-
gating in such large numbers that no predator could possibly consume
all of the individuals present.

Coevolution between different species is universal. The best-suited examples come from the evolutionary interactions between flowering plants and the insects that feed on them and pollinate them. For example, acacia trees provide food and shelter for ants, which protect the tree from herbivores and from competing plants.

Objectives

1. Explain the advantages and disadvantages to a plant of producing secondary compounds.

2. Describe experiments to show that aposematic coloration and Mullerian and Batesian mimicry confer protection on their owners.

3. Describe the main differences between Mullerian and Batesian mimicry.

4. Explain why a Batesian mimic is considered "parasitic" on its model's reputation.

5. List the four main principles of camouflage, and give an example of each.

6. Describe the importance of appropriate behavior to the adaptive advantage of protective coloration.

7. Describe how you would determine whether the pattern of coloration of an animal means that the animal is cryptic, aposematic, a Batesian model, a Batesian mimic, or a member of a Mullerian mimicry complex.

8. Tell what is meant by the following terms, and explain the importance of each to an animal's ability to find food: traplining, search image, camouflage, mimicry.

9. Tell how you would design and carry out an experiment to show that a particular physical or chemical characteristic of a plant is an affective defense against herbivores; describe such an experiment that has already been done.

10. List the benefits of mutualism to acacias and to the ants that live on them.

11. Tell how you would design and carry out an experiment to demonstrate that a particular secondary compound may function as a feeding attractant, oviposition stimulus, or repellent for herbivores, describe such an experiment that has already been done.

SUGGESTIONS FOR LECTURE PREPARATION AND ENRICHMENT (Also see Chapters 49-51.)

Supplemental Readings

Burtt, E. H. Jr. 1981. The adaptiveness of animal colors. Bioscience 31(10):723-729, Nov.

Hiam, A. 1982. Airborne models and flying mimics. Natural History 91 (4): 42-49.

Johnson, Phillip. 1985. Masters of elusion. National Wildlife 23(5): 44-50, Aug./Sept.

Owen, D. 1982. Camouflage and Mimicry. Univ. of Chicago Press, Chicago.

Pennisi, Elizabeth. 1985. Ghosts and Dragons. Discover 6(11):80-85, November, photographic essay showing fish whose forms allow them to blend into their habitats.

Prestwich, G. 1983. Chemical defenses of termites. Sci. Am., August.

Rosenthal, Gerald, 1986. The chemical defenses of higher plants. Sci. Am., January.

Steinhart, Peter, 1986. For wildlife, the struggle continues. National Wildlife 24(3):4-17, Apr./May.

Waggener, P. 1984. Agriculture and carbon dioxide. American Scientist 72(2):179-184.

Walkomir, Richard. 1986. Five decades of discovery. National Wildlife 24(3):55-65, Apr./May.

Films

Ants and Aphids (AVED, 1976, 26 min.) Describes life history of aphids and relationship of ants and aphids, and ecological aspects of underground communities of ants.

Now you see me, Now You Don't (AMP, 1977, 26 min.) Explores protective strategies of insects, including mimicry, camouflage, and release of noxious substances

Colors in Nature (EBEC, 1980, 12 min.) Examines adaptive value of coloration for a variety of organisms.

Living Machines (NOVA) (TLV, 1980, 57 min.) Covers natural engineering found in living organisms.

Secrets of Alien World (BCR, 1980, 52 min.) Deals with various features of insects including anatomy, behavior, life cycles, mimicry, etc.

Ideas for Demonstrations

1. Mimicry in Butterflies. Display mounts are available from biological supply companies.

2. Protective Coloration. Slide sets are available from biological supply companies.

Topics for Discussion and Library Research

1. Mimicry, protective coloration

2. Symbiosis: mutualism, commensalism, parasitism

3. Chemical defenses of plants and animals.

ESSAY QUESTIONS

obj 3 1. Compare Batesian mimicry with Mullerian mimicry regarding features of the model and the mimic in each case.

obj 3 2. Identify features or characteristics of models which provide the basis for mimicry.

obj 5 3. Distinguish countershading, disruptive coloration, aposematic coloration and cryptic coloration, and provide an example for each.

4. Describe three characters associated with an ideal "sit and wait" predator

5. Distinguish convergent evolution from coevolution and provide an example for each.